Directory *of* Specialized American Bookdealers

1981-1982

Prepared by the staff of *American Book Collector*

New York: The Moretus Press, Inc.

Table of Contents

How To Use This Book

Use the *Directory of Specialized American Bookdealers* as you would any good reference book. It contains a wealth of information about nearly 3,000 rare, antiquarian, used, and out-of-print bookdealers in the United States and Canada.

The *Directory* is divided into three sections. The key section is the first, the *Alphabetical Section.* Here are listed, in easily accessible form, the names, addresses, telephone numbers (where the dealers have supplied them), and the kinds of books in which each dealer specializes. In addition, we have provided a *short name* for each dealer (an abbreviation or condensation of the full name). This short name is the way in

which each dealer will be represented in the following two sections.

The *Specialties Section* contains over 450 book specialties, some broad (like Americana) and some quite specific (like Adirondacks). Each dealer who has listed a specialty in the alphabetical section will be found (in short-name form) under that specialty in this section. If you need the dealer's address or telephone number, you can easily obtain it from the alphabetical section.

Similarly, the *Geographical Section* employs the short name to list all dealers in alphabetical order under their state or province and then under their town.

Acknowledgments

The preparation of this *Directory* was no solitary effort. Many diverse hands have had a

part in its compilation, production, printing, and distribution. *Peter Sherred,* of Arco

Publishing, Inc., provided the initial encouragement for this directory, and without his and his company's efforts this book would not have been begun. *Laurence Witten,* in his correspondence, and the *Antiquarian Booksellers Association of America (ABAA),* through its publication of a directory of its membership, clarified a number of sticky points about nomenclature of book specialties and sub-specialties. Alas, this process is far from complete. *Renée Roff* came to the rescue and, with her broad background in directory compilation, specific good cheer, and organized mind, helped hold the many strands and pieces of paper in order. *Nicholas T. Smith,* publisher, bookseller, and space salesman, is responsible for the advertising included in the directory and for watching diligently for oversights and omissions that all too often accompany a project of this magnitude. *Terry Noble* and his staff at Noble Fulfillment Corporation handled all the computer work, from designing the initial system which holds the data to generating questionnaires, mailing labels, and printouts *ad nauseum.* The folks at R. R. Donnelley, especially *Ed Hokenson* and *Arvy Tumulus,* coordinated and spurred by *Jean Kahn,* set the type for this book in 96 hours, no mean feat. *Ron Gordon,* whose design for *American Book Collector* has been widely praised, designed this directory in his traditionally cheerful manner. Finally, a wide variety of bookdealers, through their helpful and encouraging comments written on questionnaires and postcards, gave support and information at just the right time.

A Reminder About All Directories— And Certainly This One

No directory of any group of people is ever error-free or even current by the time it is published. In the production of this *Directory,* the staff of *American Book Collector* has made a considerable step forward in directory production by keeping the time spent in the actual printing of the book to a minimum. The last addition to the *Directory* was made on January 24, 1981. Type was set within 96 hours after that, and corrections were made by February 2, 1981. The *Directory* should be ready to mail to advance buyers by the end of February, 1981.

This compressed production time makes this *Directory* far more valuable than earlier books for the rare, antiquarian, used, and out-of-print book trade. Because of this directory's large number of dealers and its extraordinary range of book specialties, coupled with the high-speed production employed, it is far more up-to-date when it is published than anything else in its field.

But computers have their problems, one of which is that they have rigid formulae for handling information. Thus we have had to employ a number of abbreviations of names where the names of dealers have exceeded the room available. Too, we have been forced to limit the number of specialties shown to six for each dealer. And, because electronic storing of information is not perfect, undetected small errors have been known to creep in.

All of which leads to the following *caveat:* the *Directory* which you hold in your hands is by far the most extensive book of its kind available today, but is was produced by humans with the aid of machines, which implies the possibility of error. If you see such an error, please let us know, because we wish to make a more perfect book next year. We have done our best, but, alas, we can not be responsible for errors shown here beyond making a correction to our files for the next edition.

A

A B C Theological Index
P O Box 2786, Comm St
  Station
Springfield, Mo. 65803
Short Name: **ABC Theological**
Religion & Theology;
Americana

A C H Bookshop
1916 West 7th Street
Los Angeles, Calif. 90057
(213) 483-8413
Short Name: **A C H**
Cookery & Gastronomy; Crafts
& Trades; Dictionaries;
Railroads; Religion &
Theology; Automotive

A Points Northe
3630 NW 22nd
Oklahoma City, Okla. 73107
Short Name: **A Pts Northe**
Oklahoma (& Indian Territory);
Western Americana

A To Z Book Service (Mail
  Only)
P O Box 610813
North Miami, Fla. 33161
Short Name: **A To Z**
First Editions; Poetry;
Biography; Childrens' Books;
Paperbacks (new); Search
Service, with Stock

Aah, Books!
6042 Broadway Terrace
Oakland, Calif. 94618
(415) 547-3881
Short Name: **Aah!**
Americana, Regional;
Illustrated Books; Outlaws &
Rangers; Horses; Voyages,
Travels, & Exploration; Arctica
& Antarctica

Aardvark Books
237 Church Street
San Francisco, Calif. 94114
(415) 552-6733
Short Name: **Aardvark-S F**
Out of Print, with Stock;
Railroads; Rare Books;
Medicine & Science; First
Editions, Modern; Art

Aardvark Book Shop
4829 East Speedway
Tucson, Ariz. 85712
Short Name: **Aardvark-Tuc**
American Indians; Western
Americana; Outlaws & Rangers;
Pacific Region; Rare Books

Aardvark's Booksellers
P O Box 15070
Orlando, Fla. 32858
Short Name: **Aardvark's-Orl**
Detective Fiction; Search
Service, with Stock; First
Editions, Modern

AB Bookman's Weekly
P O Box AB
Clifton, N.J. 07015
Short Name: **AB Bookman's**
Useful Publications for
Bookdealers

Abatis Books
P O Box 451
Springfield, Vt. 05156
Short Name: **Abatis**
Archaeology; Bells; Astronomy

Abbies Search Service
P O Box 36
Temple, N.H. 03084
Short Name: **Abbies**
Search Service, with Stock; Out
of Print, with Stock

Abbot Books & Prints
100-26 Benchley Place
Bronx, N.Y. 10475
Short Name: **Abbot**
Stock Market & Wall Street;
Economics & Business; Antique
Stocks and Bonds; Travel
Guides; Horses; Orientalia

Richard E Abel
1730 SE 90th
Portland, Ore. 97225
Short Name: **R E Abel**
Gardening & Horticulture;
Crafts & Trades; Hunting,
Fishing & Angling; Printing &
Printing History; Voyages,
Travels, & Exploration

Abelard Bookshop
342 Queen Street, West
Toronto, Ont. M5V 2A2
(416) 366-0021
Short Name: **Abelard**
Religion & Theology;
Philosophy; Literature; History;
Classics; Archaeology

Able Beam Books
P O Box 3771
Davenport, Iowa 52808
Short Name: **Able Beam**
Greece & Turkey; First
Editions, Modern

About Books
280 Queen Street, West
Toronto, Ont. M5V 2A1
(416) 861-1648
Short Name: **About**
First Editions, Modern;
General; Literature

About Music
357 Grove Street
San Francsico, Calif. 94102
(415) 621-1634
Short Name: **About Music**
Performing Arts; New Books;
Out of Print, with Stock

Abra Cadavar House Of
  Mystery
Rochester, N.Y. 14618
Short Name: **Abra Cadavar**
Detective Fiction; Fiction; First
Editions; History, American;
Paperbacks (new); Tobacco &
Smoking

Abraham Lincoln Book Shop
18 East Chestnut Street
Chicago, Ill. 60611
(312) 944-3085
Short Name: **Abraham Lincoln**
Americana; Appraisals &
Appraisal Services;
Autographed Material &
Autographs; Civil War &
Confederacy; History,
American; Presidents

Abraham's Magazine Service
56 East 13th Street
New York, N.Y. 10003
(212) 777-4700
Short Name: **A M S**
Periodicals; Reprints

Harvey Abrams
P O Box 732
State College, Penna. 16801
Short Name: **H Abrams-Sta**
Sports; Olympic Games;
Physical Education

Abraxas Books
133 East De La Guerra Street
Santa Barbara, Calif. 93101
Short Name: **Abraxas**
Fiction; First Editions;
Americana; Childrens' Books;
Cookery & Gastronomy

Abreyde Books
4500 Soquel Drive
Soquel, Calif. 95073
(408) 462-1279
Short Name: **Abreyde**
Classics; Art; Literature;
Fiction; Poetry; Religion &
Theology

Academic Books
P O Box 86-365
No. Vancouver, B.C. V7L 4K6
Short Name: **Academic**
Canada & Canadiana; Arctica
& Antarctica; Pacific Region;
Americana; Voyages, Travels, &
Exploration; Periodicals

Academy Book Store
10 West 18th Street
New York, N.Y. 10011
(212) 242-4848
Short Name: **Academy-NYC**
First Editions; Literature; Art;
Performing Arts; Psychiatry,
Psychology, & Psychonanalysis;
Philosophy

Academy Shop
900 South Beretania Street
Honolulu, Haw. 96814
(808) 538-3693
Short Name: **Academy-Hon**
Art; Asia; Pacific Region;
Orientalia

Acadia Bookstore
232 Queen Street, East
Toronto, Ont. M5A 1S3
Short Name: **Acadia**
Canada & Canadiana; Voyages,
Travels, & Exploration

Aceto Bookmen
5721 Antietam Drive
Sarasota, Fla. 33581
Short Name: **Aceto**
Americana, States;
Geneaologies; History,
American

Christopher Ackerman
180 East Inlet Drive
Palm Beach, Fla. 33480
Short Name: **C Ackerman**
Search Service, without Stock;
Collection Development;
Renaissance; Press Books &
Fine Printing; Foreign
Languages; Virginia

Acoma Books
P O Box 4
Ramona, Calif. 92065
(714) 789-1288
Short Name: **Acoma**
American Indians; Appraisals
& Appraisal Services;
Archaeology; Out of Print, with
Stock; Central America;
Publishing History

Acorn Books
3238 North Garey Avenue,
   Suite F
Pomona, Calif. 91767
(714) 956-5768
Short Name: **Acorn**
Out of Print, with Stock;
General; History; Art; Cookery
& Gastronomy; Search Service,
with Stock

Acres Of Books
35 East State
Trenton, N.J. 08608
(609) 392-0459
Short Name: **Acres-Tre**
Childrens' Books; Fiction;
History, American; Out of
Print, with Stock; Political
Science & Theory; Search
Service, with Stock

Acres Of Books Inc
633 Main Street
Cincinnati, Ohio 45202
Short Name: **Acres-Cin**
Science; Technology; Voyages,
Travels, & Exploration;
History; Literature; Fiction

Action Books
P O Box 393
Oceanside, N.Y. 11572
Short Name: **Action Bks**
Detective Fiction; Biography;
First Editions; Search Service,
with Stock; Childrens' Books

Richard Adamiak
1545 East 60th Street
Chicago, Ill. 60637
Short Name: **R Adamiak**
Law; Political Science &
Theory; Philosophy; History

Adams Books & Hobbies
214 North 8th Street
Columbia, Mo. 65201
Short Name: **Adams**
Appraisals & Appraisal
Services; Americana;
Paperbacks (new); Search
Service, with Stock

Adams Brown Company
P O Box 399, 4 Elm Street
Exeter, N.H. 03833
(603) 772-4067
Short Name: **Adams Brown**
Horology

Harvey Dan Adams, Bookseller
~~1633 North Rock Springs Road,~~
~~NE~~
Atlanta, Ga. 30324
(404) 872-8549
Short Name: **H D Adams**
Georgia; The South; Maps,
Atlases, & Cartography; Prints

Robert Henry Adams, Rare Books
P O Box 11131
Chicago, Ill. 60611
(312) 327-6542
Short Name: **R H Adams**
Art; Color Plate Books; Graphic Arts; Paintings; Prints; Maps, Atlases, & Cartography

K Tilden Adamson
1833 Woodrow Street
Augusta, Ga. 30904
Short Name: **K T Adamson**
Medical & Medicine

Adan Research Company Ltd
P O Box 666
Edmonton, Alb. T5J 2K8
(403) 853-2009
Short Name: **Adan**
Rare Books; Reference; Periodicals; History, American; Psychiatry, Psychology, & Psychonanalysis; Geneaologies

Jane Addams Bookstore
5 South Wabash, #1508
Chicago, Ill. 60603
(312) 782-0708
Short Name: **J Addams**
Women & Feminism; Childrens' Books; Detective Fiction; Out of Print, with Stock; Search Service, with Stock; Ephemera

Addison Book Centre
309 Raymond Street
Rockville Centre, N.Y. 11570
Short Name: **Addison**
American Literature; Women & Feminism

Richard H Adelson
North Pomfret, Vt. 05053
Short Name: **R H Adelson**
Voyages, Travels, & Exploration; Americana; Pacific Region; Africa; Childrens' Books; Appraisals & Appraisal Services

Adirondack Yesteryears
Drawer 209
Saranac Lake, N.Y. 12983
Short Name: **Adirondack**
Adirondacks

Adler's Foreign Books
162 Fifth Avenue
New York, N.Y. 10010
Short Name: **Adler's**
Foreign Languages

Adobe Booksellers
2416 Pennsylvania Street, NE
Albuquerque, N.Mex. 87110
(505) 299-1670
Short Name: **Adobe**
Americana; Southwestern America

Adrian's (Appt Only)
175 White Springs Road
Geneva, N.Y. 14456
Short Name: **Adrian's**
General; Ephemera

Adventure Books-Willis J Potthoff
427 Graeser Road
St Louis, Mo. 63141
Short Name: **Adventure**
Juveniles; Boy Scouts; Natural History; Edgar Rice Burroughs; Series Books for Boys & Girls

Adventure For Kids
2760 East Thompson
Ventura, Calif. 93003
Short Name: **Adventure Kids**
Childrens' Books

J P Adzima, Auctioneers
80 Shelton Road
Trumbull, Conn. 06611
Short Name: **J P Adzima**
Civil War & Confederacy; History; Antiques; Western Americana; Art; Collecting & Collectibles

Aeroprint
405 Monroe
Boonton, N.J. 07005
Short Name: **Aeroprint**
Aviation & Aeronautics

Aesir Books
P O Box 92893
Milwaukee, Wisc. 53202
(414) 765-9304
Short Name: **Aesir**
Fiction; Paperbacks (new); Science Fiction

Again Books
1920 Chapala Street
Santa Barbara, Calif. 93101
(805) 966-9312
Short Name: **Again**
Aviation & Aeronautics; Automotive; Militaria; Childrens' Books; Naval & Marine; Railroads

aGatherin'
P O Box 175
Wynantskill, N.Y. 12198
Short Name: **aGatherin'**
Autographed Material & Autographs; Ephemera; Manuscripts; Industry & Labor; Appraisals & Appraisal Services; Philately & Philatelic Literature

Barbara Agranoff, Books
P O Box 6501
Cincinnati, Ohio 45206
(513) 281-5095
Short Name: **B Agranoff**
Americana; Crafts & Trades; Ephemera; General; Illustrated Books; Search Service, with Stock

Ahrens Book Shop
736 Davie Street
Vancouver, B.C. V6Z 1B5
(604) 683-2014
Short Name: **Ahrens**
General; Out of Print, with Stock

Aide
962 Greenlake Circle
Cardiff, Calif. 92007
(714) 753-3392
Short Name: **Aide**
Search Service, without Stock; Out of Print, without Stock; Religion & Theology; Psychiatry, Psychology, & Psychonanalysis

Ainslie Books
10640 Bridgeport Road
Richmond, B.C. V6X 1S7
Short Name: **Ainslie**
Arctica & Antarctica; New Books; Out of Print, with Stock

Air Age Book Company
P O Box 40
Tollhouse, Calif. 93667
(209) 855-8993
Short Name: **Air Age**
Aviation & Aeronautics;
Militaria; Ephemera

Ajay Enterprises
P O Box 2018
Falls Church, Va. 22042
(703) 573-8220
Short Name: **Ajay Ent**
Aviation & Aeronautics

Al's Old & New Books
1710 West Douglas
Wichita, Kan. 67211
(316) 264-8763
Short Name: **Al's**
Biography; Black Literature &
Black Studies; Cookery &
Gastronomy; Search Service,
with Stock; Women &
Feminism; Poetry

Albatross Book Company
166 Eddy Street
San Francisco, Calif. 94102
(415) 885-6501
Short Name: **Albatross**
First Editions; Illustrated
Books; Naval & Marine; Out of
Print, with Stock; Press Books
& Fine Printing

Albert Books
P O Box 19187, Corryville
  Station
Cincinnati, Ohio 45219
(513) 542-8078
Short Name: **Albert**
Middle West; Railroads; Local
History; Trade Catalogues

Albion Bookshop
378 Broadway
Albany, N.Y. 12207
(518) 465-6179
Short Name: **Albion**
Classics; Middle Ages;
Philosophy; Religion &
Theology; Renaissance;
Linguistics

Albion Graphics
1751 San Lorenzo Avenue
Berkeley, Calif. 94707
(415) 527-0103
Short Name: **Albion Graphics**
Art; Drawings; Graphic Arts;
Illustrated Books; Prints;
Psychiatry, Psychology, &
Psychonanalysis

Alcazar Book Service
P O Box 12764
El Paso, Tex. 79912
Short Name: **Alcazar**
Southwestern America; Mexico;
New Mexico; Texas; Arizona

Aldine Books
4663 Hollywood Boulevard
Los Angeles, Calif. 90027
(213) 666-2690
Short Name: **Aldine**
First Editions; General;
Literature; Out of Print, with
Stock; Performing Arts; Search
Service, with Stock

Aldredge Bookstore
2909 1a Maple Avenue
Dallas, Tex. 75201
Short Name: **Aldredge**
General

Jon Aldrich Aero
P O Box 706, Pine Mtn Lake
  Airport
Groveland, Calif. 95321
(209) 962-6121
Short Name: **J Aldrich**
Aviation & Aeronautics;
Ephemera; Documents;
Autographed Material &
Autographs

Aleph-Bet Books
670 Waters Edge
Valley Cottage, N.Y. 10989
Short Name: **Aleph-Bet**
Childrens' Books; Illustrated
Books

Terry Alford
P O Box 1151
Springfield, Va. 22151
(703) 256-6748
Short Name: **T Alford**
Manuscripts; Appraisals &
Appraisal Services;
Autographed Material &
Autographs; General;
Documents

Matthew G Alfs-Books By Mail
3355 Queen Avenue, North
Minneapolis, Minn. 55412
(612) 522-2291
Short Name: **M G Alfs**
Bible & Bible Studies;
Watchtower Books & Jehovah's
Witnesses

Alicat Gallery
64 Ludlow Street
Yonkers, N.Y. 10705
(914) 963-4794
Short Name: **Alicat**
Art; Antiques; Religion &
Theology; Literature

All Books & Prints Store
4329 SW 8th Street
Miami, Fla. 33134
(305) 444-5001
Short Name: **All B & P**
Fiction; Out of Print, with
Stock; Paperbacks (new);
Poetry; Search Service, with
Stock

All Photography Books
P O Box 429
Yonkers, N.Y. 10702
(914) 423-6473
Short Name: **All Photo**
Out of Print, with Stock;
Photography; Rare Books;
Search Service, with Stock;
Cinema & Mass Media

All Points Of View
P O Box 321
San Antonio, Tex. 78292
(512) 732-6660
Short Name: **All Pts View**
Out of Print, with Stock;
Political Science & Theory;
Political, Social, & Cultural
History & Thought; Search
Service, with Stock; Social
Sciences; Marxism-Leninism &
Communism

Allbooks
4341 Majestic Lane
Fairfax, Va. 22033
(703) 968-7396
Short Name: **Allbks**
Geology; Natural History;
Orientalia; Out of Print, with
Stock; Science Fiction; Search
Service, with Stock

D C Allen
208 Chicago Street, Box 3
Three Oaks, Mich. 49128
(616) 756-9218
Short Name: **D C Allen**
Performing Arts; Automobiles,
Classic

Allen Books
4128 Ewing Avenue, South
Minneapolis, Minn. 55410
(612) 922-6462
Short Name: **Allen**
Out of Print, with Stock;
Literature; General; Search
Service, with Stock; Childrens'
Books; Ephemera

R R Allen-Books
5300 Bluefield Road
Knoxville, Tenn. 37921
Short Name: **R R Allen**
Florida; General

William H Allen, Bookseller
2031 Walnut Street
Philadelphia, Penna. 19103
(215) 563-3398
Short Name: **W H Allen**
Classics; Incunabula & Early
Printing; Rare Books; Latin
America; STC & Wing Books;
Scholarly Books

Allenson-Breckinridge Books
P O Box 447
Geneva, Ala. 36340
Short Name: **Allenson-Breck**
Religion & Theology; Bible &
Bible Studies; Church History;
Bibliography

Aloha Book Corner
P O Box 1430
Kaneohe, Haw. 96744
(808) 235-1562
Short Name: **Aloha Bk**
Hawaii; Pacific Region;
Voyages, Travels, &
Exploration

Alpha Omega Books
408 South Main Street
Poland, Ohio 44514
Short Name: **Alpha Omega**
Americana; Western Americana;
Literature; History; Art; Science

Alphabet Bookshop
656 Spadina Avenue
Toronto, Ont. M5S 2H9
(416) 924-4926
Short Name: **Alphabet**
Canadian Literature; First
Editions; First Editions,
Modern; Poetry; Literature;
Scholarly Books

Alpine Enterprises
P O Box 766
Dearborn, Mich. 48121
Short Name: **Alpine**
Biography; Political, Social, &
Cultural History & Thought;
Political Science & Theory

Alron Associates
46-19 66th Street
Woodside, N.Y. 11377
Short Name: **Alron**
Autographed Material &
Autographs; Documents;
Cinema & Mass Media;
Literature; Manuscripts; Art

Steve Alsberg
Skokie, Ill. 60076
Short Name: **S Alsberg**
Newspapers; Magazines;
Illustrated Books; Maps,
Atlases, & Cartography;
Periodicals; Association Books

Alta California Bookstore
P O Box 296
Laguna Beach, Calif. 92652
(714) 494-5252
Short Name: **Alta Calif**
Ephemera; Mexico;
Photography; Americana;
California

Karl Altau
800 Warwick Circle
Waynesboro, Va. 22980
Short Name: **K Altau**
Americana; Virginia; Western
Americana; The South; Civil
War & Confederacy; Sporting

J G Amadeo
P O Box 487
New York, N.Y. 10009
Short Name: **J G Amadeo**
Authors; Mystery Fiction

Amadeus Books
P O Box 18052
Denver, Colo. 80218
(303) 377-7509
Short Name: **Amadeus**
Music; Musical Instruments;
Performing Arts; Law

The Amblers
1123 Hillridge
Reynoldsburg, Ohio 43068
(614) 861-4882
Short Name: **Ambelrs**
Out of Print, without Stock

Sheila B Amdur
P O Box 151
Mansfield Center, Conn. 06250
(203) 423-3176
Short Name: **S B Amdur**
General

American Book Prices Current
121 East 78th Street
New York, N.Y. 10021
(212) 737-2715
Short Name: **Abpc**
Useful Publications for
Bookdealers

American Book Collector
274 Madison Avenue
New York, N.Y. 10016
(212) 685-2250
Short Name: **Amer Bk Coll**
Useful Publications for Book
Collectors

American Books
743 Fifth Avenue, South
St Cloud, Minn. 56301
Short Name: **Amer Bks**
Americana; Classics; European
History; South America; The
South; Canada & Canadiana

American Eagle Sporting
  Library
P O Box 51
Topsfield, Mass. 01983
Short Name: **Amer Eagle**
Hunting, Fishing & Angling;
Shooting & Firearms; Sporting;
Americana, Regional;
Automobiles, Classic

American Fragments
7127 Hollister Avenue
Goleta, Calif. 93117
Short Name: **Amer Frag**
*Childrens' Books; Color Plate
Books; Illustrated Books;
Maps, Atlases, & Cartography;
Natural History; Prints*

American Library Service South
P O Box 4549
Margate, Fla. 33063
Short Name: **Amer Lib Srvce**
*Black Literature & Black
Studies; Caribbean*

American Opinion Bookstore
4909 Canal Street
New Orleans, La. 70119
(504) 486-3841
Short Name: **Amer Opinion**
*Economics & Business; Foreign
Affairs; History, American;
Political Science & Theory;
Religion & Theology; Search
Service, without Stock*

American Print Gallery
2 Prospect
Bellingham, Wash. 98225
Short Name: **Amer Print**
*Out of Print, with Stock;
Periodicals; Prints; Search
Service, with Stock; Women &
Feminism; General*

American Southwest Books
P O Box 148
Amarillo, Tex. 79105
(806) 372-3444
Short Name: **Amer So'west**
*Texas; American Indians;
Documents; Farming, Ranching,
& Livestock; Maps, Atlases, &
Cartography; Outlaws &
Rangers*

American Worlds Books
P O Box 6162, Whitneyville
    Station
Hamden, Conn. 06517
(203) 776-3558
Short Name: **Amer Wrlds**
*Literature; Literary Criticism;
Scholarly Books; Humanities;
Americana, Regional; History,
American*

Americana Books & Gallery
36 Oak Avenue
Tuckahoe, N.Y. 10707
Short Name: **Amer Bk & Gal**
*Militaria; Western Americana;
Aviation & Aeronautics;
Hunting, Fishing & Angling;
Naval & Marine; American
Illustrative Art*

Americana Mail Auctions
Allentown, Penna. 18104
Short Name: **Amer Mail Auct**
*Americana; Autographed
Material & Autographs; Civil
War & Confederacy; History,
American; Manuscripts; Maps,
Atlases, & Cartography*

The Americanist
1525 Shenkel Road
Pottstown, Penna. 19464
Short Name: **Americanist**
*Americana; Imprints; Poetry;
Drama; Women & Feminism;
Manuscripts*

Ampersand Books
P O Box 674, Cooper Station
New York, N.Y. 10003
Short Name: **Ampersand**
*First Editions, Modern;
Ephemera; Little Magazines &
Literary Small Presses;
Appraisals & Appraisal
Services*

Anacapa Books
3090 Claremont Avenue
Berkeley, Calif. 94705
(415) 654-3517
Short Name: **Anacapa**
*First Editions; Poetry;
Ephemera*

Anchor & Dolphin Books
20 Franklin Street
Newport, R.I. 02840
(401) 846-6890
Short Name: **Anchor & Dol**
*Landscape Architecture;
Decorative Arts; Architecture;
Gardening & Horticulture;
America's Cup; Authors*

Ancient City Press
P O Box 5401
Santa Fe, N.Mex. 87502
(505) 983-2420
Short Name: **Ancient Cty Pr**
*American Indians; Americana,
Regional; Appraisals &
Appraisal Services; First
Editions; Scholarly Books; Rare
Books*

Ancient City Book Shop
P O Box 1986
Sante Fe, N.Mex. 87501
(505) 982-8855
Short Name: **Ancient Cty Bk**
*Southwestern America;
American Indians; General; Out
of Print, with Stock; Rare
Books*

**Kenneth Andersen-Books (Mail
Only)**
38 Silver Street
Auburn, Mass. 01501
(617) 832-3524
Short Name: **K Andersen**
*Hunting, Fishing & Angling;
Shooting & Firearms; Sporting;
Mountaineering; Natural
History*

Elmer L Anderson
2230 West Hoyt Avenue
St Paul, Minn. 55108
Short Name: **E L Anderson**
*Books about Books; Minnesota;
Press Books & Fine Printing*

Anderson's Bookhouse
122 West Commonwealth
Fullerton, Calif. 92632
(714) 526-5328
Short Name: **Anderson's**
*Americana; Literature; Out of
Print, with Stock; Scholarly
Books; History; Naval &
Marine*

Andover Square Books
805 Norgate Road
Knoxville, Tenn. 37919
Short Name: **Andover Square**
*Americana; History; First
Editions*

Edward Andrews
49 Main Street
Irvington-On-Hudson, N.Y.
10533
Short Name: **E Andrews**
*History; Philosophy; Greek &
Latin Classics; Music; Art;
Dance*

Homer R Andrews
P O Box 5063
Richmond, Calif. 94805
Short Name: **H R Andrews**
*Pacific Region; Outlaws &
Rangers; American Indians;
California; Western Americana*

Andromeda Book Shop
111 East Platt Street
Maquoketa, Iowa 52060
Short Name: **Andromeda**
Middle West

Angel's Books
2703 Carabel Lane, #256
Sacramento, Calif. 95821
(916) 483-8677
Short Name: **Angel's**
*Mountaineering; Arctica &
Antarctica*

Anglers & Shooters Bookshelf
Goshen, Conn. 06756
(203) 491-2500
Short Name: **Angl & Shoot**
*Hunting, Fishing & Angling;
Derrydale Press; Sporting*

The Anglican Biblopole
P O Box 99309
San Francisco, Calif. 94109
(415) 552-8881
Short Name: **Anglican Bib**
*Religion & Theology;
Biography; Music; Americana,
States; Canada & Canadiana;
Out of Print, with Stock*

Angriff Press
P O Box 2726
Hollywood, Calif. 90028
Short Name: **Angriff**
*Political Science & Theory;
Political, Social, & Cultural
History & Thought*

Annie's Book Swap
39 South Street
Westborough, Mass. 01581
(617) 366-5840
Short Name: **Annie's-Wes**
*General; Paperbacks (new);
Book Swapping*

Annie's Book Swap
60 Great Road
Acton, Mass. 01720
(617) 263-3158
Short Name: **Annie's-Act**
*General; Paperbacks (new);
Book Swapping*

Annie's Book Swap
158 East Central Street
Natick, Mass. 01760
Short Name: **Annie's-Nat**
*General; Paperbacks (new);
Book Swapping*

Hugh Anson-Cartwright
229 College Street
Toronto, Ont. M5T 1R4
(416) 979-2441
Short Name: **H Anson-Cart**
*Canada & Canadiana;
Literature; Arctica &
Antarctica; Out of Print, with
Stock*

Antheil Booksellers
2177 Isabelle Court
North Bellmore, N.Y. 11710
Short Name: **Antheil**
*Naval & Marine; Ships & The
Sea; Aviation & Aeronautics;
Militaria; World Wars*

Antic Hay Books
P O Box 1441
West Caldwell, N.J. 07006
(201) 227-0963
Short Name: **Antic Hay**
*Literature; First Editions; First
Editions, Modern; Inscribed
Books; Authors; Autographed
Material & Autographs*

The Antiquarian Shop
1329 Strongs Avenue, P O Box
L
Stevens Point, Wisc. 54481
(715) 341-3351
Short Name: **Antiq Sh-Ste**
*Americana, Regional;
Appraisals & Appraisal
Services; General; History,
American; Railroads; Search
Service, with Stock*

Antiquarian Booksellers' Center
50 Rockefeller Plaza
New York, N.Y. 10020
Short Name: **Antiq Bksllrs**
*General; Americana; Art; Color
Plate Books; Literature; Rare
Books*

Antiquarian Bookvestors
940 Harmony Drive
Haywood, Calif. 94541
Short Name: **Antiq Bkvestors**
*Americana, Regional; Science
Fiction; American Indians;
Antiques; Fantasy; Birds &
Ornithology*

Antiquarian Michiana
Allen, Mich. 49227
Short Name: **Antiq Michiana**
Local History; Americana

Antiquarian Scientist
P O Box 602
Amesbury, Mass. 01913
(617) 388-2314
Short Name: **Antiq Scientist**
*Medicine & Science;
Technology; Botany; Geology;
Mathematics; Natural History*

Antiquarian Tobacciana
5101 Willowmeade Drive
Fairfax, Va. 22030
(703) 830-8584
Short Name: **Antiq Tobacco**
Tobacco & Smoking

Antiquariat
2406 North Campbell
Tucson, Ariz. 85719
(602) 327-4081
Short Name: **Antiquariat**
*Americana, Regional; First
Editions; History, American;
Illustrated Books; Out of Print,
with Stock; Press Books & Fine
Printing*

The Antiquarium
66 Humiston Drive
Bethany, Conn. 06525
(203) 393-2723
Short Name: **The Antiquarium**
*Books about Books; Natural
History; Medicine & Science;
Rare Books; Reference;
Scholarly Books*

Antique Books
3651 Whitney Avenue
Mount Carmel, Conn. 06518
(203) 281-6606
Short Name: **Antiq Bks**
*Childrens' Books; Civil War &
Confederacy; Education;
Farming, Ranching, &
Livestock; History; Maps,
Atlases, & Cartography*

Antiques Books And Crafts
P O Box 592
Hillsborough, N.C. 27278
Short Name: **Antiques-Hil**
*Basketry; Psychiatry,
Psychology, & Psychonanalysis;
Cookery & Gastronomy*

Antiquus Bibliopole
4147 24th Street
San Francisco, Calif. 94114
(415) 285-2322
Short Name: **Antiquus**
*Americana; First Editions; First
Editions, Modern; Out of Print,
with Stock; Search Service, with
Stock; Childrens' Books*

Charles Apfelbaum, Books
39 Flower Road
Valley Stream, N.Y. 11581
Short Name: **C Appelbaum**
*Author Collections;
Autographed Material &
Autographs; Collection
Development; Manuscripts;
First Editions; Documents*

S Apfelbaum
200 I U Willets Road
Albertson, N.Y. 11507
Short Name: **S Apfelbaum**
*Numismatics; Philately &
Philatelic Literature;
IncomeOpportunities & Self
Help*

Apothecary
P O Box 702
Rahway, N.J. 07065
Short Name: **Apothecary**
*Medicine & Science; Ephemera;
Prints*

Appalachia Book Shop
1316 Pen Mar Avenue
Bluefield, W.Va. 24701
(304) 327-5493
Short Name: **Appalachia**
*Appalachia; Civil War &
Confederacy; Comic Books;
Geneaologies; Out of Print, with
Stock; Search Service, with
Stock*

Kalman Appel
1413 South 17th Street
Las Vegas, Nev. 89104
(702) 382-0768
Short Name: **K Appel**
*Judaica & Hebraica; Religion
& Theology; Middle East*

Paul P Appel
119 Library Lane
Mamaroneck, N.Y. 10543
(914) 698-8115
Short Name: **P P Appel**
*Art; First Editions, Modern;
Literary Criticism; Literature;
Out of Print, with Stock;
Humanities*

Appelfeld Gallery
1372 York Avenue
New York, N.Y. 10021
(212) 988-7835
Short Name: **Appelfeld**
*Appraisals & Appraisal
Services; Fine & Rare Bindings;
Books about Books; Color Plate
Books; Rare Books; Sets*

Applegate Books
P O Box 541
Medford, Ore. 97501
Short Name: **Applegate**
General

Appleland Books
P O Box 966
Winchester, Va. 22601
Short Name: **Appleland**
*Virginia; Civil War &
Confederacy; Americana,
Regional; Americana, States;
Americana; Out of Print, with
Stock*

Arabest Book Shop
West 224 South 6800 Guthrie
   Road
Big Bend, Wisc. 53103
(414) 662-3766
Short Name: **Arabest**
*Horses; Dogs; Voyages, Travels,
& Exploration*

W Graham Arader Iii
1000 Boxwood Court
King Of Prussia, Penna. 19406
(215) 825-6570
Short Name: **W G Arader Iii**
*American Indians; Maps,
Atlases, & Cartography;
Natural History; Voyages,
Travels, & Exploration;
Americana; Color Plate Books*

Arc Books
P O Box 16282, Roland Park
   Station
Baltimore, Md. 21210
Short Name: **Arc Bks**
*Computers; Logic; Astronautics
& Rocketry*

Arcane Books
3120 Harvey Parkway
Oklahoma City, Okla. 73118
Short Name: **Arcane**
*First Editions, Modern; Rare
Books; Appraisals & Appraisal
Services; Bibliography; Ireland
& The Irish*

Archives Historical Autographs
119 Chestnut Hill Road
Wilton, Conn. 06897
Short Name: **Archives Hist**
*Autographed Material &
Autographs*

Arctician Books
538 Queen Street, Box 691
Fredericton, N.B. E3, 4k9
(509) 457-0544
Short Name: **Arctician**
*Arctica & Antarctica; Canada
& Canadiana; General;
Hunting, Fishing & Angling;
Maps, Atlases, & Cartography;
Voyages, Travels, &
Exploration*

Arcturus Book Service
263 North Ballston Avenue
Scotia, N.Y. 12302
(518) 372-2373
Short Name: **Arcturus**
UFOs

Scott Arden
20457 Highway 126
Noti, Ore. 97461
(503) 935-1619
Short Name: **S Arden**
Railroads

Argonaut Book Shop
786-792 Sutter St
San Francisco, Calif. 94109
Short Name: **Argonaut**
Americana; History, American;
Maps, Atlases, & Cartography;
Press Books & Fine Printing;
Rare Books; Voyages, Travels,
& Exploration

Argos Book Shop
1405 Robinson Road, SE
Grand Rapids, Mich. 49506
(616) 454-0111
Short Name: **Argos**
General; Paperbacks (new);
Search Service, without Stock;
Science Fiction; Periodicals;
Michigan

Argosy Book Stores
116 East 59th Street
New York, N.Y. 10022
Short Name: **Argosy**
Americana; History of Medicine
& Science; Maps, Atlases, &
Cartography; First Editions;
Out of Print, with Stock;
Collection Development

Argus Books
1714 Capitol Avenue
Sacramento, Calif. 95814
(916) 443-2223
Short Name: **Argus**
California; Ephemera;
Americana, Regional; Visual
Synthesizers; Cookery &
Gastronomy; Horses

Arjay Books
2500 River Hills Road
Austin, Tex. 78745
(512) 263-2957
Short Name: **Arjay**
Texas; General

Ark Bookshop
1703 University Avenue
Berkeley, Calif. 94703
Short Name: **Ark**
Appraisals & Appraisal
Services; First Editions;
Medicine & Science; Rare
Books; Scholarly Books;
Technology

Ark-La-Tex Book Company
P O Box 564
Shreveport, La. 71162
Short Name: **Ark-La-Tex**
Louisiana

Arkadyan Books And Prints
926 Irving Street
San Francisco, Calif. 94122
(415) 664-6212
Short Name: **Arkadyan**
Childrens' Books; Illustrated
Books; Maps, Atlases, &
Cartography; Prints

Richard Arkway, Inc
131 Fifth Avenue, Suite 401
New York, N.Y. 10003
Short Name: **Arkway**
Voyages, Travels, &
Exploration; American
Discovery; Americana; History
of Medicine & Science; Maps,
Atlases, & Cartography

The Armchair Sailor Bookstore
Lee's Wharf
Newport, R.I. 02840
(401) 847-4252
Short Name: **Armchair Sailor**
Naval & Marine; Natural
History; Alternative Energy;
Childrens' Books

Karl Armens
621 Walnut Street
Iowa City, Iowa 52240
(319) 337-7755
Short Name: **K Armens**
Americana; First Editions,
Modern; Detective Fiction;
Literature; Out of Print, with
Stock; Science Fiction

Glenn Armitage
108 Fifth Avenue
Miamisburg, Ohio 45342
Short Name: **G Armitage**
Americana; Art; First Editions;
Humanities; Literature;
Performing Arts

Frederick Armstrong
319 North McIlhaney
Stphenville, Tex. 76401
Short Name: **F Armstrong**
Americana, Regional; History,
American; Out of Print, with
Stock; Outlaws & Rangers;
Search Service, with Stock

James E Arnay
P O Box 123
New York, N.Y. 10163
Short Name: **J E Arnay**
Jewelry

George Arndt
P O Box 319
Harvard, Mass. 01451
Short Name: **G Arndt**
Stock Market & Wall Street

Arnold's Books
511 South Union Street
Traverse City, Mich. 49684
Short Name: **Arnold's**
Rare Books; Out of Print, with
Stock

Frederick Arone
377 Ashforde
Dobbs Ferry, N.Y. 10522
(914) 693-5858
Short Name: **F Arone**
Railroads

G H Arrow Company
1133-39 North 4th Street
Philadelphia, Penna. 19123
Short Name: **G H Arrow**
Periodicals

Ars Libri, Ltd
711 Boylston Street
Boston, Mass. 02118
(617) 536-3264
Short Name: **Ars Libri**
Architecture; Art; Illustrated
Books; Incunabula & Early
Printing; Photography; Rare
Books

Art Catalogues
8227 Santa Monica Boulevard
Los Angeles, Calif. 90046
(213) 656-8788
Short Name: **Art Catalogues**
Art Catalogues, Periodicals, &
Books; Art; Out of Print, with
Stock

Artcraft Books
6701 Cherry Hill Road
Baldwin, Md. 21013
Short Name: **Artcraft**
Architecture; Art; Crafts &
Trades; Drawings; Graphic
Arts; Paintings

Arthritis Research
P O Box 5688
Santa Monica, Calif. 90405
(213) 396-5164
Short Name: **Arthritis**
Health

K George Arthurton
Apt #178, Bldg 10, Salzburg
   Village
Palmyra, N.Y. 14522
Short Name: **K G Arthurton**
American Indians; Americana;
Criminology; Law; Outlaws &
Rangers; History, American

Articles Of War Ltd
7101 North Ashland Avenue
Chicago, Ill. 60626
(312) 338-7171
Short Name: **Articles Of War**
Militaria; Naval & Marine;
History; New Books; Out of
Print, with Stock; Continental
Books

Artifacts
368 Grove Street
Glen Rock, N.J. 07450
Short Name: **Artifacts**
Americana; First Editions

Artistic Endeavors
24 Emerson Place
Boston, Mass. 02114
(617) 227-1967
Short Name: **Artistic End**
Art; Drawings; Graphic Arts;
Illustrated Books; Paintings;
Autographed Material &
Autographs

Arts & Letters Bookshop
San Francisco, Calif. 94102
Short Name: **Arts & Lett**
Architecture; Art; Books about
Books; First Editions, Modern;
Graphic Arts

As You Like It Bookshop
2185 Bullis Road
Elma, N.Y. 14059
(607) 652-0060
Short Name: **As You Like It**
Science Fiction; Childrens'
Books; Paperbacks (new); Rare
Books; Shakespeare; Cookery &
Gastronomy

Ruth Asaro
R D #1, Box 191-D
Utica, N.Y. 13502
Short Name: **R Asaro**
General

Mrs A L Ashton
49 Birch Avenue
Ottawa, Ont.
(613) 749-1741
Short Name: **Mrs A L Ashton**
Canada & Canadiana;
Childrens' Books; History;
Militaria; Poetry; Rare Books

The Asian American Materials
   Center
165 West 66th Street
New York, N.Y. 10023
Short Name: **Asian Amer**
Asia; First Editions, Modern;
Orientalia; Pacific Region;
Americana, Regional; Outlaws
& Rangers

Asian Books
12 Arrow Street
Cambridge, Mass. 02138
Short Name: **Asian-Cam**
Africa; Asia; Foreign
Languages; Middle East;
Orientalia

Asian Rare Books
507 Fifth Avenue, #307
New York, N.Y. 10017
Short Name: **Asian-NYC**
Art; Asia; Middle East;
Orientalia; Voyages, Travels, &
Exploration

Associated Book Service
P O Box 7764
Long Beach, Calif. 90807
Short Name: **Assoc Bk Svc**
California; Southwestern
America; Books about Books;
Desert; Mexico

The Associates
2601 Park Center Drive, #c-406
Alexandria, Va. 22302
Short Name: **Associates**
Authors; First Editions,
Modern; Literature

Astronomy Books (Paul Luther)
P O Box 217
Bernardston, Mass. 01337
(413) 648-9393
Short Name: **Astronomy**
Technology; Medicine &
Science; Mathematics; Out of
Print, with Stock; Search
Service, with Stock; Appraisals
& Appraisal Services

At The Sign Of The Book
4812 Folsom Boulevard
Sacramento, Calif. 95819
Short Name: **At The Sign**
War; Biography; Ephemera;
Classics; Voyages, Travels, &
Exploration; History

Athenaeum
1713 Central Street
Evanston, Ill. 60201
Short Name: **Athenaeum**
Americana; Americana,
Regional; Architecture; Art;
Bibliography; Black Literature
& Black Studies

Atherton's Books
10417 Armory Avenue
Kensington, Md. 20975
(301) 949-9411
Short Name: **Atherton's**
General

Atlanta Antiquarian Booksellers
1387 Oxford Road, NE
Atlanta, Ga. 30307
(404) 346-3590
Short Name: **Atlanta**
Psychiatry, Psychology, &
Psychonanalysis; Linguistics;
Books about Books; History of
Medicine & Science; Social
Sciences; Out of Print, with
Stock

Atlantic Book Service
P O Box 218
Charlestown, Mass. 02129
(617) 242-0188
Short Name: **Atlantic**
Out of Print, with Stock; Search
Service, with Stock; Hunting,
Fishing & Angling; Militaria;
Naval & Marine

The Attic, Inc
P O Box 449
Hodges, S.C. 29653
(803) 374-3013
Short Name: **Attic-Hodg**
Americana; Collection
Development; General;
Literature; Scholarly Books

Attic Books
388 Clarence Street
London, Ont.
(519) 432-6636
Short Name: **Attic**
General; Canada & Canadiana;
Detective Fiction; Out of Print,
with Stock; Paperbacks (new);
Search Service, with Stock

Attic Books & Records
21 Rock Street
Winsted, Conn. 06098
Short Name: **Attic-Wins**
Americana; Americana,
Regional; Literature; Fiction;
Illustrated Books; General

Atticus Books
698 Spadina Avenue
Toronto, Ont. M5S 2J2
(416) 922-6045
Short Name: **Atticus-Tor**
Philosophy; Classics;
Linguistics; History of Medicine
& Science; Psychiatry,
Psychology, & Psychonanalysis;
Literary Criticism

Atticus Books
P O Box 26668
San Diego, Calif. 92126
(714) 566-8208
Short Name: **Atticus**
First Editions, Modern; Fiction;
Autographed Material &
Autographs; Little Magazines
& Literary Small Presses;
Poetry; Beat Literature

Audubon Prints
9720 Spring Ridge Lane
Vienna, Va. 22180
(703) 759-5567
Short Name: **Audubon**
Natural History; Prints; Rare
Books

Auslender
P O Box 2133
Glenbrook, Conn. 06906
Short Name: **Auslender**
Aviation & Aeronautics;
Militaria; Naval & Marine;
Technology

Austin Book Shop
82-64 Austin Street
Kew Gardens, N.Y. 11415
(212) 441-1199
Short Name: **Austin**
Immigration; Judaica &
Hebraica; Law; American
Literature; History, American;
Women & Feminism

Authors Of The West
191 Dogwood Drive
Dundee, Ore. 97115
Short Name: **Authors Of West**
Western Americana; Americana;
First Editions; American
Indians; Literature; Poetry

Autobooks East
P O Box 1
Babylon, N.Y. 11702
Short Name: **Autobks E**
Auto Racing; Transportation;
Steamships, River Travel, &
Steamboats; World War II
Battlefield Art; Posters

Autos & Autos
P O Box 280
Elizabeth City, N.C. 27907
(919) 335-1117
Short Name: **Autos & Autos**
Autographed Material &
Autographs; Medicine &
Science; Voyages, Travels, &
Exploration; Aviation &
Aeronautics

Avenue Victor Hugo Bookshop
339 Newbury Street
Boston, Mass. 02115
(617) 266-7746
Short Name: **AVH Bkshop**
Science Fiction; Art; Detective
Fiction; Comic Books;
Periodicals; Fiction

Aviation Book Company
1640 Victory Boulevard
Glendale, Calif. 91201
(213) 240-1771
Short Name: **Aviation**
Aviation & Aeronautics

Avocet Used Books
614 SW 3rd
Corvallis, Ore. 97330
Short Name: **Avocet**
Childrens' Books; Cookery &
Gastronomy; Literature;
Natural History; Paperbacks
(new); Science Fiction

Ayrshire Books
P O Box 360
Penfield, N.Y. 14526
Short Name: **Ayrshire**
General; Fine & Rare Bindings

American Book Collector has computerized all the names, addresses, and book specialties for the 3,000 dealers found in this directory and for a growing list of dealers who will appear in subsequent editions. We can provide mailing labels for these dealers, selected by specialty if you wish, at reasonable cost. Write for our price schedule. *ABC*, 274 Madison Avenue, New York, N.Y. 10016.

B

B & B Autographs
P O Box 465
Randolph, Mass. 02368
(617) 961-2688
Short Name: **B & B**
*Autographed Material &
Autographs; Documents;
Manuscripts; Presidents;
Whaling; Drawings*

B & G Fine Books
P O Box 8895
Universal City, Calif. 91608
(213) 506-7218
Short Name: **B & G**
*Circus & Carnival; Magic;
Militaria; Cinema & Mass
Media; Out of Print, with
Stock; Western Americana*

B & K Stamps
P O Box 415
Bowie, Md. 20715
Short Name: **B & K Stamps**
*Philately & Philatelic
Literature; Horatio Alger*

Bert Babcock-Fine Books
5 East Derry Road
Derry, N.H. 03038
(603) 432-9142
Short Name: **B Babcock**
*Association Books;
Autographed Material &
Autographs; Appraisals &
Appraisal Services; Author
Collections; First Editions,
Modern; Rare Books*

Back Number-Wilkins
7 Conant Street, Box 247
Danvers, Mass. 01923
(617) 531-5058
Short Name: **Back Number**
Periodicals

Back Row Bookshop
411 West Main Street
Fairborn, Ohio 45324
(513) 879-2131
Short Name: **Back Row**
*General; Paperbacks (new);
Periodicals; Out of Print, with
Stock; Fiction; Biography*

Back Tracts, Inc
5406 North College Avenue
Indianapolis, Ind. 46220
(317) 257-3686
Short Name: **Back Tracts**
*Appraisals & Appraisal
Services; Americana, States;
Americana, Regional; First
Editions; Press Books & Fine
Printing; Out of Print, with
Stock*

Backpocket Ranch Bookshop
Star Rte #4, Box 27
Sundance, Wyom. 82729
(307) 283-2594
Short Name: **Backpocket**
*Wyoming; Western Americana;
Farming, Ranching, &
Livestock; Horses; Writing
Instruction; Search Service,
without Stock*

Backstage Books
P O Box 3676
Eugene, Ore. 97403
Short Name: **Backstage**
*Theatre; Performing Arts;
General*

Backworks
488 Greenwich Street
New York, N.Y. 10013
(212) 966-1765
Short Name: **Backworks**
*Avant Garde, Experimental, &
Modern Art*

Bailey Search Service
P O Box 326
Redondo Beach, Calif. 90277
Short Name: **Bailey Srch**
*Edgar Rice Burroughs; Pulps;
Science Fiction; Fantasy;
Authors*

Jan Bailey-Books
4080 Upham Street, #201
Wheat Ridge, Colo. 80033
(303) 422-9298
Short Name: **J Bailey**
*General; Out of Print, with
Stock; Search Service, with
Stock*

Lee J Bain
5 Lovers Lane
Rolla, Mo. 65401
Short Name: **L J Bain**
*Biography; Childrens' Books;
Comic Books; Detective Fiction;
Fiction*

Baird Press, Inc
Rte #2, Box 444
Rhinebeck, N.Y. 12572
Short Name: **Baird Press**
*Horses; Middle East; Voyages,
Travels, & Exploration*

Baker Book House
2768 East Paris
Grand Rapids, Mich. 49506
(616) 957-3110
Short Name: **Baker**
*Religion & Theology;
Philosophy*

Bakka
282 Queen Street, West
Toronto, Ont. M5V 2A1
(416) 361-1161
Short Name: **Bakka**
Science Fiction

Balaclava Books
P O Box 281
Altadena, Calif. 91001
(213) 794-4796
Short Name: **Balaclava**
*Militaria; Civil War &
Confederacy; Naval & Marine*

Baldwin Book Service
P O Box 157
Baldwin, N.Y. 11510
(516) 223-0610
Short Name: **Baldwin**
*Political, Social, & Cultural
History & Thought; Literary
Criticism*

Baldwin's Book Barn
865 Lenape Road
West Chester, Penna. 19380
Short Name: **Baldwin's Barn**
*Pennsylvania; Delaware;
Sporting; Local History*

Leonard Balish (Appt Only)
124-A Engle Street
Englewood, N.J. 07621
(201) 871-3454
Short Name: **L Balish**
*Americana; Ephemera; Color
Plate Books; Printing &
Printing History*

The Ballet Shop
1887 Broadway
New York, N.Y. 10023
Short Name: **Ballet**
Dance; Opera; Theatre

Steve Ballinger
P.O. Box 2552
Salt Lake City, Utah 96011
Short Name: **S Ballinger**
*Collection Development; Search
Service, with Stock;
Literature*

John Bambach
1062 Hastings St.
Baldwin, N.Y. 11510
(516) 546-0858
Short Name: **J Bambach**
*Art; Biography; History;
History, American; Middle
Ages; Presidents*

Rick Banda's Rare Books
P.O. Box 1115
Temple, Tex. 76501
(817) 773-4384
Short Name: **R Bandas**
Texas

Banyan Books, Inc
P O Box 431160
Miami, Fla. 33143
(305) 665-6011
Short Name: **Banyan**
*Americana, Regional;
Gardening & Horticulture;
Natural History; Botany;
History, American; Naval &
Marine*

Baptist Book Bourse
745 West Main Street
Watertown, Wisc. 53094
Short Name: **Baptist Bourse**
*Religion & Theology; History;
Poetry; Biography; Bible &
Bible Studies*

Philip E Baracca
1411 Grandview Avenue
Pittsburgh, Penna. 15211
(412) 481-8893
Short Name: **P E Baracca**
*General; Biography; Literature;
Ephemera; Political, Social, &
Cultural History & Thought;
Press Books & Fine Printing*

Barbara's Books
P O Box 22
Harrison, N.Y. 10528
Short Name: **Barbara's**
Art; Antiques

Barber's Book Store
215 West 8th Street
Fort Worth, Tex. 76102
Short Name: **Barber's**
Militaria; Texas; Petroleum

Bargain Book Store
1053 Eighth Avenue
San Diego, Calif. 92101
Short Name: **Bargain-San**
*First Editions, Modern;
Southwestern America; Stock
Market & Wall Street; Art;
Architecture*

Bargain Books
424 West 4th Street
Grand Island, Neb. 68801
Short Name: **Bargain-Gran**
*General; Out of Print, with
Stock*

Bargain Bookshop
16236 Paramount Boulevard
Paramount, Calif. 90723
(213) 531-6909
Short Name: **Bargain-Par**
*Americana; Book Trade &
Catalogues; Childrens' Books;
Antiques; Color Plate Books;
Books about Books*

Barjon's Books
104 North Broadway #440
Billings, Mont. 59101
(406) 252-4398
Short Name: **Barjon's**
*Detective Fiction; Comic Books;
Search Service, with Stock;
American Indians; Northwest;
Paperbacks (new)*

The Barn Sale
Main Street, Box 58
Farmington Falls, Maine 04940
(207) 778-3429
Short Name: **Barn Sale**
*Biography; Childrens' Books;
Fiction; General; Illustrated
Books; Paperbacks (new)*

Barn Loft Bookshop
96 Woodland Avenue
Laconia, N.H. 03246
(603) 524-4839
Short Name: **Barn Loft**
*Childrens' Books; New
England; General*

C Virginia Barnes
P O Box 112
New York, N.Y. 10025
Short Name: **C V Barnes**
*Memory & Mnemonics;
Americana, Regional;
Incunabula & Early Printing;
History, American;
Geneaologies; Americana,
States*

Glynis E C Barnes
P O Box 70, Station Q
Toronto, Ont. M4T 2L1
(416) 488-3308
Short Name: **G E C Barnes**
*Press Books & Fine Printing;
Illustrated Books; Childrens'
Books; Folklore; Books about
Books; General*

Barnette's
22727 Adams Road
South Bend, Ind. 46628
(319) 272-9880
Short Name: **Barnette's**
*Americana; History, American;
Out of Print, with Stock;
Overland Narratives; Voyages,
Travels, & Exploration*

Barnstable Books
799 Broadway, Room 506a
New York, N.Y. 10003
Short Name: **Barnstable**
*First Editions; First Editions,
Modern; Bibliography; Books
about Books; Rare Books*

Baron Books
1223 Cornaga Avenue
Far Rockaway, N.Y. 11691
Short Name: **Baron**
*First Editions; First Editions,
Modern*

Charles Baron
55 Knolls Crescent
Bronx, N.Y. 10463
(212) 548-3951
Short Name: **C Baron**
Americana; First Editions,
Modern; First Editions

Baroque Book Store
1643 North Las Palmas Avenue
Hollywood, Calif. 90028
Short Name: **Baroque**
First Editions, Modern

Barra Books, Ltd
819 Madison Avenue
New York, N.Y. 10021
(212) 988-1770
Short Name: **Barra**
Antiques; Architecture; Art;
Maps, Atlases, & Cartography;
Rare Books; Scholarly Books

Barrow Bookstore
79 Main Street
Concord, Mass. 01742
(617) 369-6084
Short Name: **Barrow**
History, American; Literature;
Childrens' Books; First
Editions; Search Service, with
Stock; General

J N Bartfield Inc
45 West 57th Street
New York, N.Y. 10019
Short Name: **J N Bartfield**
Color Plate Books; Maps,
Atlases, & Cartography; Fine &
Rare Bindings; Sets; Natural
History; Americana

Baseball Books Only
5672 East Scarlett Street
Tucson, Ariz. 85711
(602) 747-5394
Short Name: **Baseball**
Baseball; Collection
Development; Sporting; Book
Scouts

Robert Batchelder
1 West Butler Avenue
Ambler, Penna. 19002
(215) 643-1430
Short Name: **R Batchelder**
Autographed Material &
Autographs; Documents;
Manuscripts

Mark E Battersby
P O Box 527
Ardmore, Penna. 19003
(215) 649-0311
Short Name: **M E Battersby**
Fine & Rare Bindings;
Bookbinding & Restoration;
Farming, Ranching, &
Livestock; Detective Fiction;
Economics & Business; Stock
Market & Wall Street

The Battery Book Shop
P O Box 3107
Nashville, Tenn. 37219
Short Name: **Battery**
Militaria; Military (World War
II)

David Lawrence Bauman,
  Bookseller
14 South La Clede Place
Atlantic City, N.J. 08401
Short Name: **D L Bauman**
Rare Books; Voyages, Travels,
& Exploration; Law;
Humanities; First Editions

Bay Side Books
P O Box 57
Soquel, Calif. 95073
Short Name: **Bay Side**
Literature; Poetry; Philosophy;
Fiction; Anthropology; Left
Wing

Bayview Books And Bindery
P O Box 208
Northport, N.Y. 11768
(516) 757-3563
Short Name: **Bayview**
Africa; Arctica & Antarctica;
Bookbinding & Restoration;
Naval & Marine; Voyages,
Travels, & Exploration;
Whaling

Bazaar Books
P O Box 496
Chico, Calif. 95927
Short Name: **Bazaar**
Search Service, with Stock

W G Bazan-Books
P O Box 125
O'fallon, Mo. 63366
Short Name: **W G Bazan**
Medicine & Science; Medical &
Medicine

Bazemore's Books
52 Eliot Drive
Stow, Mass. 01775
(617) 897-5288
Short Name: **Bazemore's**
Book Scouts

Mary Beth Beal
3919 North Claremont Avenue
Chicago, Ill. 60618
(312) 539-0105
Short Name: **M B Beal**
Appraisals & Appraisal
Services; Collection
Development; Autographed
Material & Autographs;
Americana; Maps, Atlases, &
Cartography; Rare Books

Samuel N Bean
26 South Washington
Niantic, Conn. 06357
Short Name: **S N Bean**
General; New England

Bear Book Shop
R F D #4, Box 219
West Brattleboro, Vt. 05301
(802) 464-2260
Short Name: **Bear**
Literature; Literary Criticism;
Illustrated Books; Bibliography;
Childrens' Books; Scholarly
Books

Doug Bearce
P O Box 7081
Salem, Ore. 97303
(503) 363-1715
Short Name: **D Bearce**
Boy Scouts

S D Beare
7 East Brookland Avenue
Wilmington, Del. 19805
Short Name: **S D Beare**
History of Medicine & Science;
Technology; 19th Century
Literature

Beasley Books
~~2615 North Wilton~~ 2616 h.
~~Chicago, Ill. 60614~~ Wilton
(312) 472-4528
Short Name: **Beasley**
First Editions, Modern;
Literature; Little Magazines &
Literary Small Presses; Poetry;
Detective Fiction

James W Beattie
611 Arlyn Circle
Wayne, Penna. 19087
Short Name: **J W Beattie**
Art; Hunting, Fishing &
Angling; Typography & Type
Specimens; Voyages, Travels, &
Exploration

Beaufort Book Co
P O Box 1127
Beaufort, S.C. 29902
(803) 524-5172
Short Name: **Beaufort**
Out of Print, with Stock

Beaver Books
P O Box 974
Daly City, Calif. 94017
Short Name: **Beaver**
Americana, Regional; Canada
& Canadiana; Fur Trade

Dr Wilfred E Beaver
418 East Main Street
Sparta, Wisc. 54656
(608) 269-6205
Short Name: **W E Beaver**
History, American; Maps,
Atlases, & Cartography;
Ancient Civilizations; Voyages,
Travels, & Exploration

J Richard Becker
51 Concord Road
Acton Centre, Mass. 01720
(617) 263-3820
Short Name: **J R Becker**
Canada & Canadiana;
Photography; Ephemera;
Numismatics

Beckham's Bookshop
228 Decatur Street
New Orleans, La. 70130
(504) 522-9875
Short Name: **Beckham's**
The South; Louisiana

Bedford's Used Books
54 High Street
Ellsworth, Maine 04605
Short Name: **Bedford's**
Maine; Naval & Marine;
General

C J Bedore
P O Box 4, R R #2
New Holstein, Wisc. 53061
Short Name: **C J Bedore**
Boy Scouts

Bee Gee's Book Exchange
9225 North Bethanne Drive
Brown Deer, Wisc. 53223
(414) 354-4363
Short Name: **Bee Gee's**
Comic Books; Paperbacks
(new); Pulps; Magazines;
Science Fiction

Johann Bekker
903 South 10th Street, East
Salt Lake City, Utah 84105
(801) 359-5185
Short Name: **J Bekker**
First Editions; History;
Literature; Voyages, Travels, &
Exploration

Bel Canto Bookshop
P O Box 55
Metuchen, N.J. 08840
Short Name: **Bel Canto**
Music; Opera

Belanske & Levinger Inc
43 West 54th Street
New York, N.Y. 10019
Short Name: **Belanske & Lev**
First Editions, Modern;
Illustrated Books; Literature;
Poetry; Press Books & Fine
Printing

David B Belcher-Books
231 South Main Street
Orange, Mass. 01364
(617) 544-6655
Short Name: **D B Belcher**
Childrens' Books; Photography;
Ephemera; Rare Books;
Illustrated Books; Americana

R Bemis, Bookseller
1161 Hampton Way
Altanta, Ga. 30324
Short Name: **R Bemis**
First Editions, Modern

Ben Franklin Book Shop
318 North Broadway
Upper Nyack, N.Y. 10960
(914) 358-0440
Short Name: **Ben Franklin**
Out of Print, with Stock;
Scholarly Books; Search
Service, with Stock; Paperbacks
(new)

Bengta Woo
1 Sorgi Court
Plainview, N.Y. 11803
(516) 692-4426
Short Name: **Bengta Woo**
Detective Fiction; Out of Print,
with Stock; Search Service, with
Stock; Paperbacks (new)

Walter R Benjamin Autographs,
Inc
P O Box 255, Scribner Hollow
Road
Hunter, N.Y. 12442
Short Name: **Benjamin Autogr**
Autographed Material &
Autographs; History;
Presidents; Civil War &
Confederacy; Literature; Music

Bennett & Marshall
8214 Melrose Avenue
Los Angeles, Calif. 90046
(213) 653-7040
Short Name: **Bennett & Marsh**
Science; Printing & Printing
History; Voyages, Travels, &
Exploration; Asia

Michael E Bennett
P O Box 342
Kew Gardens, N.Y. 11415
Short Name: **M E Bennett**
New York Metropolitan Area;
Cookery & Gastronomy;
Bookbinding & Restoration;
Ephemera; Americana, States

J A Benoit
3465 Sherbrooke East, #1
Montreal, Que. H1W 1C9
(514) 527-1137
Short Name: **J A Benoit**
Canada & Canadiana; French
Books & Literature

Deborah Benson-Bookseller
River Road
West Cornwall, Conn. 06796
Short Name: **D Benson**
First Editions, Modern; Books
about Books; Out of Print, with
Stock; Chess, Checkers, &
Draughts; Miniature Books

Ken Benson-Books
98 Hawthorne Avenue
Ottawa, Ont. K1S 0B1
(613) 238-7509
Short Name: **K Benson**
Canada & Canadiana; Militaria

Howard O Berg
317 7th Street
Devils Lake, N.D. 58301
(701) 662-2343
Short Name: **H O Berg**
North Dakota; Local History;
Out of Print, with Stock

J & J Berger Booksellers
3905 MacArthur Boulevard
Oakland, Calif. 94619
(415) 530-8252
Short Name: **J & J Berger**
Childrens' Books

Fred A Berk
P O Box 1367
Studio City, Calif. 91604
Short Name: **F A Berk**
Americana; California;
Ephemera; Voyages, Travels, &
Exploration

Carl Sandler Berkowitz
P O Box 688
Monroe, N.Y. 10950
(914) 342-4154
Short Name: **C S Berkowitz**
Archaeology; Art; History;
Numismatics; Religion &
Theology; Architecture

Lillian Berliawsky
23 Bay View Street
Camden, Maine 04843
(207) 236-3903
Short Name: **L Berliawsky**
Americana; European History;
Literature; Music; Art

Steven C Bernard First Editions
138 New Mark Esplanade
Rockville, Md. 20850
(301) 340-8623
Short Name: **S C Bernard**
First Editions, Modern; First
Editions; Literature; Fiction;
Science Fiction; Autographed
Material & Autographs

William Berner, Books
P O Box 31175
San Francisco, Calif. 94131
(415) 564-6297
Short Name: **W Berner**
Sherlock Holmes & A. Conan
Doyle

F A Bernett Inc
2001 Palmer Avenue
Larchmont, N.Y. 10538
(914) 834-3026
Short Name: **F A Bernett**
Fine Arts; Architecture;
Archaeology

George A Bernstein, Bookdealer
G P O Box 1439
Brooklyn, N.Y. 11202
Short Name: **G A Bernstein**
Archaeology; Judaica &
Hebraica; Middle East;
Voyages, Travels, &
Exploration; Scholarly Books;
Technology

Berry Hill Bookshop
R D Box 118
Deansboro, N.Y. 13328
Short Name: **Berry Hill**
New York; Cinema & Mass
Media; General; Authors

Peter Berry
527 East 72nd Street
New York, N.Y. 10021
(212) 988-8351
Short Name: **P Berry**
Classics; Incunabula & Early
Printing; Press Books & Fine
Printing; Law; Printing &
Printing History; Rare Books

Howard John Besnia
Scarab Press
Sterling Junction, Mass. 01565
(617) 422-8869
Short Name: **H J Besnia**
Bookbinding & Restoration;
Graphic Arts; Illustrated Books;
Press Books & Fine Printing;
Prints; Woodcut Books

The Bethlehem Book Company
249 East Street
Bethlehem, Conn. 06751
Short Name: **Bethlehem**
Antiques; Folk Art

Ron Bever
Rte #3, Box 243-B
Edmond, Okla. 73034
Short Name: **R Bever**
Stock Market & Wall Street;
Commodities Trading;
Biography; Oklahoma (&
Indian Territory); Church
History

Elizabeth H Bevington
1625 North Street
Terre Haute, Ind. 47804
(812) 234-8989
Short Name: **E H Bevington**
General

Preston C Beyer
752a Pontiac Lane
Stratford, Conn. 06497
(203) 375-9073
Short Name: **P C Beyer**
Books about Books; First
Editions, Modern; Press Books
& Fine Printing; Printing &
Printing History; Literature;
Typography & Type Specimens

B L Bibby
1225 Sardine Creek
Gold Hill, Ore. 97525
(503) 855-1621
Short Name: **B L Bibby**
Gardening & Horticulture;
Natural History

Bible Commentary House
P O Box 2485
El Cajon, Calif. 92021
(714) 440-5871
Short Name: **Bible Comment**
Religion & Theology

Biblio Services
P O Box 671, Station A
Montreal, Que. H3C 2T8
(514) 481-2188
Short Name: **Biblio**
Bibliography; Books about
Books; Canada & Canadiana;
Economics & Business; Industry
& Labor; Railroads

Biblioctopus
Idyllwild, Calif. 92349
(714) 659-5188
Short Name: **Biblioctopus**
First Editions; Detective
Fiction; Fiction; Literature;
Manuscripts; Science Fiction

Bibliography Of The Dog
4170 Decarie Boulevard
Montreal, Que. 4h4 3k2
(514) 488-6279
Short Name: **Bibliog Of Dog**
Dogs

Biblion, Inc
P O Box 9
Forest Hills, N.Y. 11375
(212) 263-3910
Short Name: **Biblion**
History of Medicine & Science;
Incunabula & Early Printing;
Rare Books

The Bibliophile
148 West 72nd Street
New York, N.Y. 10023
Short Name: **Bibliophile-NYC**
Literature; Drama; Philosophy;
Psychiatry, Psychology, &
Psychonanalysis; History;
General

A Bibliophile's Dream
26 Holland Street
Binghamton, N.Y. 13905
Short Name: **Biblio's Dream**
Wireless Communication
History

Bibliophiles
P O Box 704
Pasadena, Calif. 91102
Short Name: **Bibliophile-Pas**
Childrens' Books; Search
Service, with Stock;
Bibliography; General; Out of
Print, with Stock

Bibliopolis
220 Williamson Buildings
Cleveland, Ohio 44114
Short Name: **Bibliopolis-Cle**
Rare Books; Incunabula &
Early Printing; First Editions;
Collection Development; Books
about Books; Fine & Rare
Bindings

Bicentennial Bookshop
820 South Westnedge
Kalamazoo, Mich. 49008
Short Name: **Bicentennial**
Michigan; Hunting, Fishing &
Angling; Gene Stratton-Porter;
Militaria; Childrens' Books

Bickerstaff & Barclay
P O Box 28452
Washington, D.C. 20005
Short Name: **Bick & Barc**
Photography; Americana;
Cinema & Mass Media;
Voyages, Travels, &
Exploration; Medicine &
Science; Periodicals

Biermaier's B H Books
809 SE 4th Street
Minneapolis, Minn. 55414
(612) 378-0129
Short Name: **Biermaier's**
Art; Literature; General; Fiction

Big John's Book Room
R D #2
Meshoppen, Penna. 18630
(717) 833-5323
Short Name: **Big John's**
Biography; Western Americana;
Travel; Natural History;
Sporting; Fiction

Bigelows' Quill Bookshop
90 Green Street
Northampton, Mass. 01060
(413) 584-3912
Short Name: **Bigelows' Quill**
New Books; Women &
Feminism; Paperbacks (new);
Fiction; Literature

Billiard Archives
1113 Dodson
San Pedro, Calif. 90732
Short Name: **Billiard**
Games & Pasttimes

Billig Works Bookstore & Tea
Room
1322 College Avenue
Boulder, Colo. 80302
Short Name: **Brillig Works**
Poetry; Metaphysics; Literary
Criticism; Fine Arts; Literature

Binders Press
23777 Adams Road
South Bend, Ind. 46628
Short Name: **Binders Press**
Bookbinders Services

The Bird & The Book
6101-B North Kings Highway
Myrtle Beach, S.C. 29577
Short Name: **Bird & Bk**
North Carolina; South
Carolina; Birds & Ornithology

Bird's Nest
136 East Broadway, Box 8809
Missoula, Mont. 59807
Short Name: **Bird's Nest**
General; Out of Print, with
Stock; Search Service, with
Stock; Biography

Bisbee Book Stall
P O Box 73, 8 Brewery Gulch
Bisbee, Ariz. 85603
Short Name: **Bisbee**
Arizona; Western Americana;
Out of Print, with Stock;
Mexico

The Bishop Of Books-Charles
Bishop
117 15th Street
Wheeling, W.Va. 26003
(304) 232-8801
Short Name: **Bishop Of Bks**
West Virginia; Western
Americana; Illustrated Books;
Hunting, Fishing & Angling;
Civil War & Confederacy;
Literature

Deron Bissett
9011 East Drive
Austin, Tex. 78753
Short Name: **D Bissett**
American Illustrative Art

Black Sun Books
667 Madison Avenue
New York, N.Y. 10021
(212) 688-6622
Short Name: **Black Sun**
Press Books & Fine Printing;
First Editions; Illustrated
Books; Drawings; Manuscripts;
Rare Books

Henry Black's Rare Books And
Prints
150 Metlcalfe Street, #106
Ottawa, Ont. K2P 1P1
Short Name: **H Black's**
Canada & Canadiana;
Literature; Illustrated Books;
Voyages, Travels, &
Exploration; Militaria; Rare
Books

H C Blackerby
1290 Irvin Bridge Road
Conyers, Ga. 30207
(404) 483-6566
Short Name: **H C Blackerby**
Comic Books

Blacktail Mountain Books
42 First Avenue, West
Kalispell, Mont. 59901
Short Name: **Blacktail Mtn**
Hunting, Fishing & Angling;
Out of Print, with Stock; Search
Service, with Stock; Shooting &
Firearms; Sporting

Warren Blake-Bookseller
131 Sigwin Drive
Fairfield, Conn. 06430
(203) 259-3278
Short Name: **W Blake**
Americana; Voyages, Travels, & Exploration

Edward G Blankman
P O Box 78
Adams Center, N.Y. 13606
Short Name: **E G Blankman**
New York; Biography

William Bledsoe, Bookseller
P O Box 763
San Carlos, Calif. 94070
(415) 593-6878
Short Name: **W Bledsoe**
Economics & Business; Foreign Affairs; Industry & Labor; Political Science & Theory; Political, Social, & Cultural History & Thought; Social Sciences

Roy Bleiweiss
92 Northgate Avenue
Berkeley, Calif. 94708
(415) 548-1624
Short Name: **R Bleiweiss**
Press Books & Fine Printing; First Editions; Books about Books; Law; Tobacco & Smoking

P H Bliss-Serials
215 East Main Street
Middletown, Conn. 06457
(203) 347-2255
Short Name: **P H Bliss**
Periodicals; Renaissance; Reprints; Search Service, with Stock; Sets

Blitz Books
P O Box 1076
Weaverville, Calif. 96093
(916) 623-5430
Short Name: **Blitz**
Search Service, with Stock; Americana; Out of Print, with Stock

Bloch & Company
P O Box 18058
Cleveland, Ohio 44118
Short Name: **Bloch & Co**
Americana; Western Americana; Ohio; Civil War & Confederacy; Prints; Black Literature & Black Studies

Dick Blomberg
6065 Newburg Road
Rockford, Ill. 61108
Short Name: **D Blomberg**
American Indians; Childrens' Books; Hunting, Fishing & Angling; Natural History; Overland Narratives; Photography

Carl Blomgren
51 Gold Hill Grade
San Raphael, Calif. 94901
Short Name: **C Blomgren**
Photography; Illustrated Books; First Editions, Modern; Ephemera; Comic Books; Childrens' Books

Annie Bloom's Books
7829 SW Capital Highway
Portland, Ore. 97219
(503) 246-0053
Short Name: **A Bloom's**
Judaica & Hebraica; Childrens' Books; Women & Feminism; Cookery & Gastronomy; Photography; Poetry

Bloomsbury Books
525 South Western Avenue
Los Angeles, Calif. 90020
(213) 389-4180
Short Name: **Bloomsbury**
Archaeology; Classics; Literature; Middle Ages; History; Anthropology

The Blors Corporation Book Brokers
P O Box 5564
Madison, Wisc. 53705
Short Name: **Blors**
General; New Books; Out of Print, without Stock; Rare Books; Scholarly Books; Medicine & Science

The Blue Jay Bookshop
P O Box 1121
Regina, Sask. S4P 3B4
Short Name: **Blue Jay**
Natural History; Birds & Ornithology

Blue Eye Books
P O Box 27
Blue Eye, Mo. 65611
Short Name: **Blue Eye**
Fiction; General; Natural History; Book Scouts; Miniature Books; Sheet Music

Blue Moon Records
307 Cedar Avenue
Minneapolis, Minn. 55454
Short Name: **Blue Moon**
Detective Fiction; First Editions, Modern; Performing Arts

Blue Rider Books (Mail Only)
65 Mt Auburn Street
Cambridge, Mass. 02138
(617) 354-4894
Short Name: **Blue Rider**
Archaeology; Architecture; Art; Graphic Arts; Horses; Photography

Blue River Books
R R #1, Box 92a
Marriston, Ind. 46161
(317) 763-6004
Short Name: **Blue River**
Middle West; Canada & Canadiana; Conservation; Fiction; Hunting, Fishing & Angling; History, American

Sidonea E Blumenauer
34-29 80th Street
Jackson Heights, N.Y. 11372
Short Name: **S E Blumenauer**
Inland Waterways

C J Boardman
Rte #3, Box 26
Camden, N.Y. 13316
(315) 245-1950
Short Name: **C J Boardman**
New York; General; Americana, States

Boardwalk Books
P O Box 283
Friday Harbor, Wash. 98250
Short Name: **Boardwalk**
Naval & Marine; Authors

Bob's Bookshop
227 East College Avenue
Appleton, Wisc. 54911
Short Name: **Bob's-App**
Wisconsin; Americana; General

Bohling Book Company
P O Box 215
Lawton, Mich. 49065
(616) 624-6002
Short Name: **Bohling**
Americana; Americana, States; Ephemera

Nelson Bond
4724 Easthill Drive
Roanoke, Va. 24018
Short Name: **N Bond**
First Editions; Authors

Book
P O Box 547, Streetsville
Mississauga, Ont. L5M 2C1
Short Name: **Book-Miss**
Ice Hockey

The Book & Tackle Shop
29 Old Colony Road
Chestnut Hill, Mass. 02167
Short Name: **Bk & Tackle**
Science; Medicine & Science; Naval & Marine; Hunting, Fishing & Angling; Cookery & Gastronomy; Art

A Book End
521 Jewett Avenue
Staten Island, N.Y. 10302
Short Name: **Bk End-Sta**
General

A Book Gallery
P O Box 99309
Tacoma, Wash. 98499
(206) 588-2503
Short Name: **Bk Gall-Tac**
Childrens' Books; First Editions, Modern; Rare Books

Book Addict
P O Box 9134
Albuquerque, N.Mex. 87119
Short Name: **Bk Addict-Albu**
Arctica & Antarctica; Mountaineering; Voyages, Travels, & Exploration; Natural History; Out of Print, with Stock; Search Service, without Stock

Book Attic
10239 Fair Oaks Boulevard
Fair Oaks, Calif. 95628
(916) 961-3703
Short Name: **Bk Attic**
Americana; First Editions, Modern; Cookery & Gastronomy; Militaria; Out of Print, with Stock; Religion & Theology

Book Barn
4570 SW Watson
Beaverton, Ore. 97005
Short Name: **Bk Barn-Bea**
Childrens' Books; Parenting; Education; Search Service, without Stock; New Books

Book Baron
12365 Magnolia Avenue
Anaheim, Calif. 92804
Short Name: **Bk Baron**
Science Fiction; First Editions; General; Detective Fiction; Search Service, with Stock; Out of Print, with Stock

Book Basement
263 King Street
Charleston, S.C. 29401
Short Name: **Bk Basement**
The South; First Editions, Modern; South Carolina; North Carolina

Book Bin
225 Princess Street
Kingston, Ont. K7L 1B3
Short Name: **Bk Bin-Kin**
Art; First Editions; Fiction; Mountaineering; Science Fiction; Voyages, Travels, & Exploration

Book Bin Inc
Dallas, Tex. 75234
(214) 357-2731
Short Name: **Bk Bin-Dal**
New Books; Out of Print, with Stock; Ephemera; Prints; Newspapers; Americana, Regional

The Book Addict-David H Foshey
71 Beckett Street
Portland, Maine 04101
(207) 774-8951
Short Name: **Bk Addict-Por**
History, American; Biography; Natural History; Sports; Adventure

The Book Barn
R R 1-304h
Sioux City, Neb. 68776
(402) 494-2936
Short Name: **Bk Barn-Sio**
Autographed Material & Autographs; First Editions; Out of Print, with Stock; Railroads; Rare Books; Authors

The Book Bazaar
755 Bank Street
Ottawa, Ont. K1S 3V3
(613) 233-4380
Short Name: **Bk Bazaar**
Canada & Canadiana; Music

The Book Block
~~14 West Putnam Avenue~~ *8 Coughlin*
~~Greenwich, Conn. 06830~~ *Cos Cob*
(203) 629-2990 *cohn .06807*
Short Name: **Bk Block-Gree**
Illustrated Books; Press Books & Fine Printing; Fine & Rare Bindings; Woodcut Books; Graphic Arts; Color Plate Books

The Book Caravan
P O Box 72
Wales, Fla. 33853
(813) 676-7035
Short Name: **Bk Caravan**
Poetry; Sherlock Holmes & A. Conan Doyle; Natural History; Americana; Art

The Book Center
282 East Clayton Street
Athens, Ga. 30601
Short Name: **Bk Center-Ath**
Americana, Regional; Childrens' Books; Fiction; New Books; Paperbacks (new); Search Service, without Stock

The Book Dales
P O Box 9776
Minneapolis, Minn. 55440
Short Name: **Bk Dales**
First Editions, Modern; Childrens' Books; Illustrated Books

The Book Dispensary
4588 Memorial Drive
Decatur, Ga. 30032
(404) 296-2186
Short Name: **Bk Dispensary**
Out of Print, with Stock; Out of Print, without Stock

The Book End
11 East Stephenson
Freeport, Ill. 61032
(815) 232-1081
Short Name: **Bk End-Free**
Classics; Fiction; General; New Books; Paperbacks (new); Periodicals

The Book End
245 Pearl Street
Monterey, Calif. 93940
Short Name: **Bk End-Mon**
Foreign Languages; Childrens'
Books; Biography; Literature

The Book Gallery
P O Box 26, Gedney Station
White Plains, N.Y. 10605
Short Name: **Bk Gall-Whit**
Art; Architecture; Graphic Arts;
Photography; Search Service,
with Stock; Search Service,
without Stock

The Book Habit
311 East Vista Way
Vista, Calif. 92083
(714) 724-0664
Short Name: **Bk Habit**
Miniature Books; Western
Americana; Whaling; Mystery
Fiction; Literature; Americana,
Regional

The Book House
209-B North Boundary Street
Williamsburg, Va. 23185
Short Name: **Bk Hse-Will**
General; Search Service, with
Stock

The Book Lady
414 Bull Street
Savannah, Ga. 31401
Short Name: **Bk Lady**
Africa; General; Literature; Out
of Print, with Stock

The Book Mart
P O Drawer 72
Lake Wales, Fla. 33853
Short Name: **Bk Mart (Mag)**
Useful Publications for Book
Collectors

The Book Peddlers
23 West Delaware Avenue
Pennington, N.J. 08534
(609) 737-3099
Short Name: **Bk Peddlers**
Childrens' Books; Cookery &
Gastronomy; New Books;
Paperbacks (new); Search
Service, without Stock

The Book Sail
1186 North Tustin
Orange, Calif. 92667
(714) 997-9511
Short Name: **Bk Sail**
Illustrated Books; Rare Books;
Fine & Rare Bindings; First
Editions, Modern; Science
Fiction; Comic Books

The Book Shelf
4 Louella Court
Wayne, Penna. 19087
·Short Name: **Bk Shelf-Way**
Antiques; Art; Cookery &
Gastronomy; Childrens' Books

The Book Shop Inc
908 Main Street
Boise, Idaho 83702
(208) 342-2659
Short Name: **Bk Sh-Boise**
Fiction; New Books; Americana,
Regional; Out of Print, with
Stock; Search Service, with
Stock; Women & Feminism

The Book Shoppe
1599 Oakland Avenue
Kettering, Ohio 45409
Short Name: **Bk Sh-Ket**
Childrens' Books; Detective
Fiction; Fiction; Science Fiction

The Book Shoppe
52081 Us 31 N
South Bend, Ind. 46637
Short Name: **Bk Sh-Sou**
Art; Black Literature & Black
Studies; Cookery &
Gastronomy; Literary Criticism;
Militaria

The Book Stall
1424 Springfield Pike
Cincinnati, Ohio 45215
(513) 761-8224
Short Name: **Bk Stall-Cin**
General; Out of Print, with
Stock; Search Service, with
Stock

The Book Stop
2504 North Campbell
Tucson, Ariz. 85719
(602) 326-6661
Short Name: **Bk Stop-Tuc**
Americana, Regional; Scholarly
Books; Out of Print, with Stock

The Book Store
108 East Fourth Avenue
Olympia, Wash. 98501
Short Name: **Bk St-Oly**
Childrens' Books; Literature;
Northwest

The Book Studio
P O Box 13865
Atlanta, Ga. 30324
Short Name: **Bk Studio**
Magic; Limited Editions Club;
Philately & Philatelic
Literature; Art

Book Broker
10 South Weinbach
Evansville, Ind. 47714
Short Name: **Bk Broker**
General; Comic Books

Book Buddy
1328 Sartori Avenue
Torrence, Calif. 90501
(213) 328-1134
Short Name: **Bk Buddy**
General

Book Case
2419 South Shepherd
Houston, Tex. 77019
(713) 527-9293
Short Name: **Bk Case-Hou**
Americana; Bibliography; Book
Trade & Catalogues; Books
about Books; History,
American; General

Book Case
610 East Olive
Fresno, Calif. 93728
(209) 266-0956
Short Name: **Bk Case-Fres**
Religion & Theology;
Americana, Regional;
Childrens' Books; Autographed
Material & Autographs

Book Case Books
461 North Lake Avenue
Pasadena, Calif. 91101
(213) 793-6527
Short Name: **Bk Case-Pas**
General; Out of Print, with
Stock; Search Service, with
Stock; Paperbacks (early &
collectible); Detective Fiction;
Science Fiction

Book Cellar
36 Main Street
Freeport, Maine 04032
(207) 865-3157
Short Name: **Bk Cellar-Fre**
*Nostalgic Fiction; Maine
Authors; Juveniles; Biography*

Book Cellar
120 Main Street
Brattleboro, Vt. 05301
Short Name: **Bk Cellar-Brat**
*Childrens' Books; Cookery &
Gastronomy; Crafts & Trades;
Literature; Out of Print, with
Stock; Poetry*

Book Cellar
2 South Main
Temple, Tex. 76501
(817) 773-7545
Short Name: **Bk Cellar-Tem**
*General; Americana, Regional;
Out of Print, with Stock; Search
Service, with Stock; Paperbacks
(new); Texas*

Book Cellar
122 Orangefair Mall
Fullerton, Calif. 92632
Short Name: **Bk Cellar-Ful**
*Scholarly Books; Art;
Illustrated Books; Women &
Feminism; Cookery &
Gastronomy; Books about
Books*

Book Chest, Inc
19 Oxford Place
Rockville Centre, N.Y. 11570
Short Name: **Bk Chest**
*Natural History; Botany;
Gardening & Horticulture;
Horses; Hunting, Fishing &
Angling; Voyages, Travels, &
Exploration*

Book City Collectables
6625 Hollywood Boulevard
Hollywood, Calif. 90028
Short Name: **Bk City Coll**
*Cinema & Mass Media; Rock
& Roll; Autographed Material
& Autographs; Photography;
Movie & Fan Magazines*

Book Clearing House
12 Hughenot Drive
Larchmont, N.Y. 10538
Short Name: **Bk Clearing**
*Technology; Reference; Stock
Market & Wall Street;
Dictionaries; Medicine &
Science*

The Book Collector
375 Elliot Street
Newton, Mass. 02164
(617) 964-3599
Short Name: **Bk Coll-Newt**
Out of Print, with Stock; Japan

Book Connection
P O Box 486
Mariposa, Calif. 95338
(209) 966-2877
Short Name: **Bk Connect**
General; Paperbacks (new)

Book Cottage
2403 Lawrence Highway
Decatur, Ga. 30033
(404) 636-1690
Short Name: **Bk Cottage**
*Childrens' Books; Classics; Out
of Print, with Stock;
Paperbacks (new); Prints;
Search Service, with Stock*

Book Den
15 East Anapanu Street, Box
   733
Santa Barbara, Calif. 93102
(805) 967-3321
Short Name: **Bk Den-San**
*Americana; Western Americana;
Magazines*

Book Den East
P O Box 721
Oak Bluffs, Mass. 02557
Short Name: **Bk Den East**
*America's Cup; Juveniles;
Naval & Marine; Voyages,
Travels, & Exploration;
Cookery & Gastronomy*

Book Dispensary
1600 Broad River Road
Columbia, S.C. 29210
Short Name: **Bk Disp-Col**
South Carolina

Book Ends
2710 North Washington
   Boulevard
Arlington, Va. 22201
(703) 524-4976
Short Name: **Bk Ends-Arl**
*Childrens' Books; General;
History, American; Out of
Print, with Stock*

Book Exchange
90 West Market Street
Corning, N.Y. 14830
(607) 936-8536
Short Name: **Bk Exch-Corn**
*Astrology; Crafts & Trades;
Apiculture; Philosophy*

Book Exchange
Holiday Village
Missoula, Mont. 59801
(406) 728-6342
Short Name: **Bk Exch-Mis**
*Comic Books; Fiction; Out of
Print, with Stock; Paperbacks
(new); Periodicals; Search
Service, with Stock*

Book Fair
1409 Oak Street
Eugene, Ore. 97401
Short Name: **Bk Fair-Eug**
General

Book Fair, Farmers Market
1200 South Congress Avenue
West Palm Beach, Fla. 33407
Short Name: **Bk Fair**
*Paperbacks (new); New Books;
Automotive; Bible & Bible
Studies; Crafts & Trades*

Book Fiend
549 Mt Pleasant Road
Toronto, Ont. M4S 2M5
Short Name: **Bk Fiend**
Out of Print, without Stock

Book Finder
80 Seneca Street
Geneva, N.Y. 14456
Short Name: **Bk Fndr-Genev**
*Fiction; General; Humanities;
Out of Print, with Stock;
Paperbacks (new); Search
Service, with Stock*

Book Finders General
145 East 27th Street
New York, N.Y. 10016
Short Name: **Bk Fndrs-NYC**
*Search Service, with Stock;
Literature; Out of Print, with
Stock; History; Medicine &
Science; Geneaologies*

Book Gallery
1150 North Main Street
Gainesville, Fla. 32601
Short Name: **Bk Gall-Gai**
*American Indians; First
Editions, Modern; Comic
Books; General; Church
Records; Search Service, with
Stock*

Book Harbor
201 North Harbor Boulevard
Fullerton, Calif. 92632
Short Name: **Bk Harbor**
*First Editions; Philosophy;
Metaphysics; Cookery &
Gastronomy; Transportation;
Heritage Press*

Book Haven
154 North Prince Street
Lancaster, Penna. 17603
Short Name: **Bk Haven-Law**
*General; Americana;
Americana, States; Illustrated
Books; Childrens' Books; First
Editions*

Book Home, Inc
P O Box 825
Colorado Springs, Colo. 80901
Short Name: **Bk Home**
*Botany; Geology; Natural
History; Scholarly Books;
South America*

Book House
218 East Front Street
Plainfield, N.J. 07060
(201) 757-6321
Short Name: **Bk Hse-Pla**
*General; Out of Print, without
Stock; Search Service, with
Stock*

Book House
805 North Emerson
Arlington, Va. 22205
(703) 527-7797
Short Name: **Bk Hse-Arl**
*Americana; Art; Civil War &
Confederacy; Illustrated Books;
Militaria; Natural History*

Book Keeper
908 South Miller
Mitchell, S.D. 57301
Short Name: **Bk Keeper-Mit**
*South Dakota; Local History;
American Indians*

Book Land
1319 East Prado
Torrence, Calif. 90501
Short Name: **Bk Land-Tor**
*Anthropology; Folklore;
Literature; History; Social
Sciences; Women & Feminism*

Book Look
51 Maple Avenue
Warwick, N.Y. 10990
Short Name: **Bk Look-War**
*Out of Print, with Stock;
Collection Development; Book
Scouts; Search Service, with
Stock; Autographed Material &
Autographs; Hudson River
Valley*

Book Mark
2049 West Rittenhouse Square
Philadelphia, Penna. 19103
(215) 735-5546
Short Name: **Bk Mark-Phil**
*Architecture; Art; Books about
Books; Literature; General*

Book Mart
985 Main Street
Brockton, Mass. 02401
(617) 588-0124
Short Name: **Bk Mart**
*Science Fiction; Comic Books;
Paperbacks (new); Ephemera;
Pulps; Sports*

Book Mart
7 Biltmore Plaza, Box 5094
Asheville, N.C. 28803
Short Name: **Bk Mart-Ash**
Authors; North Carolina

Book Mart
3127 Broadway
San Antonio, Tex. 78209
Short Name: **Bk Mart-San**
*Americana; Americana,
Regional; First Editions;
History, American; Militaria;
Outlaws & Rangers*

Book Mart Annex
3132 Avenue B'
San Antonio, Tex. 78209
Short Name: **Bk Mart Anx-San**
*Americana; Americana, States;
Railroads; Outlaws & Rangers;
Press Books & Fine Printing;
Shooting & Firearms*

Book Nook
3702 Emma Lane
Yakima, Wash. 98903
(509) 453-3762
Short Name: **Bk Nook**
*American Indians; Childrens'
Books; Out of Print, without
Stock; Philosophy; Religion &
Theology; Search Service,
without Stock*

Book Place
3129 Millwood Avenue
Columbia, S.C. 29205
Short Name: **Bk Place-Col**
*Out of Print, with Stock; Search
Service, with Stock*

Book Quest
P O Box 636
Arlington, Tex. 76010
(817) 265-8903
Short Name: **Bk Quest**
Search Service, without Stock

Book Ranger
105 Charles Street
New York, N.Y. 10014
Short Name: **Bk Ranger**
*Americana; Art; Naval &
Marine; Out of Print, with
Stock; Search Service, with
Stock; Voyages, Travels, &
Exploration*

Book Roundup
P O Box 162
Flemington, N.J. 08822
Short Name: **Bk Roundup**
*Cartoons & Caricature;
Original Art of Book
Illustrations*

Book Search
135 Sewickley-Oakmont Road
Pittsburgh, Penna. 15237
Short Name: **Bk Srch-Pit**
*Biography; Juveniles; Cookery
& Gastronomy; General; First
Editions; Americana*

Book Search
9105 Rothery Court
Springfield, Va. 22153
(703) 451-4055
Short Name: **Bk Srch-Spr**
Search Service, without Stock

Book Search Service
36 Kensington Road
Avondale Estates, Ga. 30002
Short Name: **Bk Srch-Avon**
Music

Book Search Service
P O Box 168
Brooklyn, N.Y. 11202
Short Name: **Bk Srch-Bro**
*Political Science & Theory;
Political, Social, & Cultural
History & Thought; Latin
America; Periodicals; Social
Sciences; Voyages, Travels, &
Exploration*

Book Service
P O Box 511
Santa Cruz, Calif. 95061
Short Name: **Bk Srvc-San**
*Literature; History, American;
History; Poetry; Religion &
Theology; Performing Arts*

Book Service Co
P O Box 903
Indianapolis, Ind. 46206
(317) 882-2070
Short Name: **Bk Srvc-Ind**
*General; Out of Print, with
Stock; Scholarly Books;
Literary Criticism; Literature;
History*

Book Shelf
3765 Hillsdale Drive, NE
Cleveland, Tenn. 37311
(615) 472-8408
Short Name: **Bk Shelf-Cle**
*Americana, States; Americana,
Regional; Americana; Florida;
Authors; Alabama*

Book Shoppe
10 North State Strteet
Salt Lake City, Utah 84103
(801) 532-9326
Short Name: **Bk Sh-Salt**
*Utah; Search Service, without
Stock; Voyages, Travels, &
Exploration; Americana, States;
Americana, Regional;
Americana*

Book Stacks, Inc
118 Pine Street
Burlington, Vt. 05401
Short Name: **Bk Stacks-Burl**
*Women & Feminism;
Homosexual & Gay Literature;
Remainders; Alternative
Energy; Little Magazines &
Literary Small Presses; Poetry*

The Book Stall
5899 College Avenue
Oakland, Calif. 94618
Short Name: **Bk Stall-Oak**
*Mathematics; Physics;
Childrens' Books; Cookery &
Gastronomy; Mountaineering;
History of Medicine & Science*

Book Stall Of Rockford
606 Gregory Street
Rockford, Ill. 61108
Short Name: **Bk Stall-Roc**
*Americana; Biography;
Farming, Ranching, &
Livestock; Out of Print, with
Stock; Periodicals; Technology*

Book Stop
2705 Far Hills Avenue
Dayton, Ohio 45419
(513) 293-2772
Short Name: **Bk Stop-Day**
*Out of Print, with Stock;
General; Childrens' Books;
Militaria*

Book Stop Iii
3732 East Flamingo Road
Las Vegas, Nev. 89121
(702) 456-4858
Short Name: **Bk Stop Iii**
*Childrens' Books; Classics;
First Editions; Out of Print,
with Stock; Psychiatry,
Psychology, & Psychonanalysis;
Science Fiction*

Book Store
222 North Main Street
West Bridgewater, Mass. 02379
Short Name: **Bk St-West**
*Search Service, with Stock; Out
of Print, with Stock*

Book Store
8 Depot Square
Englewood, N.J. 07631
(201) 568-6563
Short Name: **Bk St-Engl**
*Out of Print, with Stock;
General; Childrens' Books; Art*

Book Store
132 East Third Avenue
San Mateo, Calif. 94401
(415) 343-2751
Short Name: **Bk St-San**
*Art; Fiction; History;
Performing Arts; Paperbacks
(new); Paintings*

Book Store Of Naples
107 Broad Avenue, South
Naples, Fla. 33940
(813) 261-5960
Short Name: **Bk St-Nap**
Adirondacks; Florida

Book Swap
129 North Highway 101
Solana Beach, Calif. 92075
(714) 755-7323
Short Name: **Bk Swap**
*Civil War & Confederacy;
Biography*

Book Trader
P O Box 603
Fairmont, N.C. 28340
Short Name: **Bk Trader-Fai**
*Americana; Americana, States;
Civil War & Confederacy; Out
of Print, with Stock; North
Carolina; South Carolina*

Book Treasury
6707 Hollywood Boulevard
Hollywood, Calif. 90028
(213) 466-6527
Short Name: **Bk Treasury**
*Science Fiction; Detective
Fiction; First Editions, Modern;
L. Frank Baum & Oziana;
Illustrated Books*

Book Warehouse
2010 Ponce De Leon Boulevard
Coral Gables, Fla. 33134
(305) 448-3223
Short Name: **Bk Warehouse**
*Art; Americana; Humanities;
Literature; Antiques;
Photography*

Book World
P O Box 472
Petoskey, Mich. 49770
(616) 347-8149
Short Name: **Bk World**
Michigan; Americana; Fiction

Book-Friends, Inc
~~457 Third Avenue~~
New York, N.Y. 10016
(212) 689-8746
Short Name: **Bk Friends**
General; Out of Print, with Stock

Bookcell Books
90 Robinwood Road
Hamden, Conn. 06517
(203) 248-0010
Short Name: **Bkcell**
Natural History; Medicine & Science; Technology; Childrens' Books; Illustrated Books; Education

Booked Up
1209 31st Street, NW
Washington, D.C. 20007
(202) 965-3244
Short Name: **Bked Up**
Rare Books; Voyages, Travels, & Exploration; Literature; Books about Books; Literary Criticism

Bookends
1077 Parkway Mall
Napa, Calif. 94558
Short Name: **Bkends-Napa**
New Books; Paperbacks (new); Remainders

Bookery
De Witt Mall
Ithaca, N.Y. 14850
Short Name: **Bkery-Ith**
History of Medicine & Science; New York; Scholarly Books; Sets; Philosophy; Labor History

The Bookery
608 Middle Street
Fairborn, Ohio 45324
(513) 879-1408
Short Name: **Bkery-Fai**
First Editions; First Editions, Modern; Detective Fiction; Paperbacks (new)

Bookfinder
Town & Country Plaza
Pensacola, Fla. 32505
(904) 433-5994
Short Name: **Bkfnder-Pen**
Childrens' Books; New Books; Out of Print, with Stock; Paperbacks (new); Religion & Theology; Search Service, without Stock

Bookfinder
P O Box 86
Cutten, Calif. 95534
(707) 445-0507
Short Name: **Bkfndr-Cut**
General; Rare Books; Out of Print, with Stock

Bookfinders
P O Box 133
Bolivar, Ohio 44612
(816) 874-2302
Short Name: **Bkfndrs-Bol**
Childrens' Books; Detective Fiction; General; Out of Print, with Stock; Search Service, with Stock

Bookfinders Inc
P O Box 2021
Miami Beach, Fla. 33140
Short Name: **Bkfndrs-Mia**
English Literature; Psychiatry, Psychology, & Psychonanalysis; Science; Architecture; Art; Music

Bookfinders Of Fairfax
P O Box 5
Oakton, Va. 22124
Short Name: **Bkfinders-Fair**
Americana; Militaria; Paperbacks (new); Hunting, Fishing & Angling; Naval & Marine

Bookfinders Of Hawaii
211 Kingule Street
Hilo, Haw. 96720
Short Name: **Bkfndrs Hawaii**
Hawaii; Pacific Region; Whaling

Bookfinders Unltd
P O Box 734
Boston, Mass. 02102
(617) 542-3809
Short Name: **Bkfndrs Unltd**
Search Service, with Stock; General

Bookhaven
1110 North Bechtle
Springfield, Ohio 45504
Short Name: **Bkhaven-Spr**
Rare Books; Out of Print, with Stock; Childrens' Books; Paperbacks (new)

Bookhunter
175 West 87th Street
New York, N.Y. 10024
(212) 799-3318
Short Name: **Bkhunter-NYC**
Search Service, without Stock

W J Bookhunter
P O Box 2795
Denver, Colo. 80201
(303) 757-0160
Short Name: **W J Bkhunter**
Falconry; Natural History; Americana; Law; Rare Books; Out of Print, with Stock

The Bookie
116 Burnside Avenue
East Hartford, Conn. 06108
(203) 289-1208
Short Name: **Bkie**
Comic Books; Science Fiction; Paperbacks (new)

Bookie Joint
7246 Reseda Boulevard
Reseda, Calif. 91335
(213) 343-1055
Short Name: **Bkie Joint**
Judaica & Hebraica; Literature; Scholarly Books; Science Fiction; Search Service, with Stock; Social Sciences

Bookland
1025 B' Street
Hayward, Calif. 94541
Short Name: **Bkland-Hay**
Automotive

Bookleggers
6743 North Sheridan Road
Chicago, Ill. 60626
(312) 743-4195
Short Name: **Bkleggers**
First Editions, Modern; Americana; Literature; Voyages, Travels, & Exploration; Fiction; Childrens' Books

Bookmailer
2730 West Broadway
Minneapolis, Minn. 55411
(612) 588-2830
Short Name: **Bkmailer**
First Editions; General; Literary Criticism; Literature; Out of Print, with Stock; Search Service, with Stock

The Bookman
P O Box 1, 809 South Marshall
Sedalia, Mo. 65301
Short Name: **Bkman-Sed**
General

The Bookman Of Arcady
P O Box 1259
Tybee Island, Ga. 31328
(912) 786-5842
Short Name: **Bkman Arcady**
*Biography; Fiction; Literature;
Poetry; Search Service, with
Stock; Broadsides*

The Bookmark
2103 Pacific Avenue
Stockton, Calif. 95204
Short Name: **Bkmark-Sto**
*New Books; California;
Childrens' Books; Rare Books;
Cookery & Gastronomy; Out of
Print, without Stock*

The Bookmark
611 6th Street
Prosser, Wash. 99350
Short Name: **Bkmark-Pro**
*Fiction; Childrens' Books;
Dictionaries; History, American;
Gardening & Horticulture;
Cookery & Gastronomy*

Bookmart
P O Box 101
Gardiner, N.Y. 12525
(914) 255-5141
Short Name: **Bkmart-Gar**
*U.S. Government Publications;
Societies & Associations &
Their Publications; U.S.
Government Publications*

Bookphil Book Search Service
3987 Main Street
Hilliard, Ohio 43026
(614) 876-0442
Short Name: **Bkphil**
*History, American; Militaria;
British Isles; Russia & Easter·;
European Region; Middle East;
Espionage*

Bookpost
P O Box 2171
Dallas, Tex. 75221
(214) 522-2171
Short Name: **Bkpost-Dal**
*Texas; Cookery & Gastronomy;
Economics & Business; First
Editions, Modern; Railroads;
Technology*

Bookpost
962 Greenlake Court
Cardiff, Calif. 92007
(714) 753-3392
Short Name: **Bkpost-Card**
*Search Service, without Stock;
Psychiatry, Psychology, &
Psychonanalysis; Psychiatry,
Psychology, & Psychonanalysis;
Religion & Theology*

The Bookpress Ltd
Box Kp, 420 Prince George
  Street
Williamsburg, Va. 23185
(804) 229-1260
Short Name: **Bkpress**
*Americana; Architecture;
Travel; Books about Books*

Books & Things
473 NE 20th Street
Boca Raton, Fla. 33431
(305) 395-2227
Short Name: **Bks & Thngs-Boc**
*General; History; Fiction; Art;
Out of Print, with Stock*

Books 'N Things
34 East 7th Street
New York, N.Y. 10003
(212) 533-2320
Short Name: **Bks & Thngs-NYC**
*Performing Arts; Dance;
Cinema & Mass Media; Poetry;
Literature; Postcards*

Books Bohemian
P O Box 6246
Glendale, Calif. 91205
Short Name: **Bks Bohemian**
Homosexual & Gay Literature

Books By Mail
1919 Old Town Road, NW 3
Albuquerque, N.Mex. 87104
Short Name: **Bks By Mail**
*Out of Print, with Stock; Out of
Print, without Stock;
Americana, Regional*

Books Etc
P O Box 345
Hastings, Mich. 49058
Short Name: **Bks Etc-Hast**
*General; Childrens' Books;
Cookery & Gastronomy; Crafts
& Trades·*

Books For Embroidery
96 Roundwood Road
Newton, Mass. 02164
(617) 969-0942
Short Name: **Bks Embroid**
*Japan; Lace; Textiles;
Needlework*

Books For Everyone
412 Main Street
Watsonville, Calif. 95076
Short Name: **Bks For Every**
*Paperbacks (new); Social
Sciences; Fiction; Americana;
Technology*

Books Inc
33826 Kennett Park, Box 3798
Greenville, Del. 19807
Short Name: **Bks-Gre**
*General; Gardening &
Horticulture; Cookery &
Gastronomy; Childrens' Books;
Art; Natural History*

Books In Transit
412 North Palm Street
Turlock, Calif. 95380
(209) 632-6984
Short Name: **Bks In Trans**
*Crafts & Trades; Graphic Arts;
Illustrated Books; Printing &
Printing History; Typography &
Type Specimens; Woodcut
Books*

Books Of The Black Bass
402 South 55th Street
Tacoma, Wash. 98408
Short Name: **Bks Black Bass**
Hunting, Fishing & Angling

Books On File
P O Box 195
Union City, N.J. 07087
Short Name: **Bks On File-Uni**
*Search Service, with Stock; Out
of Print, with Stock*

Books Then & Now
2137 University Avenue
Madison, Wisc. 53705
(608) 233-7030
Short Name: **Bks Then & Now**
*Biography; Out of Print, with
Stock; Search Service, with
Stock*

Books Unlimited
922 East Washington
Indianapolis, Ind. 46202
(317) 634-0949
Short Name: **Bks Unltd-Ind**
*Americana, Regional;
Childrens' Books; Comic Books;
General; Out of Print, with
Stock; Paperbacks (new)*

Books Unlimited
1127 Highland Avenue
National City, Calif. 92050
(714) 477-1717
Short Name: **Bks Unltd-Nat**
*Childrens' Books; Cookery &
Gastronomy; Dictionaries;
Medicine & Science; Naval &
Marine; Technology*

Books-N-Things
504 Fox Street
Terrell, Tex. 75160
(214) 563-9867
Short Name: **Bks & Thngs-Ter**
*Childrens' Books; Civil War &
Confederacy; Paperbacks (new)*

Booksearch, Waldenbooks 834
1104 Baybrook Mall
Friendswood, Tex. 77546
(713) 488-0955
Short Name: **Bksearch-Fri**
Search Service, without Stock

Bookseller
111 North 2nd
Cherokee, Iowa 51012
Short Name: **Bkseller-Cher**
*Cookery & Gastronomy;
Childrens' Books; Iowa*

The Bookseller, Inc
521 West Exchange Street
Akron, Ohio 44302
(216) 762-3101
Short Name: **Bkseller-Akr**
*General; Militaria; Bookbinding
& Restoration; Aviation &
Aeronautics; Ohio*

Bookseller's Row
2445 North Lincoln
Chicago, Ill. 60614
(312) 348-1170
Short Name: **Bkseller's Row**
*General; Out of Print, with
Stock*

Bookshelf
534 West Faulkner
El Dorado, Ark. 71730
(501) 862-0972
Short Name: **Bkshelf-El D**
*Detective Fiction; Paperbacks
(new); Science Fiction;
Childrens' Books*

Bookshelf Inc
Greentree Mall
Clarksville, Ind. 47130
(812) 283-4313
Short Name: **Bkshelf-Cla**
*New Books; Childrens' Books;
Women & Feminism; Reference;
Cookery & Gastronomy;
Paperbacks (new)*

Bookshop
Millers Hills Center
Warner Robins, Ga. 31093
(912) 922-7231
Short Name: **Bksh-War**
*Art; Out of Print, with Stock;
Search Service, with Stock*

Booksource
P O Box 43, 7 Chester Road
Swarthmore, Penna. 19081
Short Name: **Bksource**
*Americana; Biography; Classics;
First Editions; History; Search
Service, with Stock*

Bookstack
112 West Lexington Avenue
Elkhart, Ind. 46516
Short Name: **Bkstack-Elk**
*Americana, Regional; Comic
Books; Gardening &
Horticulture; Hunting, Fishing
& Angling; Natural History;
Out of Print, with Stock*

Bookstock
7 Church Street
Bernardsville, N.J. 07924
(201) 221-9024
Short Name: **Bkstock**
*First Editions; Rare Books; Out
of Print, with Stock; Childrens'
Books; Art; Search Service,
with Stock*

The Bookstop
3369 Mt Diablo Boulevard
Lafayette, Calif. 94549
Short Name: **Bkstop-Laf**
*General; Search Service, with
Stock*

Bookstore
9 Housatonic Street
Lenox, Mass. 01240
Short Name: **Bkst-Len**
*Little Magazines & Literary
Small Presses; Literature;
Paperbacks (new); Poetry;
Religion & Theology; Women
& Feminism*

Bookstore
Jenkintown Square
Jenkintown, Penna. 19046
Short Name: **Bkst-Jenk**
*Cookery & Gastronomy;
Americana; Antiques;
Childrens' Books; Gardening &
Horticulture; Americana,
Regional*

Bookstore
4316 North Oakland Avenue
Milwaukee, Wisc. 53211
Short Name: **Bkst-Mil**
*New Books; Paperbacks (new);
Detective Fiction*

Bookstore
316 Westmoreland Drive
Vernon Hills, Ill. 60061
(312) 362-2011
Short Name: **Bkst-Vern**
*American Indians; Americana;
Arctica & Antarctica; Horses;
Search Service, with Stock;
Voyages, Travels, &
Exploration*

The Bookstore
Fairbanks, Alas. 99701
Short Name: **Bkst-Fai**
*Childrens' Books; Alaska;
Crafts & Trades; Economics &
Business; Farming, Ranching, &
Livestock; Out of Print, with
Stock*

Booktraders Inc
P O Box 9403
Winter Haven, Fla. 33880
(813) 299-4904
Short Name: **Bk Traders**
*Americana; Comic Books;
Mathematics; Paperbacks (new);
Science Fiction; Search Service,
with Stock*

Bookwood
P O Box 263
Westwood, N.J. 07675
Short Name: **Bkwood**
Soccer; Beverages; Wines

Bookworm
Baron Steuben Pl, Market &
   Center
Corning, N.Y. 14830
Short Name: **Bkworm-Cor**
*Americana; Civil War &
Confederacy; American Indians*

Bookworm & Silverfish
P O Box 516
Wytheviile, Va. 24382
(703) 686-5813
Short Name: **Bkworm & Silver**
*Appalachia; Appraisals &
Appraisal Services; Black
Literature & Black Studies;
Civil War & Confederacy;
Trade Catalogues; Technology*

The Bookwrights
P O Box 1298
Nantucket Island, Mass. 02554
Short Name: **Bkwrights**
*Science Fiction; Rare Books;
First Editions; Illustrated
Books; Fantasy*

Borderland Books
P O Box 13
Sylvania, Ohio 43560
Short Name: **Borderland**
*Americana; Kentucky; Civil
War & Confederacy*

Borene Bookstore
320 West 4th Street
Willmar, Minn. 56201
Short Name: **Borene**
General

James M W Borg
8 South Michigan Avenue
Chicago, Ill. 60603
(312) 236-5111
Short Name: **J M W Borg**
*English Literature; American
Literature; Autographed
Material & Autographs;
Americana; American Diaries &
Narratives; Association Books*

Beverly Boss
69 Riverview Place
Manchester, N.H. 03104
(603) 669-0913
Short Name: **B Boss**
*Out of Print, without Stock;
Search Service, without Stock*

Thomas G Boss
80 Monmouth Street
Brookline, Mass. 02146
Short Name: **T G Boss**
*Press Books & Fine Printing;
Imprints; Bibliography;
Literature; Fine & Rare
Bindings*

Boston Book Annex
906 Beacon Street
Boston, Mass. 02215
(617) 266-1090
Short Name: **Boston Annex**
*General; Literature; Out of
Print, with Stock; Out of Print,
without Stock*

Roy V Boswell (Mail Only)
P O Box 278
Gilroy, Calif. 95020
(408) 842-9702
Short Name: **R V Boswell**
*Out of Print, with Stock; Rare
Books; Voyages, Travels, &
Exploration; Maps, Atlases, &
Cartography*

Boulevard Books
P O Box 89
Topanga, Calif. 90290
(213) 455-1036
Short Name: **Boulevard**
Detective Fiction; Drama

W M Boulton
4003 Medford Drive, SE
Huntsville, Ala. 35802
Short Name: **W M Boulton**
*Americana, Regional; American
Indians; Americana, States;
Civil War & Confederacy; The
South*

Bound For Pleasure
31 Belmont
San Francisco, Calif. 94117
Short Name: **Bound Pleas**
Childrens' Books; History

E R Bowes
P O Box 3166
Vancouver, B.C. V6B 3X6
Short Name: **E R Bowes**
*Arctica & Antarctica; Canada
& Canadiana; Visual
Synthesizers; Voyages, Travels,
& Exploration; Illustrated
Books; Parenting*

Lance Bowling
2625 Colt Road
Rancho Palos Verdes, Calif.
   90274
(213) 427-1494
Short Name: **L Bowling**
*Americana; Cookery &
Gastronomy; Documents;
Ephemera; Reference; Music*

Judith Bowman, Books
Pound Ridge Road
Bedford, N.Y. 10506
Short Name: **J Bowman**
*Hunting, Fishing & Angling;
Natural History; Sporting*

Boysag Books
Mount Riga Road, Box 363
Salisbury, Conn. 06068
Short Name: **Boysag**
*Americana, Regional;
Southwestern America*

Bradford Books
West Road
Bennington, Vt. 05201
(802) 447-0387
Short Name: **Bradford**
*General; Out of Print, with
Stock; Search Service, with
Stock*

Van Allen Bradley
P O Box 4130, Hopi Station
Scottsdale, Ariz. 85258
Short Name: **V A Bradley**
*First Editions; Americana; Art;
Color Plate Books;
Autographed Material &
Autographs; Manuscripts*

Nancy Hubbard Brady
46 Walnut Street
East Aurora, N.Y. 14052
Short Name: **N H Brady**
Roycrofters & Elbert Hubbard

Osee H Brady
12 Elm Street
Assonet, Mass. 02702
(617) 644-5073
Short Name: **O H Brady**
*Out of Print, with Stock;
General; Biography*

Brainard Book Company
P O Box 444
La Grange, Ill. 60525
Short Name: **Brainard**
*Out of Print, with Stock; Search
Service, with Stock*

Marilyn Braiterman-Books
20 Whitfield Road
Baltimore, Md. 21210
(301) 235-4848
Short Name: **M Braiterman**
*Books about Books; Childrens'
Books; First Editions;
Illustrated Books; Press Books
& Fine Printing; Printing &
Printing History*

Branford Rare Book
221 Montowese Street
Branford, Conn. 06405
Short Name: **Branford**
*Voyages, Travels, &
Exploration; Americana; Maps,
Atlases, & Cartography*

Brassers
8701 Seminole Boulevard
Seminole, Fla. 33542
Short Name: **Brassers**
*Sporting; Paperbacks (new); Out
of Print, with Stock; Foreign
Languages; Americana,
Regional; Search Service, with
Stock*

Brattle Book Shop
25 West Street
Boston, Mass. 02111
(617) 542-0210
Short Name: **Brattle**
General

Bread, Wine & Co
R R #1, Box 97
Cream Ridge, N.J. 08514
(609) 758-3388
Short Name: **Bread, Wine**
*Biography; Industry & Labor;
Medicine & Science;
Paperbacks (new); Poetry;
Religion & Theology*

Jim Breen-Books
P O Box 7764
Stockton, Calif. 95207
Short Name: **J Breen**
Horses

Brennan Books
P O Box 9002
Salt Lake City, Utah 84109
(801) 278-7946
Short Name: **Brennan**
*Appraisals & Appraisal
Services; Americana, Regional;
Geneaologies; Orientalia; Out of
Print, with Stock; Search
Service, with Stock*

**Brentano's Rare Book
Department**
586 Fifth Avenue
New York, N.Y. 10036
Short Name: **Brentano's-NYC**
*Literature; Illustrated Books;
Fine & Rare Bindings; Press
Books & Fine Printing*

Martin Breslauer, Inc
P O Box 607
New York, N.Y. 10028
(212) 794-2995
Short Name: **M Breslauer**
*Autographed Material &
Autographs; Illustrated Books;
Fine & Rare Bindings;
Incunabula & Early Printing;
Manuscripts*

Mrs L M Brew
P O Box 246
Kiln, Miss. 39556
(601) 467-9750
Short Name: **Mrs L M Brew**
*General; Apiculture; Cookery &
Gastronomy; Needlework;
Search Service, with Stock*

Harvey W Brewer (Appt Only)
P O Box 322
Closter, N.J. 07624
(201) 768-4414
Short Name: **H W Brewer**
*Art; Architecture; Color Plate
Books; Natural History; Maps,
Atlases, & Cartography; Rare
Books*

Brick House Book Shop
Morristown Corners, Vt. 05661
(802) 888-4300
Short Name: **Brick Hse**
General

Brick Row Book Shop
278 Post Street, #303
San Francisco, Calif. 94108
(415) 398-0414
Short Name: **Brick Row**
*Literature; American Literature;
Mexico; Texas; Bibliography;
Latin America*

Herb Bridges-Bridges & Cole
Sharpsburg, Ga. 30277
Short Name: **H Bridges**
Authors

**Bridgton Book House (Summer
Only)**
Depot Street & Rte #302
Bridgton, Maine 04009
Short Name: **Bridgton**
General

British Stamp Exchange
12 Fairlawn
North Weymouth, Mass. 02191
Short Name: **British Stamp**
*Art; Arctica & Antarctica; Civil
War & Confederacy; Cookery &
Gastronomy; Sets; Medicine &
Science*

Broadfoot's Bookmark
Rte #2, Box 28-A
Wendell, N.C. 27591
Short Name: **Broadfoot's**
*Americana; Bookbinding &
Restoration; Civil War &
Confederacy; General; Maps,
Atlases, & Cartography; Prints*

Warren F Broderick, Books
695 Fourth Avenue
Lansingburgh, N.Y. 12182
(518) 235-4041
Short Name: **W F Broderick**
*Gardening & Horticulture;
Color Plate Books; Natural
History; Botany*

Broken Kettle Books
Rte #1
Akron, Iowa 51001
(712) 568-2114
Short Name: **Broken Kettle**
*Farming, Ranching, &
Livestock; Automotive; Pacific
Region; General*

Bromer Booksellers
607 Boylston Street At Copley
Sq
Boston, Mass. 02116
Short Name: **Bromer**
*Illustrated Books; Press Books
& Fine Printing; First Editions;
Juveniles; Miniature Books;
Early Printed Books*

Maury A Bromsen Associates, Inc
770 Boylston Street
Boston, Mass. 02199
(617) 266-7060
Short Name: **M A Bromsen**
*Autographed Material &
Autographs; Manuscripts;
Americana; Latin America;
Paintings; Appraisals &
Appraisal Services*

Brooklyn Gallery Of Coins
8745 Fourth Avenue
Brooklyn, N.Y. 11209
Short Name: **Bklyn Gall**
*Numismatics; Philately &
Philatelic Literature; Horology*

C W Brooks
713 Paul Street
Newport News, Va. 23605
Short Name: **C W Brooks**
*Science Fiction; Fantasy;
Illustrated Books*

Broude Brothers
56 West 45th Street
New York, N.Y. 10036
Short Name: **Broude Bros**
Music; Art; Dance

G D Brown-Books
7001 Bancroft Street
Toledo, Ohio 43617
(419) 841-4979
Short Name: **G D Brown**
*General; Great Lakes;
Americana; Archaeology; Art;
Religion & Theology*

Robert K Brown, Art & Books
120 East 86th Street
New York, N.Y. 10028
(212) 427-4014
Short Name: **R K Brown**
*Fine Arts; Illustrated Books;
Posters*

Brownstone Books
P O Box 637, Cooper Station
New York, N.Y. 10275
Short Name: **Brownstone**
*American Literature;
Americana; Bibliography;
Books about Books; Printing &
Printing History*

Browsers' Book Shop
107 North Capitol Way
Olympia, Wash. 98501
Short Name: **Browser's**
*General; Out of Print, with
Stock*

The Browsery
547 South Mendenhall Street
Greensboro, N.C. 27403
(919) 273-7259
Short Name: **Browsery**
*Americana, Regional;
Biography; Fiction; General;
Literature; Out of Print, with
Stock*

Joan Marie Bruna
1215 South Lombard
Cicero, Ill. 60650
(312) 652-3459
Short Name: **J M Bruna**
Out of Print, with Stock

Angelo Brutico Jr
P O Box 151
Paoli, Penna. 19301
(215) 647-1621
Short Name: **A Brutico Jr**
Authors

John C Bryan-Antiquarian Books
903 Clifton Avenue
Newark, N.J. 07104
Short Name: **J C Bryan**
*Out of Print, with Stock;
Technology; Science;
Philosophy; Mathematics*

Bryant's
467 Commercial Street
Provincetown, Mass. 02657
(617) 487-0134
Short Name: **Bryant's**
*Fishing & Angling; Naval &
Marine; Whaling; Cape Cod &
Martha's Vineyard; Arctica &
Antarctica; Crafts & Trades*

Bryn Mawr Book Shop
56-1/2 Whitney Avenue
New Haven, Conn. 06510
(203) 562-4217
Short Name: **Bryn Mawr-N Hav**
*Black Literature & Black
Studies; Childrens' Books;
Cookery & Gastronomy;
Detective Fiction; Paperbacks
(new); Psychiatry, Psychology,
& Psychonanalysis*

Bryn Mawr Bookshop
19 Dove Street
Albany, N.Y. 12210
Short Name: **Bryn Mawr-Alb**
*General; Rare Books; Printing
& Printing History; Phonograph
Records; Music; Childrens'
Books*

Buccaneer Books Inc
P O Box 518
Laguna Beach, Calif. 92652
(714) 494-4243
Short Name: **Buccaneer**
Search Service, with Stock

Jutta Buck
4 East 95th Street
New York, N.Y. 10028
(212) 289-4577
Short Name: **J Buck**
*Color Plate Books; Illustrated
Books; Botany; Natural
History; Prints*

K Buck
P O Box 11155
San Francisco, Calif. 94101
Short Name: **K Buck**
*Natural History; Illustrated
Books; Printing & Printing
History; Architecture; Woodcut
Books*

Buckabest Books And Bindery
247 Fulton Street
Palo Alto, Calif. 94301
(415) 325-2965
Short Name: **Buckabest**
*Bookbinding & Restoration;
Performing Arts; Appraisals &
Appraisal Services;
Conservation; Search Service,
with Stock; General*

John C Buckley Book Search Service
2701 Highland Park
Richland, Mich. 49083
Short Name: **J C Buckley**
Search Service, without Stock

E Don Bullian, Back Number Magazine
7-D Ridge Road
Greenbelt, Md. 20770
(301) 345-7430
Short Name: **E D Bullian**
*Periodicals; Specialized
Publications*

Bullock's Old Books
269 Dalhousie Street
Amherstburg, Ont. N9U 1W8
Short Name: **Bullock's**
Canada & Canadiana;
Childrens' Books; History;
General; Incunabula & Early
Printing

Bunker Books (Mail Only)
704 Safford Avenue, Box 1638
Spring Valley, Calif. 92077
(714) 469-3296
Short Name: **Bunker**
Childrens' Books; Cookery &
Gastronomy; Fiction;
Periodicals; Reference; Science
Fiction

Bunkhouse Books
R F D #5
Gardiner, Maine 04345
Short Name: **Bunkhse**
Maine Authors; Local History;
Sporting; Militaria; Americana,
Regional

Bunter Books
P O Box 1557
Evanston, Ill. 60204
Short Name: **Bunter**
Search Service, without Stock;
Out of Print, without Stock;
Collection Development;
General; Fiction; Religion &
Theology

Joanne Burger
57 Blue Bonnet Court
Lake Jackson, Tex. 77566
Short Name: **J Burger**
Science Fiction; Illustrated
Books

William J B Burger
P O Box 832, Gloria Lane
Pine Grove, Calif. 95665
(209) 296-7970
Short Name: **W J B Burger**
Americana; Western Americana;
Paintings; Prints; Manuscripts;
Autographed Material &
Autographs

Virginia Burgman
3198 Hidden Valley Drive
Santa Rosa, Calif. 95404
Short Name: **V Burgman**
Little Magazines & Literary
Small Presses; Periodicals;
Hunting, Fishing & Angling;
Americana, States; Women &
Feminism

James H Burke
315 East 68th Street
New York, N.Y. 10021
(212) 861-7462
Short Name: **J H Burke**
Autographed Material &
Autographs; First Editions,
Modern; Press Books & Fine
Printing; Out of Print, with
Stock; Poetry

Burke's Book Store, Inc
634 Poplar Avenue
Memphis, Tenn. 38105
(901) 527-7484
Short Name: **Burke's**
Americana, Regional; First
Editions; Civil War &
Confederacy; Out of Print, with
Stock; Rare Books; Search
Service, with Stock

Burkwood Books
P O Box 172
Urbana, Ill. 61801
Short Name: **Burkwood**
Western Americana; Africa;
Fore-Edge Painting; Fine &
Rare Bindings; Autographed
Material & Autographs;
Biography

Julian Burnett, Books
P O Box 229
Atlanta, Ga. 30301
(404) 252-5812
Short Name: **J Burnett**
Arctica & Antarctica; Civil War
& Confederacy; Naval &
Marine; Voyages, Travels, &
Exploration; Whaling; Panama
& Panama Canal

Thomas W Burrows
P O Box 400
Downers Grove, Ill. 60515
Short Name: **T W Burrows**
Classics; First Editions;
Literature; Rare Books;
Scholarly Books; Search
Service, with Stock

Harold M Burstein
16 Park Place
Waltham, Mass. 02154
Short Name: **H M Burstein**
Rare Books; Americana;
Bibliography; Reference; First
Editions; Childrens' Books

Joan & Walt Bursten
527 Madison Avenue
New York, N.Y. 10022
Short Name: **J & W Bursten**
Ephemera; Childrens' Books;
Automobiles, Classic; Trade
Cards; Trade Catalogues;
Photography

Burt's Books
3220 North Main Street, #102
Dayton, Ohio 45405
Short Name: **Burt's**
Dogs

John Burtniak
P O Box 304
Thorold, Ont. L2V 3Z3
Short Name: **J Burtniak**
Americana, Regional; Printing
in Canada

Burton's Bookstore
300-B Main Street
Greenport, N.Y. 11944
(516) 477-1161
Short Name: **Burton's**
General; First Editions,
Modern; Authors; Author
Collections; Out of Print, with
Stock; Paperbacks (new)

A Buschke
80 East 11th Street
New York, N.Y. 10003
(212) 254-2555
Short Name: **A Buschke**
Chess, Checkers, & Draughts;
Periodicals; Autographed
Material & Autographs; Russia
& Eastern European Region;
Rare Books; Prints

G F Bush
P O Box 82
Stonington, Maine 04681
(207) 367-2484
Short Name: **G F Bush**
Fiction; Poetry; General;
Biography

467 COMMERCIAL STREET
PROVINCETOWN, MA 02657

We are looking for material on the **Fisheries as an Industry, Its Methods, Appliances and Watercraft,** such as, but not limited to the following:

Publications of U.S. Commission of Fish and Fisheries; (U.S.) Commissioner of Fisheries; (U.S.) Bureau of Commercial Fisheries; (U.S.) National Marine Fisheries Service; U.S. Department of State; U.S. National Museum; (U.S.) Department of the Navy; U.S. Life-Saving Service; (U.S.) Light-House Board; U.S. Coast Guard; Boston Fish Bureau; Gloucester Fishermen's Institute; Gloucester Master Mariners Association.

Also, *Record of American and Foreign Shipping; Merchant Vessels of the U.S.; Canada/List of Shipping; Official Reference Book of Fishermen's Union of the Atlantic; Fishermen of the Atlantic; Fishing Gazette; Atlantic Fisherman's Almanac; Fishes of the Western North Atlantic.*

Publications of any British or Canadian commercial fisheries' agencies, the Atlantic Coast Fisheries Co. Also fishing charts, cold storage refrigeration of fish (1890-1940), any register of American yachts, trade catalogs about commercial fisheries or boatbuilding (Higgins and Gifford), reports of any state fish commission.

The works of: Harold Innes, Edward Ackerman, Frederick Wallace, Shebnah Rich, Henry Bigelow, Lorenzo Sabine, David Storer, G.B. Goode, Howard Chapelle, Dana Story, George Barker, Raymond Mc Farland, Albert Church, John Cook.

*

We are also looking for material on **Provincetown, Massachusetts:**

Copies of *Provincetown Banner; Provincetown Advocate; Beacon; New Beacon; The First Resident Directory of Provincetown, Mass.,* 1886; *The Second Resident Directory of Provincetown, Mass.,* 1890; *Resident and Business Directory of Cape Cod, Mass.,* 1901.

Also the works of Henry J. James, Mary Heaton Vorse, Harry Kemp, Frank Shay, Susan Glaspell, Donald Mac Millan, John Dos Passos, John Reed, Louise Bryant, Wilbur Steele, N.W.P. Smith, Ida Rauh, Jeremiah Digges.

Carol Butcher, Books
3955 New Road
Youngstown, Ohio 44515
(216) 793-2030
Short Name: **C Butcher**
*Dogs; Hunting, Fishing &
Angling; Horses*

Buteo Books
P O Box 481
Vermillion, S.D. 57069
(605) 624-4343
Short Name: **Buteo**
*Natural History; Birds &
Ornithology; Zoology; Science*

Roger Butterfield, Inc
White House, Rte #205
Hartwick, N.Y. 13348
(607) 293-8823
Short Name: **R Butterfield**
*Americana; New York;
Political, Social, & Cultural
History & Thought*

John R Butterworth
742 West 11th Street
Claremont, Calif. 91711
(714) 626-0763
Short Name: **J R Butterworth**
*Author Collections;
Autographed Material &
Autographs; Fiction; First
Editions, Modern; Literature;
Scholarly Books*

Button Company
1712 Julie Court, Comstock
  Place
Cornwells Heights, Penna.
  19020
Short Name: **Button**
C. S. Forester

Bygone Books
91 College Street
Burlington, Vt. 05401
(802) 864-4486
Short Name: **Bygone**
*Geography; Out of Print, with
Stock; Search Service, with
Stock*

C

Cabin In The Pines Bookshop
Rte #2
Potsdam, N.Y. 13676
(315) 265-9036
Short Name: **Cabin In Pines**
*Americana, Regional; Fiction;
Biography; History, American;
Science Fiction; Search Service,
with Stock*

A Cabinet Of Books
P O Box 195
Watertown, Conn. 06795
(203) 274-4825
Short Name: **Cabinet Of**
*Americana; Hunting, Fishing &
Angling; Illustrated Books;
Natural History; Shooting &
Firearms; Skating*

The Cache
7157 West U S 34
Loveland, Colo. 80537
(303) 667-1081
Short Name: **Cache**
*Colorado; Western Americana;
Zane Grey; Paperbacks (new);
Out of Print, with Stock; Search
Service, with Stock*

Cadenza Booksellers
8 Brilner Drive
Smithtown, N.Y. 11787
Short Name: **Cadenza**
Music

Richard H Cady
1265 Sterling Avenue
Palatine, Ill. 60067
(312) 358-5389
Short Name: **R H Cady**
*First Editions; Books about
Books; Autographed Material
& Autographs; Fine & Rare
Bindings; Press Books & Fine
Printing; Appraisals &
Appraisal Services*

Caissa Books
121 SE 5th Street
Minneapolis, Minn. 55414
(612) 379-7841
Short Name: **Caissa**
Chess, Checkers, & Draughts

Calderwoods Books
P O Box F
Long Valley, N.J. 07853
(201) 876-3001
Short Name: **Calderwoods**
*Derrydale Press; Horses;
Hunting, Fishing & Angling;
Press Books & Fine Printing;
Sporting*

**California Book Auction
  Galleries**
1749 North La Brea Avenue
Hollywood, Calif. 90046
(415) 775-0426
Short Name: **CBAG-Hol**
Auctions & Auctioneers

**California Book Auction
  Galleries**
358 Golden Gate Avenue
San Francisco, Calif. 94102
Short Name: **CBAG-S F**
Auctions & Auctioneers

Call Me Ishmael Books
P O Box 595
Saugatuck, Mich. 49493
Short Name: **Call Me Ishmael**
*Great Lakes; Out of Print, with
Stock; Search Service, with
Stock*

Callahan & Company Booksellers
130 South Washington Street
Easton, Md. 21601
Short Name: **Callahan & Co**
Hunting, Fishing & Angling; Birds & Ornithology; Natural History; Shooting & Firearms; Conservation

Camden House Book Company
4395 Mt Royal Boulevard
Allison Park, Penna. 15101
(412) 486-2693
Short Name: **Camden Hse**
General

Camelot Books
7603 Mulberry Bottom Lane
Springfield, Va. 22153
(703) 455-9540
Short Name: **Camelot**
Art; First Editions, Modern; Illustrated Books; Inscribed Books; Little Magazines & Literary Small Presses; Press Books & Fine Printing

Cameron's Books & Magazines
336 SW Third Avenue
Portland, Ore. 97204
Short Name: **Cameron's**
General; Search Service, with Stock; Magazines

Campbell Book Shop
428 East Campbell Avenue
Campbell, Calif. 95008
Short Name: **Campbell-Camp**
California; Poetry; Out of Print, with Stock

Campbell's Books
P O Box 2125
Livermore, Calif. 94550
Short Name: **Campbell's**
Militaria; Search Service, with Stock

Canada Book Auction Galleries
35 Front Street
Toronto, Ont. M5E 1B3
(416) 368-4326
Short Name: **Canada Bk Auct**
Auctions & Auctioneers

Canine Connection-E Kirchner-Dean
10606 Manor Court
Manassas, Va. 22110
Short Name: **Canine Conn**
Dogs

J S Canner Co
49-65 Lansdowne
Boston, Mass. 02215
Short Name: **J S Canner**
Periodicals; Reference; Little Magazines & Literary Small Presses; U.S. Government Publications

Canterbury Bookshop
P O Box 177
Georgetown, Conn. 06829
Short Name: **Canterbury-Geo**
Science Fiction; Detective Fiction; Childrens' Books; Edgar Rice Burroughs; Horatio Alger; Search Service, with Stock

Canterbury Bookshop
63 East Adams Street, #300
Chicago, Ill. 60603
Short Name: **Canterbury-Chi**
Books about Books; Out of Print, with Stock; Biography; Hunting, Fishing & Angling; Scholarly Books; First Editions

Cantrells' Books
15 South Pearl Street, Box 311
North East, Penna. 16428
(814) 725-3681
Short Name: **Cantrells'**
Inland Waterways

Cape Cod Clutter
3523 Fifth Avenue
San Diego, Calif. 92103
(714) 291-8088
Short Name: **Cape Cod-San**
Americana; Books about Books; Cookery & Gastronomy; Latin America; Out of Print, with Stock

Caravan Book Store
550 South Grand Avenue
Los Angeles, Calif. 90071
Short Name: **Caravan-L A**
California; Cookery & Gastronomy; Fine & Rare Bindings; Rare Books; Aviation & Aeronautics; Ships & The Sea

Caravan Books
233 South Knoblock
Stillwater, Okla. 74074
(405) 372-6227
Short Name: **Caravan-Sti**
Americana; Architecture; Childrens' Books; Religion & Theology; Science Fiction; Search Service, with Stock

Caravan-Marittime Books, Mail Only
87-06 168th Place
Jamaica, N.Y. 11432
Short Name: **Caravan-Marit**
Arctica & Antarctica; Naval & Marine; Manuscript Logbooks; Nautica; Voyages, Travels, & Exploration; Yachts, Yachting, & Sailing

Denis Carbonneau
P O Box 50, Cooper Station
New York, N.Y. 10276
(212) 989-2737
Short Name: **D Carbonneau**
Folklore; Search Service, with Stock; Collection Development; Scholarly Books; Social Sciences

Art Carduner
6228 Greene Street
Philadelphia, Penna. 19144
Short Name: **A Carduner**
Americana; Fiction; History, American; Literature; Paperbacks (new); Performing Arts

Bernard Conwell Carlitz
1901 Chestnut Street
Philadelphia, Penna. 19103
(215) 563-6608
Short Name: **B C Carltiz**
Americana; First Editions; Illustrated Books; Manuscripts; Maps, Atlases, & Cartography; Medicine & Science

Carlos Book Stall
1115 San Carlos Avenue
San Carlos, Calif. 94070
(415) 593-3392
Short Name: **Carlos**
Rare Books; General; California; Fore-Edge Painting

Carmel Bookshop
P O Box 682
Carmel, Ind. 46032
(317) 534-4862
Short Name: **Carmel**
Search Service, with Stock

Carmichael's Bookstore
1582 Bardstown Road
Louisville, Ken. 40205
(502) 456-6951
Short Name: **Carmichael's**
*First Editions, Modern; Fiction;
New Books; Search Service,
with Stock; Women &
Feminism*

Carnegie Book Shop, Inc
140 East 59th Street
New York, N.Y. 10022
(212) 755-4861
Short Name: **Carnegie**
*Rare Books; Autographed
Material & Autographs;
Manuscripts; Americana*

Carney Books
44 Elm Street
Oneonta, N.Y. 13820
(607) 432-5360
Short Name: **Carney**
General; Ephemera

Carolina Bookshop
1601 East Independence
   Boulevard
Charlotte, N.C. 28205
(704) 375-7305
Short Name: **Carolina**
*Americana, Regional; Black
Literature & Black Studies;
Civil War & Confederacy;
History, American; North
Carolina; Out of Print, with
Stock*

L E Carpenter
P O Box 96
Bartlow, Ohio 45712
(304) 678-2602
Short Name: **L E Carpenter**
Search Service, without Stock

Carrocel Bookshop
P O Box 2294
Rockville, Md. 20852
Short Name: **Carrocell**
*Childrens' Books; First
Editions; Foreign Languages;
Cookery & Gastronomy*

Carry Back Books
Route 10, Dartmouth College
   Highway
Haverhill, N.H. 03765
(603) 989-5943
Short Name: **Carry Back**
*Americana; Vermont;
Americana, Regional; First
Editions; Photography;
Ephemera*

Cartesian Bookstore
2445 Dwight Way
Berkeley, Calif. 94704
(415) 549-3973
Short Name: **Cartesian**
*Philosophy; Theology; Classics;
Ancient Civilizations; Church
History; Archaeology*

Cartographics
P O Box 67, Main Street
North Stonington, Conn. 06359
(203) 535-3152
Short Name: **Cartographics**
*Maps, Atlases, & Cartography;
Prints; Appraisals & Appraisal
Services*

Sally S Carver
179 South Street
Chestnut Hill, Mass. 02167
Short Name: **S S Carver**
Postcards

Roger F Casavant
88 Dudley Road
Wayland, Mass. 01778
Short Name: **R F Casavant**
*Americana; American
Literature; Juveniles;
Illustrated Books; Ephemera;
Voyages, Travels, &
Exploration*

John Cashman Books
10 East Rogues Path
Huntington Station, N.Y. 11746
Short Name: **J Cashman**
*Periodicals; Newspapers;
Literature; First Editions;
Cinema & Mass Media; Books
about Books*

Casperson Books
1303 Buchanan Road, Box 634
Niles, Mich. 49120
(616) 683-2888
Short Name: **Casperson**
General

Barry Cassidy Rare Books
2003 T' Street
Sacramento, Calif. 95814
(916) 456-6307
Short Name: **B Cassidy**
*Autographed Material &
Autographs; Manuscripts;
Association Books; First
Editions; Ephemera; First
Editions, Modern*

William J Cassidy
109 East 65th Street
Kansas City, Mo. 64113
Short Name: **W J Cassidy**
Economics & Business; Dance

Brian E Cassie-Ibis Books
349 Exchange Street
Millis, Mass. 02054
(617) 376-2294
Short Name: **B E Cassie**
*Natural History; Birds &
Ornithology; Mollusks*

Castalia Books
P O Box 92534
Milwaukee, Wisc. 53202
Short Name: **Castalia**
*First Editions; First Editions,
Modern; Incunabula & Early
Printing; Rare Books; Science
Fiction*

M Castelli
55 Terrace
San Anselmo, Calif. 94960
Short Name: **M Castelli**
*Childrens' Books; Color Plate
Books; Illustrated Books;
Literature; Poetry*

Jo-Ann And Richard Casten
Little Bay Road
Wading River, N.Y. 11792
Short Name: **J & R Casten**
*Maps, Atlases, & Cartography;
Rare Books*

Cat Book Center
P O Box 112, Wykagyl Station
New Rochelle, N.Y. 10804
Short Name: **Cat Center**
Cats

Catawba River Books
Rte #10, Box 120
Morganton, N.C. 28655
(704) 433-5478
Short Name: **Catawba River**
*General; Out of Print, with
Stock; Social Sciences;
Humanities*

James P Cather
2501 Seventh Avenue, South
Birmingham, Ala. 35233
Short Name: **J P Cather**
*Alabama; Civil War &
Confederacy; Americana; The
South*

Catholic Book Collector
381 Wrentham Road
Bellingham, Mass. 02019
(617) 883-4344
Short Name: **Cath Bk Coll**
*Religion & Theology;
Bibliography; Reference; Out of
Print, with Stock*

Cathryn Books
P O Box 7433 W
Trenton, N.J. 08628
Short Name: **Cathryn**
*Medicine & Science; Performing
Arts; Literature; First Editions,
Modern; Poetry; Literary
Criticism*

Tracy Catledge
P O Box 583
Fern Park, Fla. 32730
Short Name: **T Catledge**
*Boy Scouts; Series Books for
Boys & Girls*

Kathleen Caughren
284 Purdue
Berkeley, Calif. 94708
Short Name: **K Caughren**
Cookery & Gastronomy; Wines

Caveat Emptor
208 South Dunn
Bloomington, Ind. 47401
(812) 332-9995
Short Name: **Caveat Emptor**
*Science Fiction; Scholarly
Books; Out of Print, with Stock;
First Editions; Detective
Fiction; Search Service, with
Stock*

Celestial Books
P O Box 1066
La   Ca   91011
(213) 790-4984
Short Name: **Celestial**
*Astronomy; Physics; Medicine
& Science; Rare Books; Optics*

Cellar Book Shop
18090 Wyoming
Detroit, Mich. 48221
(313) 861-1776
Short Name: **Cellar**
*Pacific Region; Voyages,
Travels, & Exploration*

H Celnick
2144 Muliner Avenue
Bronx, N.Y. 10462
(212) 823-5731
Short Name: **H Clenick**
*Gardening & Horticulture;
Judaica & Hebraica; Medicine
& Science; Natural History;
Natural Healing*

Celtic Cross Books
P O Box 728
Windsor, Vt. 05089
Short Name: **Celtic Cross**
*Catholica; Religion &
Theology; Philosophy*

Centauri Books & Herbs
Duverus Building
Seligman, Mo. 65745
(314) 662-7700
Short Name: **Centauri**
*Out of Print, without Stock;
Search Service, without Stock;
New Books; Herbology &
Herbs; Americana*

Walter Chadde-Books By Mail
Star Rte #3, Box 629
Grand Marais, Minn. 55604
Short Name: **W Chadde**
*Fiction; Literature; Paperbacks
(new)*

Chafey's Old And Rare Books
2920 Central Avenue, SE
Albuquerque, N.Mex. 87106
(505) 265-9473
Short Name: **Chafey's**
*Americana, Regional; Fine &
Rare Bindings; Childrens'
Books; First Editions;
Literature; Rare Books*

Richard Chalfin
118 West 72nd Street
New York, N.Y. 10023
Short Name: **R Chalfin**
Detective Fiction; Book Scouts

Chamblin Bookmine
4148 Herschel Street
Jacksonville, Fla. 32210
Short Name: **Chamblin**
*American Indians; Americana,
Regional; Comic Books;
Incunabula & Early Printing;
Natural History; Voyages,
Travels, & Exploration*

Chamisa Bookshop
3611 Simms Avenue, SE
Albuquerque, N.Mex. 87108
(505) 266-1229
Short Name: **Chamisa**
*Construction, Building
Materials, & Materials Science;
Cookery & Gastronomy;
Southwestern America; Search
Service, without Stock*

Charles Chandler
14010 Cardwell
Livonia, Mich. 49154
(313) 522-0920
Short Name: **C Chandler**
Locks; Trade Catalogues

Bev Chaney Jr-Books
60 Radnor Avenue
Croton-On-Hudson, N.Y. 10520
Short Name: **B Chaney Jr**
*First Editions, Modern;
Literature; Books about Books*

A Change Of Hobbit
1371 Westwood Boulevard
Los Angeles, Calif. 90024
(213) 473-2873
Short Name: **Change Hobbit**
*Science Fiction; Out of Print,
with Stock; New Books;
Paperbacks (new); Search
Service, with Stock; Fantasy*

Chanticleer Books
1120 Michigan
Fort Wayne, Ind. 46804
(219) 424-0746
Short Name: **Chantiicleer**
*Americana, States; Americana,
Regional; Out of Print, with
Stock*

Stephanie F Chapin
R D #7, 303
Reading, Penna. 19606
(215) 779-1512
Short Name: **S F Chapin**
Childrens' Books; Illustrated
Books

Chapman & Berryman
  Booksellers
2377 Teviot Street
Los Angeles, Calif. 90039
(213) 667-2430
Short Name: **Chapman & Berry**
Pacific Region; Hawaii;
Australia & Oceania; Ephemera

Darlene Chapman
Rte #1, Box 36
Merrimac, Wisc. 53561
Short Name: **D Chapman**
General

Mary Chapman, Bookseller
P O Box 304
College Park, Md. 20740
Short Name: **M Chapman-Coll**
Textiles; Needlework; Lace

Chappaqua Bookshop
95 King Street
Chappaqua, N.Y. 10514
Short Name: **Chappaqua**
Childrens' Books; Cookery &
Gastronomy; Criminology;
General; Psychiatry,
Psychology, & Psychonanalysis;
Search Service, without Stock

Don M Chase Books
8569 Lawrence Lane
Sebastopol, Calif. 95472
Short Name: **D M Chase**
Western Americana; American
Indians; Archaeology; History,
American; Outlaws & Rangers

Chatham Bookseller
8 Village Green Road
Madison, N.J. 07940
(201) 822-1361
Short Name: **Chatham**
Medicine & Science;
Technology; Literary Criticism;
Literature; Rare Books; Fiction

Checker Book World
3520 Hillcrest
Dubuque, Iowa 52001
Short Name: **Checker**
Chess, Checkers, & Draughts

Cheng & Tsui Company, Inc
25-31 West Street
Boston, Mass. 02111
(617) 426-6074
Short Name: **Cheng & Tsui**
Asia; Collection Development;
Foreign Affairs; Foreign
Languages; Orientalia; Pacific
Region

Cherokee Book Shop
6607 Hollywood Boulevard, Box
  3427
Hollywood, Calif. 90028
(213) 463-6090
Short Name: **Cherokee**
Fine & Rare Bindings; First
Editions; Childrens' Books;
Illustrated Books; Militaria;
Americana

Arthur Cheslock
2510 Smith Avenue
Baltimore, Md. 21209
Short Name: **A Cheslock**
Astronautics & Rocketry;
Computers; Mathematics; Logic

Chestnut Ridge Books
P O Box 353
Rutherford, N.J. 07070
(201) 438-5850
Short Name: **Chestnut Ridge**
Dogs; Hunting, Fishing &
Angling; Shooting & Firearms;
Sporting; Horses; Voyages,
Travels, & Exploration

Chicago Book Mart
P O Box 636-Y
Chicago Heights, Ill. 60411
Short Name: **Chicago**
General; Out of Print, with
Stock; Search Service, without
Stock

The Chickadee, Inc
702 Marshall Street
Houston, Tex. 77006
Short Name: **Chickadee**
Natural History; Out of Print,
with Stock; New Books; Birds
& Ornithology

Childs Gallery
169 Newbury Street
Boston, Mass. 02116
(617) 266-1108
Short Name: **Childs Gall**
Prints; Americana; Drawings

Chimney Smoke Books
74 Waller Road
Bridgeport, Conn. 06606
Short Name: **Chimney Smoke**
Illustrated Books; Books about
Books; Natural History;
Americana; Art; Gardening &
Horticulture

Chimney Sweep Books
220a Mount Hermon Road
Scotts Valley, Calif. 95066
Short Name: **Chimney Sweep**
Childrens' Books; Religion &
Theology; Detective Fiction;
Gardening & Horticulture

Chiricahua Book Company
P O Box 672
Douglas, Ariz. 85607
(602) 364-3273
Short Name: **Chiricahua**
American Indians; Americana;
Americana, Regional; Farming,
Ranching, & Livestock; Outlaws
& Rangers; Overland
Narratives

The Chirorgical Bookshop
1211 Cathedral Street
Baltimore, Md. 21201
Short Name: **Chirorgical**
History of Medicine & Science

Chiswick Book Shop, Inc
Walnut Tree Hill Road
Sandy Hook, Conn. 06482
(203) 426-3220
Short Name: **Chiswick**
Press Books & Fine Printing;
Rare Books; Printing &
Printing History; Typography &
Type Specimens; Ephemera;
Calligraphy

Chloe's Books
P O Box 255673
Sacramento, Calif. 95825
Short Name: **Chloe's**
First Editions; First Editions,
Modern; Literature; Poetry;
Press Books & Fine Printing;
Little Magazines & Literary
Small Presses

Choctaw Traders
P O Box 471
Ridgeland, Miss. 39157
Short Name: **Choctaw Traders**
Mississippi; Authors;
Mississippi River; Civil War &
Confederacy; The South;
History

Choreographica
103 Charles Street
Boston, Mass. 02114
Short Name: **Choreogr**
Dance; Art; Illustrated Books;
Photography; Literature;
General

The Christian Bookfellowship
P O Box 763
Millbrook, N.Y. 12545
(914) 677-3013
Short Name: **Christian-Mil**
Appraisals & Appraisal
Services; Judaica & Hebraica;
Psychiatry, Psychology, &
Psychonanalysis; Religion &
Theology; Search Service, with
Stock; Out of Print, with Stock

Christian Classics
P O Box 30
Westminster, Md. 21157
(301) 848-3065
Short Name: **Christian**
Religion & Theology; Rare
Books

Christiania Press
Star Route Box 132
Staples, Minn. 56479
Short Name: **Christiania**
Bibliography; Crafts & Trades;
Graphic Arts; Printing &
Printing History; Religion &
Theology; Woodcut Books

A Christiansen
66 Spencer Road
Basking Ridge, N.J. 07920
Short Name: **A Christiansen**
Apiculture; Stereoviews;
Violins; Scandinavia

Christie's Rare Book
  Department
502 Park Avenue
New York, N.Y. 10022
Short Name: **Christie's**
Auctions & Auctioneers

J J Christoffersen
221 South Barry Avenue
Mamaroneck, N.Y. 10543
Short Name: **Christoffersen**
Rare Books; Illustrated Books;
Press Books & Fine Printing

Christopher's Book Room
116 North Grant Street
Bloomington, Ind. 47401
Short Name: **Christopher's**
Middle Ages; Scholarly Books;
Philosophy; History; Religion &
Theology; Art

Churchilliana Company
4629 Sunset Drive
Sacramento, Calif. 95822
(916) 488-7053
Short Name: **Churchilliana**
Sir Winston Churchill

Gerald J Cielec
2248 North Kedvale Avenue
Chicago, Ill. 60639
(312) 235-2326
Short Name: **G J Cielec**
Americana; Art; Autographed
Material & Autographs;
Graphic Arts; Photography; Out
of Print, without Stock

Cinema Books By Post
P O Box 20092-Broadway
  Station
Seattle, Wash. 98102
Short Name: **Cinema-Sea**
Cinema & Mass Media;
Performing Arts; Out of Print,
with Stock; Search Service, with
Stock; Ephemera

Cipriano's Books
P O Box 5071
Santa Rosa, Calif. 95402
Short Name: **Cipriano's**
Out of Print, with Stock

City Book And Coin Store
521 Crockett Street
Shreveport, La. 71101
Short Name: **City Bk & Coin**
Astrology; Comic Books;
Paperbacks (new); Metaphysics;
IncomeOpportunities & Self
Help

City Wide Books
150 Manhattan Avenue
Brooklyn, N.Y. 11206
Short Name: **City Wide**
Paperbacks (new); Magazines;
General

Cityana Gallery (Appt Only)
16 East 53rd Street
New York, N.Y. 10022
(212) 752-2079
Short Name: **Cityana Gall**
New York Metropolitan Area;
Prints; Rare Books

Civic Center Books
360 Golden Gate Avenue
San Francisco, Calif. 94102
(415) 885-5072
Short Name: **Civic Center**
Paperbacks (new); Performing
Arts; Fiction; Science Fiction;
Newspapers; U.S. Government
Publications

Claitor's Law Books
3165 South Arcadian, Box 3333
Baton Rouge, La. 70821
(504) 344-0476
Short Name: **Claitor's**
Law

Roy W Clare
47 Woodshire Street
Getzville, N.Y. 14068
Short Name: **R W Clare**
Incunabula & Early Printing;
Illustrated Books; Rare Books;
Woodcut Books; Medicine &
Science; STC & Wing Books

Arthur H Clark Company
1264 South Central Avenue
Glendale, Calif. 91204
(213) 245-9119
Short Name: **A H Clark**
Americana; Pacific Region;
American Indians; Outlaws &
Rangers; Americana, Regional;
Voyages, Travels, &
Exploration

Taylor Clark
2623 Government Street
Baton Rouge, La. 70806
Short Name: **T Clark**
Color Plate Books; Maps,
Atlases, & Cartography;
Natural History; Paintings;
Sporting

Clark's Old Bookstore
318 West Sprague Avenue
Spokane, Wash. 99204
Short Name: **Clark's**
Americana, Regional;
Childrens' Books; Classics;
Gardening & Horticulture;
History; Poetry

Albert G Clegg
312 West Broad Street
Eaton Rapids, Mich. 48827
Short Name: **A G Clegg**
Geology; Arctica & Antarctica;
Documents; Science

Evelyn Clement
45 Central Street
Franklin, N.H. 03235
(603) 934-5496
Short Name: **E Clement**
Americana, Regional;
Technology; Biography; Science
Fiction

William T Clermont, Books
87 Rowland Avenue
Hackensack, N.J. 07601
(201) 343-5495
Short Name: **W T Clermont**
American Literature; English
Literature; First Editions;
Literary Criticism; Biography;
Literature

C E Clift
2032 Ascot Drive, #8
Moraga, Calif. 94556
Short Name: **C E Clift**
Tobacco & Smoking

Jack Clinton Nautical Books
High Street, Box 1098
Hope Valley, R.I. 02832
Short Name: **J Clinton**
Whaling; Naval & Marine;
Yachts, Yachting, & Sailing

Clipper Ship Books
P O Box 1211
Canoga Park, Calif. 91304
(213) 888-8631
Short Name: **Clipper Ship**
Appraisals & Appraisal
Services; Autographed Material
& Autographs; Author
Collections; First Editions,
Modern; Detective Fiction;
Manuscripts

Coach House Press
401 Huron Street, Rear
Toronto, Ont.
Short Name: **Coach Hse**
Poetry; Fiction; Photography

Taylor Coffman
1441 Astor Avenue
Cambria, Calif. 93428
Short Name: **T Coffman**
Biography; History, American;
Art; History

Cogitator Bookstore
1165 Wilmette Avenue
Wilmette, Ill. 60091
Short Name: **Cogitator**
Literary Criticism; First
Editions; Childrens' Books; Out
of Print, with Stock; Press
Books & Fine Printing; Fiction

Albert Cohen
2343 Selma Avenue
Youngstown, Ohio 44504
Short Name: **A Cohen**
First Editions; Illustrated
Books; Rare Books

John Cole's Book Shop
P O Box 1132
La Jolla, Calif. 92038
Short Name: **Cole's-La J**
Art; Mexico; Childrens' Books;
Travel

Colebrook Book Barn
Rte #183, Box 108
Colebrook, Conn. 06021
(203) 379-3185
Short Name: **Colebrook**
Out of Print, with Stock;
General; Americana; Book
Trade & Catalogues; First
Editions; Publishing History

Colgate University Bookstore
O'Connor Campus Center
Hamilton, N.Y. 13346
Short Name: **Colgate**
General

Collector Books
P O Box 3009
Paducah, Ken. 42001
(502) 898-6211
Short Name: **Coll-Pad**
Trade Catalogues; Authors;
Jesse Stuart; Kentucky

A Collector's List, Inc
77 North Centre Avenue
Rockville Centre, N.Y. 11570
Short Name: **Coll's List**
Illustrated Books; Art; Poetry;
Theatre; Cinema & Mass
Media; First Editions

A Collector's Library
520 North Greece Road
Hilton, N.Y. 14468
(716) 392-7720
Short Name: **Coll's Libr**
Hunting, Fishing & Angling;
General; Search Service,
without Stock

Collector's Bookcase
820 East Chapman
Fullerton, Calif. 92631
Short Name: **Coll's Bkcase**
First Editions; Collecting &
Collectibles; Science Fiction;
Cinema & Mass Media; Series
Books for Boys & Girls; Comic
Books

Collector's Choice
P O Box 83
Waterville, Ohio 43566
(419) 878-1511
Short Name: **Coll's Ch-Wat**
First Editions, Modern;
Illustrated Books; Science
Fiction

Collector's Corner
2 Highwood Avenue
Tenafly, N.J. 07670
Short Name: **Coll's Crnr**
New Jersey; Hudson River
Valley; Miniature Books; Books
about Books; Shakespeare;
Illustrated Books

Collectors' Center Rare Books
601-05 Ogden Street
Denver, Colo. 80218
Short Name: **Colls' Cntr-Den**
Americana; Americana, States;
Bibliography; Books about
Books; Childrens' Books;
Folklore

Collectors' Editions
P O Box 5049, F D R Station
New York, N.Y. 10150
Short Name: **Colls' Edtns**
Photography; Press Books &
Fine Printing; Illustrated
Books; Posters

Collectors' Old Bookshop
707 East Franklin Street
Richmond, Va. 23219
Short Name: **Coll's Old**
Americana, States; Civil War &
Confederacy; Americana,
Regional; Americana;
Appraisals & Appraisal
Services; Geneaologies

Colleen's Books
6880 Telephone Road
Houston, Tex. 77061
Short Name: **Colleen's**
Search Service, with Stock; Out
of Print, with Stock;
Americana, Regional;
Technology; Militaria; Naval &
Marine

College Hill Books
306 Cattell Street
Easton, Penna. 18042
(215) 250-0890
Short Name: **College Hill**
Out of Print, with Stock; Search
Service, with Stock

College Nook Book Shop
988 Hempstead Turnpike
Uniondale, N.Y. 11553
Short Name: **College Nook**
Mathematics; Medicine &
Science; Technology;
Psychiatry, Psychology, &
Psychonanalysis; Literature;
Social Sciences

Anthony P Collins
P O Box 58, Franklin Avenue
Millbrook, N.Y. 12545
(914) 677-9256
Short Name: **A P Collins**
Drawings; Paintings; Rare
Books; Militaria; Prints;
Autographed Material &
Autographs

Louis Collins Books
898 Carolina Street
San Francisco, Calif. 94107
Short Name: **L Collins**
Africa; American Indians;
Architecture; Collection
Development; First Editions,
Modern; Folklore

Rowland L Collins
English Dept, Univ Of
   Rochester
Rochester, N.Y. 14627
Short Name: **R L Collins**
Authors; Early Printed Books

S F Collins' Bookcellar
266 Concord Drive
Pottstown, Penna. 19464
(215) 323-2495
Short Name: **S F Cullins'**
Childrens' Books; Illustrated
Books; Books about Books;
Press Books & Fine Printing;
Printing & Printing History

Colonial Out-Of-Print Book
   Service
P O Box 451
Pleasantville, N.Y. 10570
Short Name: **Colonial**
Out of Print, with Stock;
Literary Criticism; Literature;
Biography

Colophon Book Shop
700 South 6th Avenue
La Grange, Ill. 60525
(312) 354-0022 mass
Short Name: **Colophon**
First Editions, Modern;
Bibliography; Press Books &
Fine Printing; Books about
Books; Printing & Printing
History; Typography & Type
Specimens

Colorado Bookman
P O Box 156
Norwood, Colo. 81423
(303) 327-4616
Short Name: **Colo Bkman**
Americana, States; Antiques;
Illustrated Books; Photography;
Natural History

Columbia Books
P O Box 27
Columbia, Mo. 65205
(314) 449-6678
Short Name: **Columbia**
Childrens' Books; Illustrated
Books; Art; Fiction; Scholarly
Books; Search Service, with
Stock

Comic Art Shop
319 Sixth Avenue
New York, N.Y. 10014
Short Name: **Comic Art**
Comic Books; Original Art of
Book Illustrations

Common Reader Bookshop
P O Box 32
New Salem, Mass. 01355
(617) 544-3002
Short Name: **Common Reader**
Women & Feminism; Out of
Print, with Stock; First
Editions; Ephemera;
Performing Arts; Biography

Computer Book Locators
P O Box 1805
Hawaiian Gardens, Calif. 90716
Short Name: **Computer Locate**
Search Service, with Stock; Out
of Print, with Stock; General;
Childrens' Books; Economics &
Business; History

Comstock's Bindery & Bookshop
7903 Rainier Avenue
Seattle, Wash. 98118
Short Name: **Comstock's**
Aviation & Aeronautics;
Militaria; Mountaineering;
Naval & Marine; Out of Print,
with Stock; Search Service, with
Stock

The Confederate Bookstore
957 Johnson Avenue
San Luis Obispo, Calif. 93401
Short Name: **Confederate**
Autographed Material &
Autographs; Books about
Books; Civil War &
Confederacy; Paperbacks (new);
Science Fiction; Inscribed Books

James E Conner
1315 Pleasant Valley Drive
Baltimore, Md. 21228
Short Name: **J E Conner**
Printing & Printing History;
Typography & Type Specimens;
Calligraphy; Miniature Books

Conrad's
955 23rd Road
Grand Junction, Colo. 81501
Short Name: **Conrad's**
American Indians; Americana;
Americana, Regional;
Archaeology; Militaria;
Shooting & Firearms

Constant Reader Bookshop Ltd
1901 North Prospect Avenue
Milwaukee, Wisc. 53202
(414) 291-0452
Short Name: **Constant Reader**
Americana; Cinema & Mass
Media; Fiction; Hunting,
Fishing & Angling; Literary
Criticism; Religion & Theology

The Conversation Piece
7439 East Main Street
Reynoldsburg, Ohio 43068
Short Name: **Conversation**
Americana; Childrens' Books;
General; Out of Print, with
Stock; Religion & Theology;
Scholarly Books

Mrs Dorothy Cook
61 Cornell Drive
Rancho Mirage, Calif. 92270
(714) 328-2506
Short Name: **Mrs D Cook**
Books about Books; Childrens'
Books; Illustrated Books; Doll
Books & Paper Dolls

Michael L Cook-Bookseller
3318 Wimberg Avenue
Evansville, Ind. 47712
Short Name: **M L Cook**
Americana, States;
Genealogies; History,
American; Reprints

Cookery Bookery
Inn At Huntington,
   Worthington Road
Huntington, Mass. 01050
(413) 667-3633
Short Name: **Cookery Bkery**
Cookery & Gastronomy

Coosa Valley Book Shop
15 East Third Avenue
Rome, Ga. 30161
(404) 291-7517
Short Name: **Coosa Valley**
Americana; Americana, States;
Americana, Regional

Nathan Copeland
72 Groveside Street
Portland, Maine 04101
(207) 773-3647
Short Name: **N Copeland**
Naval & Marine; Voyages,
Travels, & Exploration;
Illustrated Books; Maps,
Atlases, & Cartography;
Wireless Communication
History

Copper Fox Farm-Books
P O Box 763
Millbrook, N.Y. 12545
Short Name: **Copper Fox**
Appraisals & Appraisal
Services; Gardening &
Horticulture; History;
Paperbacks (new); Rare Books;
Search Service, with Stock

Core Collection Books
11 Middle Neck Road
Great Neck, N.Y. 11021
(516) 466-3676
Short Name: **Core Coll**
Poetry; Reference; Bibliography

Corn Mill Books
5505 Lindo Pasco
San Diego, Calif. 92115
Short Name: **Corn Mill**
Astronomy; History of Medicine
& Science; Mammalogy; Mark
Twain

Corner Book Shop
102 Fourth Avenue
New York, N.Y. 10003
(212) 254-7714
Short Name: **Corner-NYC**
Cookery & Gastronomy; Wines;
Theatre; Cinema & Mass
Media; Dance

Corner Book Shop
418 Spring Street
Newport, R.I. 02840
Short Name: **Corner-Newp**
Out of Print, with Stock;
General; First Editions,
Modern; First Editions

Corner Book Shop
511 East 2nd Street
Casper, Wyom. 82601
(307) 266-6124
Short Name: **Corner-Cas**
Childrens' Books; General; New
Books; Homosexual & Gay
Literature

Corner Shelf
102-B North Main Street, Box
87
Culpeper, Va. 22701
Short Name: **Corner Shelf-Cul**
Civil War & Confederacy;
Virginia; Falconry; Thomas
Jefferson

Corner Stone Bookshop
110 Margaret Street
Plattsburgh, N.Y. 12901
Short Name: **Corner Stone**
Comic Books; General;
Adirondacks; Religion &
Theology; Phonograph Records

Cornhill Books
P O Box 544
La Mirada, Calif. 90637
Short Name: **Cornhill**
Medicine & Science;
Technology

Cornwall House Books (Dr L
   Bendes)
54 Cornwall Lane
Sands Points, N.Y. 11050
(516) 883-4366
Short Name: **Cornwall Hse**
Art; Books about Books;
Photography; Prints; Press
Books & Fine Printing; Rare
Books

Cortese Sporting Books
1254 Henderson Avenue, #3
Sunnyvale, Calif. 94086
(408) 247-8789
Short Name: **Cortese**
Hunting, Fishing & Angling;
Dogs; Sporting; Shooting &
Firearms; Natural History; Out
of Print, without Stock

Cosmic Aeroplane Books
258 East First Street, South
Salt Lake City, Utah 84111
Short Name: **Cosmic Aero**
Mormons; Western Americana;
Science Fiction; Illustrated
Books; First Editions

Cosmopolitan Books
7007 Melrose Avenue
Los Angeles, Calif. 90038
Short Name: **Cosmopolitan**
*Show Business; Psychiatry,
Psychology, & Psychonanalysis;
Criminology; Social Sciences;
Cookery & Gastronomy;
Phonograph Records*

Country Bookshelf
933 North State Road, #49
Chesterton, Ind. 46304
Short Name: **Country Bkshlf**
*Indiana; Authors; Gene
Stratton-Porter; Juveniles*

Country Connection
90 East 10th Street
New York, N.Y. 10003
(212) 533-0578
Short Name: **Country Connect**
*Fiction; History; Literature; Out
of Print, with Stock; Poetry;
Religion & Theology*

The Country Craftsman
4796 Usona Road
Mariposa, Calif. 95338
Short Name: **Country Craft**
*American Indians; Out of Print,
with Stock; Natural History;
Americana, Regional*

Country Lane Books
38 Country Lane
Collinsville, Conn. 06022
(203) 693-2245
Short Name: **Country Lane**
*Americana; Arctica &
Antarctica; Childrens' Books;
Color Plate Books; First
Editions; Natural History*

**Court Place Antiquarian
　Bookshop**
1445 Court Place
Denver, Colo. 80202
(303) 893-0819
Short Name: **Court Place**
*Americana; First Editions;
Americana, Regional; Militaria;
Geology; General*

Court's Book Store
535 West Reed Street
Moberly, Mo. 65270
(816) 263-4279
Short Name: **Court's**
*New Books; Out of Print,
without Stock*

Coventry Books, Inc
1824 Coventry Road
Cleveland Heights, Ohio 44118
Short Name: **Coventry**
*Out of Print, without Stock;
Classics; Fiction; First Editions,
Modern; Women & Feminism;
Literature*

Nathaniel Cowen
16 Schoonmaker Lane
Woodstock, N.Y. 12498
Short Name: **N Cowen**
Out of Print, with Stock

Crabtree Booksellers
2905 Taft Highway, Box 282
Signal Mountain, Tenn. 37377
(615) 886-5944
Short Name: **Crabtree**
*Out of Print, with Stock; Rare
Books; Search Service, with
Stock; Civil War &
Confederacy; The South;
Tennessee*

Edward J Craig
P O Box 547
Jamestown, R.I. 02835
(401) 423-1632
Short Name: **E J Craig**
*Manuscripts; Documents;
Autographed Material &
Autographs; Caribbean;
Ephemera; History, American*

John Craig
P O Box 656
Norfolk, Conn. 06058
Short Name: **J Craig**
*Photography; Cinema & Mass
Media; Graphic Arts*

Craighouse-Home Of Fine Books
Patchen Village
Lexington, Ken. 40502
(606) 269-4611
Short Name: **Craighse-Pat**
Horses; Kentucky

Craighouse-Home Of Fine Books
Mall At Lexington Center
Lexington, Ken. 40507
(606) 233-0104
Short Name: **Craighse-Mall**
Horses; Kentucky

Cranbury Book Worm
54 North Main Street
Cranbury, N.J. 08512
Short Name: **Cranbury**
General

Creative Arts Book Company
833 Bancroft Way
Berkeley, Calif. 94710
Short Name: **Creative Arts**
Literature

Creedmoor Bookstore
2323 West Foster
Chicago, Ill. 60625
(312) 769-4232
Short Name: **Creedmoor**
*General; Gardening &
Horticulture; Hunting, Fishing
& Angling*

John Criscione
10 Churchill Drive
New Hyde Park, N.Y. 11040
Short Name: **J Criscione**
*Rare Books; Illustrated Books;
Childrens' Books; Sporting;
Voyages, Travels, &
Exploration; Printing &
Printing History*

Crofter's Books
P O Box 226
Washington, Conn. 06793
Short Name: **Crofter's**
*Cinema & Mass Media;
Zeppelin & Dirigibles;
Television; Naval & Marine;
History, American; Labor
History*

Cross Hill Books
P O Box 798
Bath, Maine 04530
(207) 443-5652
Short Name: **Cross Hill**
*Maine; Naval & Marine;
Voyages, Travels, &
Exploration; Whaling; Nautica;
Yachts, Yachting, & Sailing*

Leroy Cross
21 Columbia Avenue
Brunswick, Maine 04011
Short Name: **L Cross**
Mountaineering

Croton Book Service
P O Box 131
Croton-On-Hudson, N.Y. 10520
(914) 271-6575
Short Name: **Croton**
*Americana, Regional; Militaria;
Hudson River Valley*

Cumberland Literary Agency
P O Box 50331
Nashville, Tenn. 37205
Short Name: **Cumberland**
Religion & Theology

James Cummins Bookseller, Inc
667 Madison Avenue, Suite 1005
New York, N.Y. 10021
(212) 371-4151
Short Name: **J Cummins**
Sporting; Press Books & Fine Printing; Color Plate Books; Voyages, Travels, & Exploration; First Editions; Illustrated Books

The Curiosity Shoppe
223 North Dewey
Eau Claire, Wisc. 54701
Short Name: **Curiosity-Eau**
First Editions; Biography; Fiction; Voyages, Travels, & Exploration

Curiosity Shoppe
3720 Red Arrow Highway
St Joseph, Mich. 49085
Short Name: **Curiosity-St J**
Americana; Fine & Rare Bindings; Childrens' Books; Illustrated Books; Rare Books

A Curious Bookshop
14-1/2 Bosworth Place
Boston, Mass. 02108
Short Name: **Curious-Bost**
General; Literature; Americana, Regional; Childrens' Books; Illustrated Books; History, American

Curious Book Shop
307 East Grand River
East Lansing, Mich. 48823
(517) 332-0112
Short Name: **Curious-East**
Science Fiction; Illustrated Books; General; Out of Print, with Stock; Detective Fiction; Comic Books

Curious Bookshoppe
198 West Main Street
Los Gatos, Calif. 95030
(408) 354-5560
Short Name: **Curious-Los G**
Cinema & Mass Media; Criminology; Detective Fiction; Rare Books; Science Fiction

The Current Company
P O Box 46, 12 Howe Street
Bristol, R.I. 02809
(401) 253-7824
Short Name: **Current**
First Editions; Voyages, Travels, & Exploration; Americana; Literature; Rare Books; Naval & Marine

L W Currey Inc
Church Street
Elizabethtown, N.Y. 12932
(518) 873-6477
Short Name: **L W Currey**
Americana; First Editions; Press Books & Fine Printing; Rare Books; Science Fiction

John Parke Custis Booksellers
P O Box N
Cool, Calif. 95614
Short Name: **J P Custis**
Literature

Kenneth Cutler
123 Plumtree Lane
Willingboro, N.J. 08046
Short Name: **K Cutler**
Books about Books; Science; Rare Books; History, American

Mitchell R Cutler
61 West 37th Street
New York, N.Y. 10018
(212) 921-9234
Short Name: **M R Cutler**
Art; Crafts & Trades; Reference

Cypress-Park Bookstore
3024 West Ball Road
Anaheim, Calif. 92804
Short Name: **Cypress-Park**
Automotive; Construction, Building Materials, & Materials Science; Doll Books & Paper Dolls; Foreign Languages

Cyrano's Bookshop
Main Street
Highlands, N.C. 28741
Short Name: **Cyrano's**
Juveniles; Natural History; North Carolina; Out of Print, with Stock; Art; Fine Arts

D

D & D Books
Ridgefarm, Ill. 61870
Short Name: **D & D**
C. S. Forester; Authors; General

D J Book Search Service
3269 North E' Street, Box 3352
San Bernardino, Calif. 92413
(714) 883-5712
Short Name: **D J**
Out of Print, with Stock; American Indians; Alaska; Occult & Metaphysics; Search Service, with Stock

Q M Dabney
P O Box 9883
Washington, D.C. 20015
(301) 881-1470
Short Name: **Q M Dabney**
Militaria; Americana; European History; Law; U.S. Government Publications

Daedalus
121 Fourth Street, NE
Charlottesville, Va. 22901
Short Name: **Daedalus**
General

William & Victoria Dailey
8216-1/2 Melrose Avenue
Los Angeles, Calif. 90046
(213) 658-8515
Short Name: **W & V Dailey**
*Rare Books; Prints; Art; Press
Books & Fine Printing;
Illustrated Books; Science*

Howard C Daitz
P O Box 530, Old Chelsea
   Station
New York, N.Y. 10113
Short Name: **H C Daitz**
*Photography; Out of Print, with
Stock; Art; Black Literature &
Black Studies; Collection
Development; Medicine &
Science*

Dakota Books
505 Main Street
Webster, S.D. 57274
Short Name: **Dakota**
*Americana; History; Fiction;
Outlaws & Rangers; Rare
Books; Bibliography*

The Daly Collection (Appt Only)
66 Chilton Street
Cambridge, Mass. 02138
(617) 547-8228
Short Name: **Daly Coll**
*General; Sporting; Women &
Feminism*

Nathaniel Dame
127-133 Walden Street
Cambridge, Mass. 02140
Short Name: **N Dame**
*New Books; Fiction; Juveniles;
Science Fiction*

Dan's Book Nook
135 East Rocks Road
Norwalk, Conn. 06851
(203) 846-9635
Short Name: **Dan's**
*Autographed Material &
Autographs; First Editions;
History; Political, Social, &
Cultural History & Thought;
Search Service, without Stock*

Dana's Doorway
216 King Road
Chalfont, Penna. 18914
(215) 249-9374
Short Name: **Dana's Doorway**
*Childrens' Books; Ephemera;
General*

The Dance Mart
P O Box 48, Homecrest Station
Brooklyn, N.Y. 11229
(212) 624-0477
Short Name: **Dance Mart**
*Performing Arts; Rare Books;
Prints; Autographed Material
& Autographs; Ephemera;
Antiques*

Dance, Etc
5897 College Avenue
Oakland, Calif. 94618
(415) 658-8198
Short Name: **Dance Etc**
Dance

Danville Books
176 South Hartz Avenue
Danville, Calif. 94526
Short Name: **Danville**
*Americana; California; Civil
War & Confederacy; First
Editions; Orientalia; John
Steinbeck*

Darby Books
842 Main Street
Darby, Penna. 19023
(215) 583-4550
Short Name: **Darby**
*Literary Criticism; Literature;
Humanities; Folklore; Out of
Print, with Stock; Reprints*

Darian Ltd
P O Box 456
Independence, Mo. 64051
Short Name: **Darian**
*Rare Books; History, American;
Militaria; Religion & Theology;
Mormons; Americana*

Herman M Darvick
P O Box 467
Rockville Centre, N.Y. 11571
(516) 766-0093
Short Name: **H M Darvick**
*Autographed Material &
Autographs; Documents;
Manuscripts*

John C Daub
554 79th Terrace, North
St Petersburg, Fla. 33702
Short Name: **J C Daub**
*Americana; Americana,
Regional; Militaria*

Dauber & Pine Inc
66 Fifth Avenue
New York, N.Y. 10011
(212) 675-6340
Short Name: **Dauber & Pine**
*History; Americana; American
Literature; English Literature;
Art; Fine & Rare Bindings*

David's Books
622 East Liberty
Ann Arbor, Mich. 48104
(313) 665-8017
Short Name: **David's**
*Paperbacks (new); Poetry;
General; Foreign Languages;
Bookbinding & Restoration*

Owen Davies-Bookseller
200 West Harrison Street
Oak Park, Ill. 60304
(312) 848-1186
Short Name: **O Davies**
Railroads; Naval & Marine

Curtis Carroll Davis
500 West University Parkway,
   #16r
Baltimore, Md. 21210
Short Name: **C C Davis**
Espionage; Logic

Doris Davis Books
271 Streetsboro Street
Hudson, Ohio 44236
(216) 653-5780
Short Name: **D Davis**
*Childrens' Books; Illustrated
Books; Voyages, Travels, &
Exploration*

Ernest Davis
P O Box 423
Harrodsburg, Ken. 40330
(606) 734-3165
Short Name: **E Davis**
*American Indians; Americana;
Civil War & Confederacy; Color
Plate Books; Voyages, Travels,
& Exploration; Kentucky*

Davis & Schorr Art Books
1547 Westwood Boulevard
Los Angeles, Calif. 90024
(213) 477-6636
Short Name: **Davis & Schorr**
Art; Search Service, with Stock;
Natural History; Collection
Development; Graphic Arts; Out
of Print, with Stock

Davison Books
14 Boxwood Drive
Stamford, Conn. 06906
(203) 323-4622
Short Name: **Davison**
American Indians; Childrens'
Books; Graphic Arts; Illustrated
Books; Voyages, Travels, &
Exploration; Typography &
Type Specimens

Bob Dawson
P O Box 38
Hazlet, N.J. 07730
Short Name: **B Dawson**
Americana; First Editions,
Modern; Childrens' Books;
Illustrated Books; Literature

Dawson's Book Shop
535 North Larchmont
　Boulevard
Los Angeles, Calif. 90004
(213) 469-2186
Short Name: **Dawson's**
Western Americana; Books
about Books; Miniature Books;
Mountaineering; Orientalia;
Printing & Printing History

Day's Arms & Antiques
P O Box 1846
Quincy, Calif. 95971
Short Name: **Day's**
Out of Print, with Stock; Search
Service, with Stock

Gene De Chene-Bookseller
11556 Santa Monica
Los Angeles, Calif. 90025
(213) 477-8734
Short Name: **G De Chene**
Psychiatry, Psychology, &
Psychonanalysis

De Haviland Rare Book Service
852 Sheppard Avenue, West
Downsview, Ont. M3H 2T5
(416) 635-1359
Short Name: **De Haviland**
Canada & Canadiana; History;
History, American; Psychiatry,
Psychology, & Psychonanalysis;
Playing Cards

John E De Turck
210 Penn Terrace
Mount Penn, Penna. 19606
Short Name: **J E De Turck**
Natural History; Pennsylvania;
Local History; Authors

De La Pena Books
924 Canyon Road
Sante Fe, N.Mex. 87501
(505) 982-1299
Short Name: **De La Pena**
New Mexico; Western
Americana; Civil War &
Confederacy; Mexico;
Ephemera

Gerry & Helen De La Ree
7 Cedarwood Lane
Saddle River, N.J. 07458
(201) 327-6621
Short Name: **G & H De La Ree**
Science Fiction; Wierd Fiction;
Fantasy; Pulps

De Simon Company (Appt Only)
111 West 24th Street
New York, N.Y. 10011
(212) 242-1252
Short Name: **De Simon**
Reference; Bibliography; Books
about Books; Printing &
Printing History; Bookbinding
& Restoration; Bibliography

De Victor's Book & Art Gallery
3 Dov Place
Kendall Park, N.J. 08824
(201) 297-0296
Short Name: **De Victor's**
Art; Illustrated Books; Prints;
Childrens' Books; Illustrated
Books

De Ville Books
132 Carondelet Street
New Orleans, La. 70130
(504) 522-2363
Short Name: **De Ville**
Antiques; Architecture; Art;
General; Out of Print, without
Stock; Search Service, without
Stock

Wilfrid De Freitas, Bookseller
P O Box 863, Stock Exchange
　Towers
Montreal, Que. H4Z 1K2
Short Name: **W De Freitas**
First Editions, Modern;
Authors; Sherlock Holmes & A.
Conan Doyle

Robert Dean-Art Books
1781 Beach
San Francisco, Calif. 94123
(415) 922-7099
Short Name: **R Dean**
Photography; Architecture; Art;
California; Avant Garde,
Experimental, & Modern Art;
Art Catalogues, Periodicals, &
Books

Debra Books
153 Jonathan Drive
Easton, Penna. 18042
Short Name: **Debra**
First Editions, Modern; English
Literature; Science Fiction;
Natural History; Childrens'
Books; Detective Fiction

Dee Cee Books
P O Box 506
Nyack, N.Y. 10960
(914) 358-3989
Short Name: **Dee Cee**
Africa; Asia; First Editions;
Political Science & Theory;
Russia & Eastern European
Region; Social Sciences

Deeds Book Shop
8012 Main Street, Box 85
Ellicott City, Md. 21043
Short Name: **Deeds**
Juveniles; Authors; Literature;
Maryland

George Deeds
6435 Green Valley Circle, #316
Culver City, Calif. 90230
Short Name: **G Deeds**
Civil War & Confederacy;
Illustrated Books; Victorian
Literature; Color Plate Books;
Reference; Natural History

Happy & Eleanor Deines
1707 Country Club Road
Fort Collins, Colo. 80524
Short Name: **H & E Deines**
Western Americana; Childrens'
Books

Delta Books
1016 9th Street
Sacramento, Calif. 95814
(916) 448-0226
Short Name: **Delta**
History; Humanities; Militaria;
Pacific Region

Robert Demarest Bookseller
1166 Royal Palm
Naples, Fla. 33940
(813) 262-3363
Short Name: **R Demarest**
Out of Print, with Stock; Drug
Culture; Psychopharmacology

Denbry Books
3555 Rochambeau Avenue
Bronx, N.Y. 10467
Short Name: **Denbry**
General

H O Dendurent Books
79 Central Street
Bangor, Maine 04401
(207) 947-4187
Short Name: **H O Dendurent**
General; Out of Print, with
Stock; Search Service, with
Stock; Americana, States;
Maine; Literature

Dennis Books
P O Box 99142
Seattle, Wash. 98199
(206) 283-0532
Short Name: **Dennis**
Childrens' Books; Comic Books;
Childrens' Books; Sheet Music

Bonnie Denver
5060 Franklin Avenue
Hollywood, Calif. 90027
(213) 661-4393
Short Name: **B Denver**
General; Aviation &
Aeronautics; Illustrated Books

Joseph A Dermont
P O Box 654
Onset, Mass. 02558
Short Name: **J A Dermont**
Author Collections; First
Editions, Modern; First
Editions; Inscribed Books; Little
Magazines & Literary Small
Presses; Poetry

C Derowitsch
P O Box 6
Gilbert, Penna. 18331
(215) 681-5654
Short Name: **C Derowitsch**
Americana, States;
Autographed Material &
Autographs; First Editions;
Civil War & Confederacy; Color
Plate Books

John A Desch-Bookseller
2522 University Boulevard West
Silver Spring, Md. 20902
(301) 946-9609
Short Name: **J A Desch**
Militaria; Biography;
Americana; Childrens' Books;
Paperbacks (new)

Deskins And Greene
  Antiquarians
P O Box 1092
Atlantic City, N.J. 08404
(609) 646-6920
Short Name: **Deskins/Greene**
Homosexual & Gay Literature;
Erotica; Poetry; Women &
Feminism

Rebecca B Desmarais
Nixon Road, P O Box 2286
Framingham, Mass. 01701
Short Name: **R B Desmarais**
Literature; First Editions; Press
Books & Fine Printing; Books
about Books; Americana;
Autographed Material &
Autographs

Detering Book Gallery
2311 Bissonnet
Houston, Tex. 77005
(713) 526-6974
Short Name: **Detering**
Fine & Rare Bindings; First
Editions; Press Books & Fine
Printing; Humanities;
Illustrated Books; Rare Books

Miriam H Detweiler,
  Booksearcher
1108 Rte #113
Souderton, Penna. 18964
Short Name: **M H Detweiler**
Out of Print, with Stock; Search
Service, with Stock

Diablo Books
1317 Canyon Wood Court, #1
Walnut Creek, Calif. 94595
Short Name: **Diablo**
Authors; John Muir; Jack
London; California; Voyages,
Travels, & Exploration;
Railroads

Diamond Book Store
5035 Sherbrook Street, West
Montreal, Que. H4A 1S8
(514) 482-2641
Short Name: **Diamond-Mon**
Canada & Canadiana; Out of
Print, with Stock; Search
Service, with Stock

Harold B Diamond, Bookseller
P O Box 1193
Burbank, Calif. 91507
Short Name: **H B Diamond**
Shakespeare; Foreign
Languages; Literary Criticism;
Literature; Latin America;
Social Sciences

Ray Diamond-Collections
178 Alexander Street
Rochester, N.Y. 14607
(716) 454-1276
Short Name: **R Diamond**
Americana; First Editions,
Modern; Illustrated Books;
Press Books & Fine Printing;
Art; Voyages, Travels, &
Exploration

D C Dickinson
8451 Malvern Place
Tucson, Ariz. 85710
Short Name: **D C Dickinson**
*Bibliography; Black Literature
& Black Studies; First Editions,
Modern; Poetry*

Dickson Street Books
318 West Dickson Street
Fayetteville, Ark. 72701
(501) 442-8182
Short Name: **Dickson St**
*Arkansas; Ozarks; Authors;
Irish & Scottish History;
Literature*

The Dictionary
1809 Pisgah Church Road
Greensboro, N.C. 27408
Short Name: **Dictionary**
*Computers; Childrens' Books;
Russia & Eastern European
Region; First Editions, Modern;
General*

Luther Diehl
4030 Yaqui #2
Flagstaff, Ariz. 86001
Short Name: **L Diehl**
*Fantasy; Wierd Fiction; British
Isles; Illustrated Books;
Periodicals*

Different Drummer
333 Fifth Street
West Des Moines, Iowa 50265
(515) 279-2969
Short Name: **Diff Drum-Wes**
*Fiction; Poetry; History;
Philosophy; Biography*

Different Drummer Books
420 Broadway, East
Seattle, Wash. 98102
Short Name: **Diff Drum-Sea**
*Northwest; Science Fiction;
Women & Feminism*

Different Store
P O Box 246
Addison, Mich. 49220
(517) 547-3764
Short Name: **Diff St**
*Out of Print, with Stock; Search
Service, with Stock; Michigan*

Peter C Dillon
24 Kings Highway South
Westport, Conn. 06880
Short Name: **P C Dillon**
*Science Fiction; Fantasy;
Mystery Fiction*

**Dinkytown Antiquarian
  Bookstore**
1316 SE 4th Street
Minneapolis, Minn. 55414
(612) 378-1286
Short Name: **Dinkytown**
*First Editions, Modern;
Literature; Juveniles*

Don Discher-Book Scout
4830 Audrey Drive
Castro Valley, Calif. 94546
Short Name: **D Discher**
*Detective Fiction; Reference;
Science Fiction; Search Service,
without Stock; Mystery Fiction*

Dish Hollow Books
Rte #8
Beck, Mass. 01223
Short Name: **Dish Hollow**
*General; Juveniles; Theatre;
Dance; Cookery & Gastronomy;
Gardening & Horticulture*

Joseph Distefano
4401 Montgomery Street, Ne,
  #195
Albuquerque, N.Mex. 87109
Short Name: **J Distefano**
*Western Americana; Science
Fiction; Childrens' Books;
Americana*

Diva Books
6 Mariposa Avenue
San Anselmo, Calif. 94960
(415) 453-7456
Short Name: **Diva**
*Childrens' Books; History,
American; Illustrated Books;
Out of Print, with Stock;
Periodicals; Psychiatry,
Psychology, & Psychonanalysis*

Dobbs Books
P O Box 3416
San Clemente, Calif. 92672
(714) 498-2214
Short Name: **Dobbs**
*The South; General; Search
Service, with Stock*

Carol Docheff
1605 Spruce Street
Berkeley, Calif. 94709
(415) 841-0770
Short Name: **C Docheff**
*Childrens' Books; Illustrated
Books; Color Plate Books*

Doctor Nostalgia
3237 Downing Drive
Lynchburg, Va. 24503
Short Name: **Dr Nostlgia**
*Childrens' Books; Comic Books;
Ephemera; Fiction; Series
Books for Boys & Girls*

D R Doerres
P O Box 676
Wilton, Iowa 52778
(319) 732-2874
Short Name: **D R Doerres**
*Locks; Railroads; Zeppelin &
Dirigibles; Iowa; Guns; Western
Americana*

Dog Inc
46 Cooper Lane
Larchmont, N.Y. 10538
(914) 834-9029
Short Name: **Dog Inc**
Dogs

Dolphin Book Shop
2743 Broadway
New York, N.Y. 10025
(212) 866-8454
Short Name: **Dolphin-NYC**
*Books about Books; Scholarly
Books; Out of Print, with Stock*

Don's Book Store
663 Bridge, NW
Grand Rapids, Mich. 49504
(616) 454-7300
Short Name: **Don's**
*Americana; Americana,
Regional; Art; Civil War &
Confederacy; First Editions;
History, American*

Donaldson's
2711 Holbrook Drive
Knoxville, Tenn. 37918
(615) 687-8872
Short Name: **Donaldsons**
*Illustrated Books; Childrens'
Books; General; Out of Print,
with Stock*

Donan Books Inc
235 East 53rd Street
New York, N.Y. 10022
Short Name: **Donan**
*Out of Print, with Stock; Out of
Print, without Stock; Search
Service, with Stock; Search
Service, without Stock*

Donegan Books
620 Philip
Akron, Ohio 44305
(216) 535-8830
Short Name: **Donegan**
*Americana, Regional;
Childrens' Books; Illustrated
Books; Miniature Books;
Petroleum*

Richard E Donvan
305 Massachusetts
Endicott, N.Y. 13760
Short Name: **R E Donovan**
*Art; First Editions, Modern;
Golf*

Michael C Dooling
193 Meadow Street
Naugatuck, Conn. 06770
Short Name: **M C Dooling**
*Americana; Architecture; Art;
Natural History; Psychiatry,
Psychology, & Psychonanalysis;
Voyages, Travels, &
Exploration*

Dennis Doonan (Graphics I)
345 Main Street
Racine, Wisc. 53403
(414) 632-6602
Short Name: **D Doonan**
*Sherlock Holmes & A. Conan
Doyle; Art; Photography*

Webb Dordick
15 Ash Avenue
Somerville, Mass. 02145
Short Name: **W Dordick**
*Medicine & Science; Psychiatry,
Psychology, & Psychonanalysis;
Genetics; History of Medicine &
Science*

Mrs K R Dorn
8 Walnut Avenue
Johnstown, N.Y. 12905
(518) 762-9466
Short Name: **Mrs K R Dorn**
*Americana; Americana,
Regional; Hunting, Fishing &
Angling; Natural History; Out
of Print, with Stock; Shooting
& Firearms*

Douglas Books
1 North Main Street
Jackson, Calif. 95642
(209) 223-3780
Short Name: **Douglas**
*California; Civil War &
Confederacy; Western
Americana*

Mrs Lee Douglas
Birney Star Rte, Box 79b
Sheridan, Wyom. 82801
(307) 737-2222
Short Name: **Mrs L Douglas**
Western Americana

J Dowd
38 West 281, Tom's Trail
St Charles, Ill. 60174
(312) 584-1930
Short Name: **J Dowd**
*American Indians; Western
Americana; Out of Print, with
Stock*

Michael W Dowhan
93 Linden Street
Williamstown, Mass. 01267
(413) 458-4415
Short Name: **M W Dowhan**
Bibliography; Reference

Paul J Drabeck
2886 Roosevelt Avenue
Bronx, N.Y. 10465
Short Name: **P J Drabeck**
*Archery; Falconry; Hunting,
Fishing & Angling; Shooting &
Firearms; Voyages, Travels, &
Exploration; Derrydale Press*

Dragoman Books
38 West Street
Annapolis, Md. 21401
Short Name: **Dragoman**
*Out of Print, with Stock;
American Indians; Archaeology;
Foreign Languages; Rare Books*

The Dragon's Lair, Inc
110 West Fifth Street
Dayton, Ohio 45402
(513) 222-1479
Short Name: **Dragon's Lair**
*Science Fiction; Periodicals;
Comic Books; General;
Illustrated Books; Paperbacks
(new)*

Drama Books
511 Geary
San Francisco, Calif. 94102
(415) 441-5343
Short Name: **Drama**
*Performing Arts; Cinema &
Mass Media; Periodicals; Out
of Print, with Stock; Ephemera*

Drew's Bookshop
P O Box 163
Santa Barbara, Calif. 93101
(805) 966-3311
Short Name: **Drew's**
*Americana; Literary Criticism;
Prints; Maps, Atlases, &
Cartography; Ephemera;
General*

Emily Driscoll
P O Box 834
Shepherdstown, W.Va. 25443
(304) 876-2202
Short Name: **E Driscoll**
*Autographed Material &
Autographs; Manuscripts;
Drawings*

Drusilla's Books
P O Box 16
Lutherville, Md. 21093
(301) 321-6687
Short Name: **Drusilla's**
*Childrens' Books; Ephemera;
Illustrated Books; Out of Print,
with Stock*

Margaret Du Priest
434 Hudson Street
New York, N.Y. 10014
Short Name: **M Du Priest**
*Out of Print, with Stock; Rare
Books; Press Books & Fine
Printing; Scholarly Books*

The Dugout And Depot
8 Gerry Road
Poughkeepsie, N.Y. 12603
(914) 462-6241
Short Name: **Dugout & Depot**
Militaria; Railroads

P Dumas
3875 St Urbain
Montreal, Que. H2W 1V1
Short Name: **P Dumas**
Canada & Canadiana; History of Medicine & Science; Art; Literature

Ann Dumler
P O Box 534
Southport, Conn. 06490
(203) 255-9049
Short Name: **A Dumler**
Childrens' Books; Detective Fiction

Reginald P Dunaway
6138 Delmar Boulevard
St Louis, Mo. 63112
Short Name: **R P Dunaway**
Literary Criticism; Books about Books; Fiction; History; Out of Print, with Stock; Scholarly Books

Elizabeth F Dunlap
6063 Westminster Place
St Louis, Mo. 63112
(314) 863-5068
Short Name: **E F Dunlap**
Maps, Atlases, & Cartography; Americana; Americana, Regional; History, American; Civil War & Confederacy; Search Service, without Stock

Allen A Dunn
1255 Oak Villa Road
Dallas, Ore. 97338
(503) 623-5136
Short Name: **A A Dunn**
Dogs; Hunting, Fishing & Angling; Natural History; Americana, Regional; Shooting & Firearms

Michale Dunn-Books
P O Box 436
Newport, Vt. 05855
(802) 334-2768
Short Name: **M Dunn**
Americana; Canada & Canadiana; Vermont; Hunting, Fishing & Angling; Mountaineering; Bibliography

D N Dupley
9118 Pauline Street
Omaha, Neb. 68124
(402) 393-2906
Short Name: **D N Dupley**
American Indians; Americana; Farming, Ranching, & Livestock; General; Out of Print, with Stock; Nebraska

Thomas Durflinger
3398 California Street, #15
San Francisco, Calif. 94118
(415) 346-6639
Short Name: **T Durflinger**
Technology; Hunting, Fishing & Angling; Sporting; Farming, Ranching, & Livestock; Militaria; Shooting & Firearms

Philip C Duschnes, Inc
699 Madison Avenue
New York, N.Y. 10021
(212) 838-2635
Short Name: **P C Duschnes**
Books about Books; First Editions, Modern; IlluminatedManuscripts; Illustrated Books; Press Books & Fine Printing; Limited Editions Club

Charles Dvorak
Bowden Lane
Glen Head, N.Y. 11545
Short Name: **C Dvorak**
Americana; Overland Narratives; Rare Books; South America; Voyages, Travels, & Exploration

Raymond Dworcyk Rare Books
2114 West Rogers Street
Milwaukee, Wisc. 53204
Short Name: **R Dworcyk**
Color Plate Books; Americana; Juveniles; Literature; Aviation & Aeronautics; War

Dwyer's Bookstore
P O Box 426
Northampton, Mass. 01061
Short Name: **Dwyer's**
Printing & Printing History; Books about Books; British Isles; Press Books & Fine Printing; American Literature; Ireland & The Irish

Jeff Dykes-Western Books
P O Box 38
College Park, Md. 20740
(301) 864-0666
Short Name: **J Dykes**
Western Americana; Outlaws & Rangers

Dymant Books-Scholars' Bookstore
1126 Bank Street
Ottawa, Ont. K1S 3X6
(613) 235-0565
Short Name: **Dyment**
Philosophy; Political Science & Theory; Literature; Political, Social, & Cultural History & Thought; Psychiatry, Psychology, & Psychonanalysis

E

E K Book Exchange
14 Washington Place
New York, N.Y. 10003
(212) 254-2857
Short Name: **E K**
*Education; General;
Mathematics; Out of Print, with
Stock; Philosophy; Scholarly
Books*

Eagle Books
P O Box 12010
Lexington, Ken. 40579
(606) 272-4612
Short Name: **Eagle**
*Book Trade & Catalogues;
Militaria; Out of Print, with
Stock; Rare Books; Shooting &
Firearms*

Eagle's Nest-Books (Dec-May)
2924 Eagle Trail
Vero Beach, Fla. 32960
Short Name: **Eagle's-Vero**
*Juveniles; Cookery &
Gastronomy; First Editions*

**Eagle's Nest Books (May-
    December)**
P O Box 400
Chelsea, Mich. 48118
Short Name: **Eagle's-Chel**
*Juveniles; Cookery &
Gastronomy; First Editions*

Earthworks, Inc
1724 20th Street, NW
Washington, D.C. 20009
(202) 332-4323
Short Name: **Earthworks**
Drug Culture

East & West Shop
4 Apple Blossom Lane
Newtown, Conn. 06470
Short Name: **East & West**
*Orientalia; Chinese Civilization;
Japan; Asia; Middle East*

East West Books, Inc
506 West Diversey
Chicago, Ill. 60614
(312) 525-5157
Short Name: **East West**
*Holistic Health & Nutrition;
Philosophy; Psychiatry,
Psychology, & Psychonanalysis;
Orientalia; Religion &
Theology*

Harland H Eastman
66 Main Street, Box 276
Springvale, Maine 04083
(207) 324-2797
Short Name: **H H Eastman**
*Maine; Childrens' Books; Series
Books for Boys & Girls; Prints;
General*

Hanns Ebensten & Company
705 Washington Street
New York, N.Y. 10014
Short Name: **H Ebensten**
Travel Guides

Echo Books
52 Turning Mill Road
Lexington, Mass. 02173
(617) 862-6379
Short Name: **Echo**
*Childrens' Books; Folklore;
Illustrated Books; Literary
Criticism*

Edenite Society
Imlaystown, N.J. 08526
(609) 259-7517
Short Name: **Edenite Soc**
*Religion & Theology; Out of
Print, with Stock; Philosophy;
Scholarly Books; Reprints;
Prints*

William H Edgerton
P O Box 88
Darien, Conn. 06820
(203) 655-9510
Short Name: **W H Edgerton**
*Music; Mechanical Musical
Instruments; Technology*

Edgewood Books
359 Edgewood Avenue
New Haven, Conn. 06520
Short Name: **Edgewood**
*Literary Criticism; Literature;
Out of Print, without Stock;
Scholarly Books; Search
Service, without Stock; World
Wars*

J S Edgren
P O Box 326
Carmel, Calif. 93921
(408) 625-2575
Short Name: **J S Edgren**
*Appraisals & Appraisal
Services; Asia; Collection
Development; Orientalia;
Paintings; Rare Books*

Ernest And Margaret Ediger
12680 SW Farmington Road
Beaverton, Ore. 97005
(503) 643-7222
Short Name: **E & M Ediger**
Fiction; Biography; Militaria

Edison Hall Books
5 Ventnor Drive
Edison, N.J. 08817
Short Name: **Edison Hall**
*General; First Editions,
Modern; Childrens' Books;
Education; Americana; Rare
Books*

Editions Limited
20 Clark Road
Bernardsville, N.J. 07924
Short Name: **Edtns Ltd**
Detective Fiction

Educo Services Ltd
P O Box 226
Valhalla, N.Y. 10595
Short Name: **Educo**
*Periodicals; Scholarly Books;
Collection Development; Out of
Print, with Stock; Economics &
Business*

G F Edwards
P O Box 1461
Lawton, Okla. 73502
(405) 248-6870
Short Name: **G F Edwards**
Fiction; General; New Books;
Out of Print, with Stock;
Paperbacks (new)

Anthony Egan
172 East 4th Street
New York, N.Y. 10009
(212) 260-3706
Short Name: **A Egan**
Science Fiction; Fantasy;
Horror; Curiosa; Pulps

I Ehrlich
P O Box 994, Station B
Montreal, Que. H38 3k5
(514) 842-7000
Short Name: **I Ehrlich**
Americana; Arctica &
Antarctica; Canada &
Canadiana; Pacific Region;
Voyages, Travels, &
Exploration

The Eight-Cent Nickel
310 South Main Street
Liberty, N.Y. 12754
Short Name: **Eight-Cent**
Humor; Search Service, with
Stock; Out of Print, with Stock;
General

R M Eisenberg
436 New London Road
Newark, Del. 19711
(302) 731-9445
Short Name: **R M Eisenberg**
Natural History; Botany;
Gardening & Horticulture;
General; First Editions,
Modern; Americana

El Cascajero-Old Spanish Book
    Mine
506 West Broadway
New York, N.Y. 10012
(212) 254-0905
Short Name: **El Cascajero**
Latin America; Scholarly
Books; American Indians;
Archaeology; Architecture; Art

El Piasano Books
1000 Park Avenue, SW
Albuquerque, N.Mex. 87102
(505) 242-9121
Short Name: **El Piasano**
Americana, Regional; General

Charles Elder-Bookseller
2115 Elliston Place
Nashville, Tenn. 37203
(615) 327-1867
Short Name: **C Elder**
First Editions; First Editions,
Modern; Poetry; Civil War &
Confederacy; Rare Books;
Literature

Eldorado Books
P O Box 14-036
San Francisco, Calif. 94114
Short Name: **Bkman-Gran**
Appraisals & Appraisal
Services; Literature;
Autographed Material &
Autographs; Press Books &
Fine Printing; Printing &
Printing History; Manuscripts

Electric Glory
P O Box 1581
Sausalito, Calif. 94965
(415) 383-1125
Short Name: **Electric Glory**
Illustrated Books; Press Books
& Fine Printing

Elgen Books
336 De Mott Avenue
Rockville Centre, N.Y. 11570
(516) 536-6276
Short Name: **Elgen**
Medicine & Science;
Technology; Mathematics;
Biography; Botany; Voyages,
Travels, & Exploration

Elliot's Books
P O Box 6
Northford, Conn. 06472
(203) 484-2184
Short Name: **Elliot's**
Search Service, with Stock;
Scholarly Books; Social
Sciences; Humanities;
Collection Development; Out of
Print, with Stock

Anne M Ellis Sales
P O Box 854
Kentfield, Calif. 94914
Short Name: **A M Ellis**
Americana; Black Literature &
Black Studies; Cinema & Mass
Media; Ephemera; Performing
Arts; Presidents

Bill Ellis
P O Box 436
Qn Charl. City, B.C. V0T 1S0
Short Name: **B Ellis**
American Indians; Art; Canada
& Canadiana

Patricia Ellis
P O Box 518
Parkman, Ohio 44080
Short Name: **P Ellis**
Railroads

Elm
8815 Churchfield Lane
Laurel, Md. 20811
Short Name: **Elm**
Espionage

Elmcress Books
161 Bay Road, Rte #1a
South Hamilton, Mass. 01982
(617) 468-3261
Short Name: **Elmcress**
Books about Books; General;
Horses; Naval & Marine; Press
Books & Fine Printing; Printing
& Printing History

Dorothy Elsberg
Richmond Road, Box 178
West Stockbridge, Mass. 01266
(413) 232-8560
Short Name: **D Elsberg**
Music

Allan Elsner Book Shop
900 First Avenue
New York, N.Y. 10022
(212) 688-4577
Short Name: **A Elsner**
General

Elysian Fields
81-13 Broadway
Elmhurst, N.Y. 11373
Short Name: **Elysian Fields**
Homosexual & Gay Literature;
Sexology; Transgenderism;
Erotica

R & D Emerson
The Old Church, Main Street
Falls Village, Conn. 06031
Short Name: **R & D Emerson**
Art; Geology; Medicine &
Science; Press Books & Fine
Printing; Rare Books; Scholarly
Books

Howard R Emler
4609 Bayard Street
Pittsburgh, Penna. 15213
Short Name: **H R Emler**
*Black Literature & Black
Studies; Childrens' Books;
Autographed Material &
Autographs; Illustrated Books;
Ephemera; Opera*

Encyclopedias Bought & Sold
14071 Windsor Place
Santa Ana, Calif. 92705
(714) 838-3643
Short Name: **Encyclopedias**
Encyclopedias; Classics

Enterprise Books
P O Drawer 289
Ripley, Tenn. 38083
(901) 635-1771
Short Name: **Enterprise**
*Tennessee; Papermaking &
Marbling; Bookbinding &
Restoration; Books about
Books; Printing & Printing
History; Typography & Type
Specimens*

**Ellen Enzler, Trophy Room
    Books**
4858 Dempsey Avenue
Encino, Calif. 91436
(213) 784-3801
Short Name: **E Enzler**
*Africa; Asia; Color Plate
Books; Hunting, Fishing &
Angling; Natural History;
Voyages, Travels, &
Exploration*

**The Epistemologist Scholarly
    Books**
P O Box 63
Bryn Mawr, Penna. 19010
Short Name: **Epist Scholar**
*Psychiatry, Psychology, &
Psychonanalysis; Philosophy;
Social Sciences*

Erie Book Store
717 French Street
Erie, Penna. 16501
(814) 452-3354
Short Name: **Erie**
*General; Western Pennsylvania;
Petroleum; Great Lakes*

D J Ernst-Books
27 North Market Street
Selingsgrove, Penna. 17870
(717) 374-9464
Short Name: **D J Ernst**
*Pennsylvania; Americana;
General*

Escargot
503 Rte #71
Brielle, N.J. 08730
Short Name: **Escargot**
*New Jersey; Childrens' Books;
Rare Books; Comic Books*

Gary L Estabrook Books
P O Box 61453
Vancouver, Wash. 98166
Short Name: **G L Estabrook**
*Hunting, Fishing & Angling;
Derrydale Press; Game Birds;
Dogs*

Estate Book Sales
2824 Pennsylvania Avenue, NW
Washington, D.C. 20007
(202) 965-4274
Short Name: **Estate**
*Art; Naval & Marine;
Americana, Regional;
Geneaologies; Illustrated Books;
Natural History*

Estes Book Service
13 Haley Street
Lewiston, Maine 04240
(207) 782-0887
Short Name: **Estes Service**
*Books about Books; Natural
History; Geology; Playing
Cards; Reprints; Philosophy*

Richard O Estes, Sr-Bibles
Rte #2
Hartville, Mo. 65667
(314) 443-3607
Short Name: **R O Estes, Sr**
*Appraisals & Appraisal
Services;
IlluminatedManuscripts;
Incunabula & Early Printing;
Bible & Bible Studies;
Watchtower Books & Jehovah's
Witnesses*

Et Cetera
196 East Third Street
Chico, Calif. 95926
Short Name: **Et Cetera**
*California; Western Americana;
Press Books & Fine Printing;
Fine & Rare Bindings*

Ethnographic Arts Publications
1040 Erica Road
Mill Valley, Calif. 94941
(415) 383-2998
Short Name: **Ethnograph Arts**
*Africa; American Indians; Art;
Out of Print, with Stock; Pacific
Region; Central America*

Eu Be Co
P O Box 377
Williamsburg, Va. 23185
(804) 564-3107
Short Name: **Eu Be Co**
*Bookbinding & Restoration;
Papermaking & Marbling*

Eubiotics Ltd
90 New York Avenue
West Hempstead, N.Y. 11552
Short Name: **Eubiotics**
Dogs; Cats; Botany

Euclid Books
227 Euclid Street
Santa Monica, Calif. 90402
(213) 393-5963
Short Name: **Euclid**
*First Editions, Modern; Fiction;
Poetry; Press Books & Fine
Printing; Literary Criticism;
Little Magazines & Literary
Small Presses*

Leighton Evans
Green Valley Auction Barn
Mount Crawford, Va. 22841
Short Name: **L Evans**
*Civil War & Confederacy;
Virginia; Authors; Western
Americana; Local History;
Imprints*

Lonnie E Evans
8 Burbank Boulevard
Savannah, Ga. 31406
(912) 925-5455
Short Name: **L E Evans**
*Childrens' Books; Detective
Fiction; Illustrated Books;
Color Plate Books; First
Editions, Modern; Search
Service, with Stock*

Olin O Evans
371 West Spring Street
Woodstock, Va. 22664
Short Name: **O O Evans**
*Farming, Ranching, &
Livestock; Game Birds;
National Geographic Magazine;
Civil War & Confederacy;
Americana, Regional*

Evergreen Books
P O Box 2725
Cherry Hill, N.J. 08034
Short Name: **Evergreen**
*Americana; Americana, States;
Americana, Regional*

Ex Libris
160a East 70th Street
New York, N.Y. 10021
Short Name: **Ex Libris-NYC**
*Avant Garde, Experimental, &
Modern Art; Architecture;
Graphic Arts; Little Magazines
& Literary Small Presses;
Posters; Photography*

Ex Libris Mazel
P O Box 419
Larchmont, N.Y. 10538
Short Name: **Ex Libris Mazel**
*Psychiatry, Psychology, &
Psychonanalysis*

Ex Libris Books
23 Franklin Street
Bangor, Maine 04401
Short Name: **Ex Libris-Ban**
*Mystery Fiction; Literature;
History; Maine; General*

Examino Books
P O Box 448
Fremont, Neb. 68025
Short Name: **Examino**
*Adventure; Mining &
Metallurgy; Treasure Hunting;
Self-Sufficiency; Self Help*

F

F & I Books
P O Box 1900
Santa Monica, Calif. 90406
(213) 394-7886
Short Name: **F & I**
*Australia & Oceania; Arctica &
Antarctica; Asia; Pacific
Region; Voyages, Travels, &
Exploration; Whaling*

Facsimile Book Shop
16 West 55th Street
New York, N.Y. 10019
Short Name: **Facsimile**
*Ireland & The Irish; Irish &
Scottish History; Folklore;
Poetry*

Fain's First Editions
Pacific Palisades, Calif. 90272
Short Name: **Fain's First**
*First Editions, Modern; Art;
Medicine & Science; Literary
Criticism; Biography*

Anthony Fair Rare Books
274 Madison Avenue
New York, N.Y. 10016
(212) 685-2475
Short Name: **A Fair**
*Fine & Rare Bindings;
Illustrated Books; Voyages,
Travels, & Exploration; Rare
Books; Emblem Books;
Literature*

Edward C Fales
Turnpike Road
Salisbury, N.H. 03268
(603) 648-2484
Short Name: **E C Fales**
*Americana; Appraisals &
Appraisal Services; Cookery &
Gastronomy; Gardening &
Horticulture; General;
Manuscripts*

Mrs Carlton Fallert
203 North Vine Street
Hinsdale, Ill. 60521
Short Name: **Mrs C Fallert**
Search Service, without Stock

Family Bookshop
4951 Glacier Drive
Los Angeles, Calif. 90041
(213) 257-3069
Short Name: **Family**
*Golf; Arctica & Antarctica;
Alaska; Hunting, Fishing &
Angling*

The Family Album
R D #1
Glen Rock, Penna. 17327
(717) 235-2134
Short Name: **Family Album**
*Americana; Appraisals &
Appraisal Services;
IlluminatedManuscripts;
Illustrated Books; Incunabula
& Early Printing; Rare Books*

Fantasy Archives
71 Eighth Avenue
New York, N.Y. 10014
(212) 929-5391
Short Name: **Fant Archives**
*Inscribed Books; Science
Fiction; First Editions;
Manuscripts; Search Service,
with Stock; Out of Print, with
Stock*

Fantasy, Etc
808 Larkin Street
San Francisco, Calif. 94109
(415) 441-7617
Short Name: **Fantasy**
*Science Fiction; Detective
Fiction; New Books; Out of
Print, with Stock; Horror; First
Editions*

Far Corners Book Search
2000 Dauphin Street
Mobile, Ala. 36605
Short Name: **Far Corners-Mob**
Americana; The South

Carolyn Farkas
71 North Simpers Road
Elkton, Md. 21921
Short Name: **C Farkas**
*Author Collections; Classics;
Dictionaries; Literature;
Reference; Sets*

Farley's Old And Rare Books
2031 Morningside Drive
Pensacola, Fla. 32503
(904) 432-8194
Short Name: **Farley's**
*Americana; Childrens' Books;
Technology; Humanities*

Barbara Farnsworth
West Cornwall, Conn. 06796
(203) 672-6333
Short Name: **B Farnsworth**
*Out of Print, with Stock;
Illustrated Books; Childrens'
Books; Press Books & Fine
Printing; Graphic Arts; Search
Service, with Stock*

Don Fay
4329 Acon-Caledonia Road, Rte
#5
Caledonia, N.Y. 14423
Short Name: **D Fay**
*Literature; Americana;
Psychopharmacology;
Childrens' Books; Detective
Fiction*

C L Feick, Books (Mail Only)
10 North Mill Road
Cranbury, N.J. 08512
Short Name: **C L Feick**
*Arctica & Antarctica; American
Literature; Poetry; Black
Literature & Black Studies*

Bob Fein
139 Joralemon Street
Brooklyn, N.Y. 11201
(212) 522-1309
Short Name: **B Fein**
*American Indians; Archaeology;
Art; Latin America; South
America*

Joseph J Felcone, Books
P O Box 366
Princeton, N.J. 08540
(609) 924-8371
Short Name: **J J Felcone**
*New Jersey; Americana;
Americana, States; Americana,
Regional*

A L Feldman-Fine Arts
Cleveland, Ohio 44114
Short Name: **A L Feldman**
*Art; Illustrated Books;
Miniature Books; Press Books
& Fine Printing; Printing &
Printing History*

Henry Feldstein
P O Box 588, Corona-Elmhurst
Flushing, N.Y. 11373
Short Name: **H Feldstein**
Photography

Peter R Feltus
5709 Keith Avenue
Oakland, Calif. 94618
(415) 658-9627
Short Name: **P R Feltus**
*Middle East; Travel Guides;
Philately & Philatelic
Literature*

Bruce P Ferrini, Rare Books
933 West Exchange Street
Akron, Ohio 44302
(216) 867-2665
Short Name: **B P Ferrini**
*Rare Books; Manuscripts;
Prints; Drawings*

Ferryman Antiquarian Books
P O Box 61
Greensboro Bend, Vt. 05842
(802) 533-2912
Short Name: **Ferryman Ant**
*Literature; Humanities;
Detective Fiction; Science
Fiction; Search Service, with
Stock*

Kenneth And Jane Field
14 North Street
Georgetown, Mass. 01833
(617) 352-6641
Short Name: **K & J Field**
*General; Out of Print, with
Stock; Militaria*

Fields Bookstore
1419 Polk Street
San Francisco, Calif. 94109
(415) 673-2027
Short Name: **Fields**
*Psychiatry, Psychology, &
Psychonanalysis; Out of Print,
with Stock; Religion &
Theology; Art; Folklore*

50,000 Books, Inc
123 North Magnolia
El Cajon, Calif. 92020
(714) 444-6191
Short Name: **50,000**
*Economics & Business;
Gambling; Paperbacks (new);
Stock Market & Wall Street*

Bob Finch
P O Box 1362
Torrance, Calif. 90505
(213) 378-2771
Short Name: **B Finch**
*Arctica & Antarctica; Naval &
Marine; Voyages, Travels, &
Exploration; Whaling; Ships &
The Sea*

Find A Book
P O Box 6190
Arlington, Va. 22206
Short Name: **Find A Bk**
*Americana; Photography;
Literature; Psychiatry,
Psychology, & Psychonanalysis*

Steve Finer
173 L' Street
Turner's Falls, Mass. 01376
(413) 863-2375
Short Name: **S Finer**
*Americana; Gambling;
Photography; Search Service,
with Stock; Technology*

Leonard H Finn
40 Greaton Road
West Roxbury, Mass. 02132
(617) 327-7053
Short Name: **L H Finn**
*Numismatics; Medals (books
on); Counterfeit Stamps &
Coins; Ephemera*

Jack Finney
Box 152-F
Indianapolis, Ind. 46234
(317) 271-9030
Short Name: **J Finney**
Auto Racing

Fir Tree Books
P O Box 07416
Milwaukee, Wisc. 53207
Short Name: **Fir Tree**
*Architecture; City & Urban
Planning; Fine & Rare
Bindings; Prints; Printing &
Printing History*

Fireside Books
72 North Williams Street
Crystal Lake, Ill. 60014
Short Name: **Fireside**
*Out of Print, with Stock; Search
Service, with Stock; Geography*

First Impressions
26w580 Butterfield Road
Wheaton, Ill. 60187
(312) 668-9418
Short Name: **First Impress**
*Childrens' Books; Illustrated
Books; First Editions, Modern;
Out of Print, with Stock;
Detective Fiction; Little
Magazines & Literary Small
Presses*

Firstborn Books
1007 East Benning Road
Galesville, Md. 20765
(301) 867-7050
Short Name: **Firstborn**
*Out of Print, with Stock;
Western Americana; Music;
Appraisals & Appraisal
Services*

A S Fischler Rare Books
604 South 15th Street
San Jose, Calif. 95112
(408) 297-7090
Short Name: **A S Fischler**
*Press Books & Fine Printing;
First Editions, Modern;
California; Western Books;
Signed, Limited Editions;
Western Americana*

C G Fisher
62 East Main Street
Cobleskill, N.Y. 12043
Short Name: **C G Fisher**
*Americana; Americana, States;
General; Maps, Atlases, &
Cartography; Natural History;
Search Service, with Stock*

Jim Fisher
453 Laury Lane
New Wilmington, Penna. 16142
Short Name: **J Fisher**
Criminology

Peter Thomas Fisher
41 Union Square, West
New York, N.Y. 10003
Short Name: **P T Fisher**
*Americana; German Books &
Literature; Search Service, with
Stock*

**Richard Fitch-Maps, Prints &
Books**
2324 Calle Halcon
Santa Fe, N.Mex. 87501
(505) 982-2939
Short Name: **R Fitch**
*Maps, Atlases, & Cartography;
Prints; Voyages, Travels, &
Exploration; Geography;
Geology; Reference*

E Fithian Books
1538 Ingalls Street
Lakewood, Colo. 80214
(303) 238-6283
Short Name: **E Fithian**
*Detective Fiction; Science
Fiction; Out of Print, with
Stock*

Five Quail Books
P O Box 91
Rancho Santa Fe, Calif. 92067
Short Name: **5 Quail**
*Hunting, Fishing & Angling;
Southwestern America; U.S.
Government Publications*

John F Fleming, Inc
322 East 57th Street
New York, N.Y. 10022
(212) 755-3242
Short Name: **J F Fleming**
*First Editions; Rare Books;
Manuscripts*

Fletcher's Books
Main Street & Mill Creek Drive
Salado, Tex. 76571
Short Name: **Fletcher's**
*Appraisals & Appraisal
Services; General; Specialized
Publications; Fine & Rare
Bindings*

Fleuron Books
541 Chipping Lane
Sarasota, Fla. 33577
Short Name: **Fleuron**
*Sporting; Authors; Hunting,
Fishing & Angling*

Floating Mountain Books
Star Route
Redway, Calif. 95560
Short Name: **Floating Mtn**
*Louis Icart; Voyages, Travels,
& Exploration; Childrens'
Books; Fiction; New Books;
Natural History*

Fly Creek Bookstall
P O Box 114
Fly Creek, N.Y. 13337
Short Name: **Fly Creek**
*Poetry; General; Press Books &
Fine Printing; Miniature Books*

**T T Foley, Bookseller (Appt
Only)**
307 East Wood Street
Paris, Ill. 61944
(217) 466-8585
Short Name: **T T Foley**
*Archaeology; Art; Childrens'
Books; Cookery & Gastronomy*

Folger Shakespeare Bookstore
201 East Capitol Street, SE
Washington, D.C. 20003
(202) 546-2626
Short Name: **Folger**
*Shakespeare; Renaissance;
Prints; Press Books & Fine
Printing; Art; Literature*

Folkways, Scholarly Books
5305 Mc Kinley Street
Bethesda, Md. 20014
Short Name: **Folkways**
*Medicine & Science; Social
Sciences; Psychiatry,
Psychology, & Psychonanalysis;
Religion & Theology*

Folkways Scholarly Books
5305 McKinley Street
Bethesda, Md. 20014
Short Name: **Folkways**
*Social Sciences; Psychiatry,
Psychology, & Psychonanalysis;
Medicine & Science; Economics
& Business; Political Science &
Theory; Criminology*

The Footnote
179 Washington Park
Brooklyn, N.Y. 11205
Short Name: **Footnote**
*Dance; Opera; Music; Cookery
& Gastronomy; Americana*

Alla T Ford, Rare Books
114 South Palmway
Lake Worth, Fla. 33460
(305) 585-1442
Short Name: **A T Ford**
*Childrens' Books; First
Editions; Miniature Books;
Rare Books; Science Fiction; L.
Frank Baum & Oziana*

Fordham Book Company
P O Box 6
New Rochelle, N.Y. 10801
Short Name: **Fordham**
Search Service, without Stock

Forest Bookshop
P O Box 5206
Charlottesville, Va. 22905
(804) 296-3824
Short Name: **Forest**
*Book Scouts; Natural History;
Out of Print, without Stock;
Search Service, without Stock*

Forest Park Bookshop
1412 Delaware Avenue
Fort Wayne, Ind. 46805
(219) 424-1058
Short Name: **Forest Park**
*Americana, Regional;
Childrens' Books; Detective
Fiction; Illustrated Books; Out
of Print, with Stock; Search
Service, with Stock*

Forsyth Travel Library
9154 West 57th Street, Box
2975
Shawnee Mission, Kan. 66201
(913) 384-3440
Short Name: **Forsyth Travel**
*Travel; Maps, Atlases, &
Cartography; Voyages, Travels,
& Exploration; Antiques;
Periodicals*

Fortunate Finds Bookstore
16 West Natick Road
Warwick, R.I. 02886
(401) 737-8160
Short Name: **Fortunate Fnds**
*Ephemera; Trade Cards;
Postcards; Trade Catalogues;
Documents; Maps, Atlases, &
Cartography*

Fortune Finders Press
P O Box 1
Islip, N.Y. 11751
(516) 581-4545
Short Name: **Fortune Finders**
*Childrens' Books; Automotive;
Aviation & Aeronautics;
Periodicals; Americana;
IncomeOpportunities & Self
Help*

Fox & Sutherland
15 South Moger Avenue
Mount Kisco, N.Y. 10549
(914) 666-5957
Short Name: **Fox & Suther**
*Americana; Philosophy;
Photography; Religion &
Theology; Natural History; Out
of Print, without Stock*

Alan C Fox (Appt Only)
13440 Ventura Boulevard
Sherman Oaks, Calif. 91423
(213) 981-2888
Short Name: **A C Fox**
*Mark Twain; Printing &
Printing History; Press Books
& Fine Printing; Illustrated
Books; Incunabula & Early
Printing*

Fox Books
1420 Neely Bend Road
Madison, Tenn. 37115
(615) 868-2078
Short Name: **Fox-Mad**
*Americana; Americana,
Regional; Tennessee; Civil War
& Confederacy; Authors;
Childrens' Books*

Fox Hill Books
436 Main Street
Palmer, Mass. 01069
(413) 283-7681
Short Name: **Fox Hill**
General; Americana

Leonard Fox
667 Madison Avenue
New York, N.Y. 10021
(212) 888-5480
Short Name: **L Fox**
*Illustrated Books; Graphic Arts;
Performing Arts; Color Plate
Books; Avant Garde,
Experimental, & Modern Art*

Francis And Yellin
P O Box 2403
Sepulveda, Calif. 91343
Short Name: **Francis & Yell**
*First Editions, Modern; Science
Fiction; Fantasy; Detective
Fiction; Signed, Limited
Editions*

Franklin Book Shop
302 South Main Street
Athens, Penna. 18810
(717) 888-1552
Short Name: **Franklin**
*Americana, States; Biography;
Civil War & Confederacy; First
Editions; Political Science &
Theory; Religion & Theology*

**Fransen's Bks & Prints (Mail
Only)**
Anderson Island, Wash. 98303
Short Name: **Fransen's**
*Americana; Books about Books;
First Editions; Militaria; Out of
Print, with Stock; Science
Fiction*

James L Fraser
309 South Willard Street
Burlington, Vt. 05401
Short Name: **J L Fraser**
*Economics & Business; Stock
Market & Wall Street; Industry
& Labor; Biography*

Fraser's Books
13760 Valley Vista
Sherman Oaks, Calif. 91423
Short Name: **Fraser's**
*History; Philosophy; Music;
Literature; Political Science &
Theory; Frank L. Munsey*

Mildred Frazier
402 North 6th Street
Marshall, Ill. 62441
Short Name: **M Frazier**
*Miniature Books; Press Books
& Fine Printing*

Palmer D French (Appt Only)
2014 MacArthur Boulevard,
   Box 2704
Oakland, Calif. 94602
(415) 530-1648
Short Name: **P D French**
Voyages, Travels, &
Exploration; Orientalia; Fine
Arts; Prints

Fricelli Associates
P O Box 247, Bath Beach
   Station
Brooklyn, N.Y. 11214
Short Name: **Fricelli**
Autographed Material &
Autographs

Howard Frisch
P O Box 75, Old Post Road
Livingston, N.Y. 12541
Short Name: **A Frisch**
General

Froghollow Books
1 Sullivan Street
Cazenovia, N.Y. 13035
(315) 655-2006
Short Name: **Froghollow**
Literature; Americana; Women
& Feminism; Poetry; Childrens'
Books; Illustrated Books

Doris Frohnsdorff
P O Box 2306
Gaithersburg, Md. 20760
(301) 869-1258
Short Name: **D Frohnsdorff**
Fine & Rare Bindings;
Childrens' Books; Drawings;
Illustrated Books; Miniature
Books; Rare Books

From Another Time
P O Box 6903
Houston, Tex. 77005
(713) 666-2044
Short Name: **From Another**
Antiques

Frontier America Corporation
P O Box 3698
Bryan, Tex. 77801
(713) 846-4462
Short Name: **Fron Amer**
Americana; Americana,
Regional; Voyages, Travels, &
Exploration; Photography; Civil
War & Confederacy; Press
Books & Fine Printing

Frontier Pioneer Bookshop
1357-1/2 East Colorado Street
Glendale, Calif. 91205
(213) 243-0221
Short Name: **Frontier P'neer**
Arctica & Antarctica; Canada
& Canadiana; Cookery &
Gastronomy; Paperbacks (new);
General; Childrens' Books

Fuller's-Books
12 Holcomb Street
West Haven, Conn. 06516
(203) 933-9569
Short Name: **Fuller's**
General; Out of Print, with
Stock; Civil War &
Confederacy; World Wars;
Americana; Colonial America &
Revolutionary War Era

W Bruce Fye
1607 North Wood Avenue
Marshfield, Wisc. 54449
(715) 384-8128
Short Name: **W B Fye**
Medicine & Science; History of
Medicine & Science;
Bibliography; Neurosciences;
American Mercury Magazine;
Autographed Material &
Autographs

G

G B I Antiques
P O Box 185
Smithtown, N.Y. 11787
(516) 724-7781
Short Name: **G B I**
Paintings; Prints; Drawings;
Dogs; Fiction; Paperbacks (new)

G F S Books
P O Box 12
Great River, N.Y. 11739
(516) 581-7076
Short Name: **G F S**
Out of Print, with Stock

G J M Enterprises
P O Box 795
Santa Monica, Calif. 90406
Short Name: **G J M**
Books about Books; Fishing &
Angling; Psychiatry,
Psychology, & Psychonanalysis;
Religion & Theology

G N Gabbard
P O Box 781
New Boston, Tex. 75570
Short Name: **G N Gabbard**
Science Fiction; Paperbacks
(new); Comic Books;
Humanities; Middle Ages;
Detective Fiction

John Gach Books
5620 Waterloo Road
Columbia, Md. 21045
(301) 465-9023
Short Name: **J Gach**
Psychiatry, Psychology, &
Psychonanalysis; Appraisals &
Appraisal Services; Collection
Development; Rare Books

Jean Gagnon, Libraire
498 Rue D'aiguillon, B.P. 653
   H.-V.
Quebec, Que. G1R 4S2
Short Name: **J Gagnon**
Canada & Canadiana; French
Books & Literature

Kendall G Gaisser, Booksellers
1242 Broadway
Toledo, Ohio 43609
Short Name: **K G Gaisser**
Rare Books; Militaria; History;
Literature; Art

H Galewitz
143 Northern Parkway
Plainview, N.Y. 11803
(516) 938-4167
Short Name: **H Galewitz**
Humor; Fiction; Childrens'
Books; Performing Arts;
General

Lorraine Galinsky
P O Box 744
Huntington, N.Y. 11743
Short Name: **L Galinsky**
Antiques; Art; Childrens'
Books; Fiction; Illustrated
Books; Poetry

I Galis-Bound To Please Books
357 Atlantic Avenue
Marblehead, Mass. 01945
(617) 631-5351
Short Name: **I Galis**
Biography; Book Scouts;
Militaria; Naval & Marine;
Presidents; British Isles

Gallery Of The Old West
P O Box 262
Lakeside, Mont. 59922
(406) 844-3568
Short Name: **Gall Old West**
Montana; Shooting & Firearms;
Sporting; Hunting, Fishing &
Angling; Western Americana

Galvez Books & Silver, Inc
208 South Florida Blanca Street
Pensacola, Fla. 32501
(904) 432-2874
Short Name: **Galvez**
General; Americana, Regional

Gambler's Book Club
630 South 11th Street
Las Vegas, Nev. 89101
(702) 382-7555
Short Name: **Gambler's**
Gambling

Garciagarst Books
112 East Monte Vista
Turlock, Calif. 95380
Short Name: **Garciagarst**
General; Childrens' Books;
Appraisals & Appraisal
Services; Out of Print, with
Stock; Paperbacks (new)

A & R Gardiner (Appt Only)
60 Mill Road
Stamford, Conn. 06903
(203) 322-1129
Short Name: **A & R Gardiner**
Americana; Maps, Atlases, &
Cartography; Voyages, Travels,
& Exploration; Newspapers;
Trade Catalogues; Ephemera

Charles E Gardiner
39-20 220th Street
Bayside, N.Y. 11361
Short Name: **C E Gardiner**
Railroads; Shooting &
Firearms; Out of Print, with
Stock

Frederick R Gardner
20 Marilyn Avenue, Box 836
Amityville, N.Y. 11701
Short Name: **F R Gardner**
Childrens' Books

Ralph Gardner
135 Central Park West
New York, N.Y. 10023
Short Name: **R Gardner**
Authors; Autographed Material
& Autographs; Bibliography;
Books about Books; Childrens'
Books; First Editions

Anthony Garnett, Fine Books
P O Box 4918
St Louis, Mo. 63108
(314) 367-8080
Short Name: **A Garnett**
Press Books & Fine Printing;
First Editions; English
Literature

Charles Garvin, Rare Books
203b Dey Street, Box 621
Ithaca, N.Y. 14850
(607) 277-4225
Short Name: **C Garvin**
Rare Books; Detective Fiction;
Science Fiction; First Editions;
Authors; Press Books & Fine
Printing

W C Gates-Books (Mail Only)
1279 Bardstown
Louisville, Ken. 40204
(503) 451-3295
Short Name: **W C Gates**
Americana; Kentucky; Fiction;
First Editions; Illustrated
Books

The Gateway
Ferndale, Penna. 18921
(215) 847-5644
Short Name: **Gateway**
Religion & Theology;
Astrology; Folklore; Search
Service, with Stock; Out of
Print, with Stock

John Taylor Gatto
235 West 76th Street
New York, N.Y. 10023
Short Name: **J T Gatto**
Mushrooms; Science Fiction;
Fantasy; Popular Culture;
Television; Firearms &
Weapons

William T Gavin
86 Maple Avenue
Leominster, Mass. 01453
(617) 534-4038
Short Name: **W T Gavin**
Americana; Color Plate Books;
Natural History; Presidents;
Maps, Atlases, & Cartography;
Rare Books

Gem Antiques
1088 Madison Avenue
New York, N.Y. 10028
Short Name: **Gem Antiq**
Antiques; Reference

Gene & Kit's Books
R D #2
Mars, Penna. 16046
Short Name: **Gene & Kit's**
Mountaineering

Genealogists Bookshelf
343 East 85th Street, Box 468
New York, N.Y. 10028
(212) 879-1699
Short Name: **Genealogists**
Geneaologies; Heraldry;
Theatre; Local History

Genessee Book Shop
1966 Monroe Avenue
Rochester, N.Y. 14618
Short Name: **Genessee**
Americana; Literature; Religion & Theology; Economics & Business; Art; Local History

Geological Book Center
P O Box 235
Falls Village, Conn. 06031
(203) 824-0442
Short Name: **Geological**
Geology; Medicine & Science; Natural History; Technology; Petroleum; Paleontology

Robert L George
3705 Northwood Drive, NW
Cleveland, Tenn. 37311
(615) 472-7750
Short Name: **R L George**
Religion & Theology; Judaica & Hebraica; Science Fiction; Childrens' Books; Boy Scouts; Series Books for Boys & Girls

George Sand Books
9011 Melrose Avenue
Los Angeles, Calif. 90069
(213) 858-1648
Short Name: **George Sand**
Literature; Biography; Cinema & Mass Media; Little Magazines & Literary Small Presses; Performing Arts; Poetry

Lois Gereghty
9521 Orion Avenue
Sepulveda, Calif. 91343
(213) 892-1053
Short Name: **L Gereghty**
General; Search Service, with Stock

Victor F Germack
1199 Park Avenue
New York, N.Y. 10028
Short Name: **V Germack**
Photography

German & International Bookstore
1767 North Vermont Avenue
Los Angeles, Calif. 90027
Short Name: **German & Int'l**
Foreign Languages; First Editions, Modern; Judaica & Hebraica

Neil W Getman
624 Rossmore Road
Goleta, Calif. 93017
Short Name: **N W Getman**
Book Scouts; Americana, States; Americana, Regional

Ghent Bookworm
1407-09 Colley Avenue
Norfolk, Va. 23517
(804) 627-2267
Short Name: **Ghent Bkworm**
General; Search Service, with Stock; Out of Print, with Stock

Michael Gibbs Books
3206 Raintree Drive
Plano, Tex. 75074
(214) 424-4864
Short Name: **M Gibbs**
Americana; Appraisals & Appraisal Services; Farming, Ranching, & Livestock; Geology; Industry & Labor; Outlaws & Rangers

Gierspeck & Roper Booksellers
1132 West Dallas
Conroe, Tex. 77301
(713) 756-6188
Short Name: **Gierspeck & Rop**
Juveniles; Judaica & Hebraica; Out of Print, with Stock

D & P Gilbert
Rte #3
Lebanon, Mo. 65536
(417) 532-9869
Short Name: **D & P Gilbert**
Science Fiction; Fantasy; Illustrated Books; Childrens' Books; Mystery Fiction

Richard Gilbo
P O Box 12
Carpinteria, Calif. 93013
Short Name: **R Gilbo**
Americana; Black Literature & Black Studies; Humanities; Literature

Gilfillan Book Barn
999 Lincoln
San Jose, Calif. 95126
Short Name: **Gilfillan**
General

Duff & M E Gilfond
1722 19th Street, NW
Washington, D.C. 20009
(202) 387-1418
Short Name: **D & M E Gilford**
Search Service, with Stock

R Geneva Gill
P O Box 493
Bantam, Conn. 06750
Short Name: **R G Gill**
General; Fiction; Voyages, Travels, & Exploration; Out of Print, without Stock; Performing Arts

Jascha Giller-Quality Book Shop
P O Box 130
Westbury, N.Y. 11590
Short Name: **J Giller**
Art; Prints; Posters

Stanley Gilman
P O Box 131, Cooper Station
New York, N.Y. 10276
Short Name: **S Gilman**
General

The Ginger Press Bookstore
R R #3
Owen Sound, Ont. N4K 5N5
Short Name: **Ginger**
Antiques; Books about Books; Calligraphy; Press Books & Fine Printing; Crafts & Trades; Hobbies

Louis Ginsberg
P O Box 1502
Petersburg, Va. 23803
(804) 732-8188
Short Name: **L Ginsberg**
Americana, Regional; Beverages; Civil War & Confederacy; Medicine & Science; Overland Narratives; Rare Books

Michael Ginsberg Books, Inc
P O Box 402
Sharon, Mass. 02067
(617) 784-8181
Short Name: **M Ginsberg**
Americana; Canada & Canadiana; Latin America; Overland Narratives; Voyages, Travels, & Exploration; Western Americana

Givens Books
2345 Lakeside Drive
Lynchburg, Va. 24501
(804) 237-3440
Short Name: **Givens**
First Editions; General; New Books; Out of Print, with Stock; Rare Books; Search Service, with Stock

Keith Glackin Books
561 Grand
Astoria, Ore. 97103
(503) 325-7416
Short Name: **K Glackin**
Childrens' Books; Fiction; First Editions, Modern; Out of Print, without Stock; Science Fiction; Search Service, without Stock

Glad Day Bookshop
648a Yonge Street
Toronto, Ont. M4Y 2A6
(416) 961-4161
Short Name: **Glad Day-Tor**
Homosexual & Gay Literature

Glad Day Bookshop
22 Bromfield Street
Boston, Mass. 02108
(617) 542-0144
Short Name: **Glad Day-Bos**
Homosexual & Gay Literature

G F Glaeve
132 East Main Street
Mount Horeb, Wisc. 53572
(608) 437-8992
Short Name: **G F Glaeve**
Prints; Auctions & Auctioneers; Ephemera; Antiques; Search Service, with Stock; Maps, Atlases, & Cartography

Edwin V Glaser
25 Rodeo Avenue, #1, Box 1765
Sausalito, Calif. 94965
(415) 332-1194
Short Name: **E V Glaser**
Botany; Astrology; Continental Books; Mathematics; Medicine & Science

Richard Glassman-Out Of Print Books
15 First Street
Corte Madera, Calif. 94925
(415) 924-0410
Short Name: **R Glassman**
Biography; Fiction; History; Literature; Natural History; Modern Library (Publishers)

Glenn Books, Inc
1227 Baltimore
Kansas City, Mo. 64105
Short Name: **Glenn**
Americana; Western Americana; Printing & Printing History; Press Books & Fine Printing; Illustrated Books; Fine & Rare Bindings

Global Book Research
P O Box 153
Belding, Mich. 48809
(616) 794-3992
Short Name: **Global**
Militaria; Hunting, Fishing & Angling; Crafts & Trades; Shooting & Firearms; Americana, States; History

The Globe
P O Box A3398
Chicago, Ill. 60690
(312) 528-6228
Short Name: **Globe-Chic**
Maps, Atlases, & Cartography; Voyages, Travels, & Exploration

The Globe Bookstore
2509 Thames Street
Los Angeles, Calif. 90046
Short Name: **Globe-L A**
Metaphysics; History of Medicine & Science

Bob Godshall
P O Box 207
Fairview Village, Penna. 19409
Short Name: **B Godshall**
Pennsylvania; New Jersey

Judy Goffman Fine Art
P O Box 350a
Blue Bell, Penna. 19422
(215) 643-6310
Short Name: **J Goffman**
Art; Illustrated Books; Paintings; American Illustrative Art

Golden Age Collectables
1501 Pike Place
Seattle, Wash. 98101
(206) 622-9799
Short Name: **Golden Age**
Comic Books

Golden Hill Antiquarian
2456 Broadway
San Diego, Calif. 92101
(714) 236-9883
Short Name: **Golden Hill**
Antiques; Americana; General; Search Service, with Stock; Search Service, without Stock

Frank Goldman
P O Box 1165
Delray Beach, Fla. 33444
Short Name: **F Goldman**
Herbology & Herbs

Judith Goldman
384 Briarcliffe Road
Teaneck, N.J. 07666
Short Name: **J Goldman**
Books about Books; Calligraphy; Illustrated Books; Press Books & Fine Printing; Printing & Printing History

Yosef Goldman
6396 Overbrook Avenue
Philadelphia, Penna. 19151
Short Name: **Y Goldman**
Judaica & Hebraica; Rare Books

Lucien Goldschmidt
1117 Madison Avenue
New York, N.Y. 10028
Short Name: **L Goldschmidt**
Drawings; Illustrated Books; Psychiatry, Psychology, & Psychonanalysis; Architecture

Morton Goldsholl
420 Frontage Road
Northfield, Ill. 60093
Short Name: **M Goldsholl**
Architecture; Calligraphy; Cinema & Mass Media; Ephemera; Graphic Arts; Photography

Herbert Goodkind
25 Helena Avenue
Larchmont, N.Y. 10538
Short Name: **H Goodkind**
Violins; Music

Alfred Goodman
P O Box 724, Grand Central
  Station
New York, N.Y. 10163
(212) 544-1026
Short Name: **A Goodman**
Autographed Material &
Autographs; Canada &
Canadiana; Manuscripts;
Militaria; Naval & Marine;
Rare Books

Goodspeed's Book Shop
18 Beacon Street
Boston, Mass. 02108
(617) 523-5970
Short Name: **Goodsp'd's-Beac**
Americana; Autographed
Material & Autographs; Prints;
Geneaologies; Maps, Atlases, &
Cartography; Manuscripts

Goodspeed's Book Shop
2 Milk Street
Boston, Mass. 02108
(617) 523-5970
Short Name: **Goodsp'd's-Milk**
Americana; Autographed
Material & Autographs; Prints;
Geneaologies; Maps, Atlases, &
Cartography; Manuscripts

Goodwin & Zeintek-Left Bank
  Bkstll
104 South Oak Park Avenue
Oak Park, Ill. 60302
Short Name: **Goodwin & Zein**
Chicago; Illinois; Great Lakes;
Women & Feminism; Little
Magazines & Literary Small
Presses; Authors

Jerrold R Goodwin-Books
P O Box 4174
Berkeley, Calif. 94704
(415) 653-8329
Short Name: **J R Goodwin**
Mountaineering; Mathematics;
Out of Print, with Stock; Search
Service, with Stock; Societies &
Associations & Their
Publications

Elliot Gordon
250 West 94th Street, #6f
New York, N.Y. 10025
Short Name: **E Gordon**
Art; Avant Garde,
Experimental, & Modern Art;
Bibliography; Books about
Books; Photography; Reference

Martin Gordon, Inc
25 East 83rd Street
New York, N.Y. 10028
Short Name: **M Gordon**
Art; Reference; Prints;
Catalogues Raisonnes

Marian L Gore
P O Box 433
San Gabriel, Calif. 91775
(213) 287-2946
Short Name: **M L Gore**
Beverages; Cookery &
Gastronomy; Hotels

Gotham Book Mart
41 West 47th Street
New York, N.Y. 10036
(212) 757-0367
Short Name: **Gotham**
First Editions, Modern; Cinema
& Mass Media; Literature;
Little Magazines & Literary
Small Presses; Performing Arts;
Poetry

Leonard M Gottlieb-Books
P O Box 176
Cedar Grove, N.J. 07009
Short Name: **L M Gottlieb**
Bookbinding & Restoration;
Books about Books; Press
Books & Fine Printing; Printing
& Printing History

D W Goudy
264 Indian Road
Toronto, Ont. M6R 2X2
(416) 762-8992
Short Name: **D W Goudy**
Napoleon

Denis Gouey
41 Union Square
New York, N.Y. 10003
(212) 929-2123
Short Name: **D Gouey**
Bookbinders Services

Bartlett Gould
15 Walnut Street
Newburyport, Mass. 01950
Short Name: **B Gould**
Aviation & Aeronautics

Charles P Gould
1200 Old Mill Road
San Marino, Calif. 91108
(213) 795-1942
Short Name: **C P Gould**
Press Books & Fine Printing

Grady's Books
142 Rutherford Avenue
Redwood City, Calif. 94061
Short Name: **Grady's**
California; Western Americana;
American Indians; Childrens'
Books

Graedon Books, Inc
R D #1
New Hope, Penna. 18938
Short Name: **Graedon**
Art; Biography; Western
Americana; Press Books & Fine
Printing; Americana; Arctica &
Antarctica

William A Graf-Books
717 Clark Street
Iowa City, Iowa 52240
(319) 337-7748
Short Name: **W A Graf**
Books about Books; History,
American; Americana;
Militaria; Press Books & Fine
Printing; Typography & Type
Specimens

Ron Graham
8167 Park Avenue
Forestville, Calif. 95436
Short Name: **R Graham**
Music; Cartoons & Caricature;
Poetry

Jerry Granat-Manuscripts
P O Box 92
Woodmere, N.Y. 11598
(516) 374-7809
Short Name: **J Granat**
Autographed Material &
Autographs; Presidents; Books
about Books

L S Granby, Rare Books & Art
1168 Lexington Avenue
New York, N.Y. 10021
(212) 249-2651
Short Name: **L S Granby**
First Editions; Graphic Arts;
Photography; Press Books &
Fine Printing; Rare Books; Sets

Grand Book, Inc
659-C Grand Street
Brooklyn, N.Y. 11211
(212) 384-4089
Short Name: **Grand**
Comic Books; Fiction; General;
Out of Print, with Stock;
Paperbacks (new); Periodicals

Grandpa's House
Rte #1, Box 208
West Troy, N.C. 27371
(919) 572-3484
Short Name: **Grandpa's Hse**
North Carolina; Out of Print,
with Stock; Ephemera;
Periodicals; Rare Books;
General

Gary L Granger
2166 Belding Court
Okemos, Mich. 48864
Short Name: **G L Granger**
Trade Catalogues; Gardening &
Horticulture; Printing &
Printing History; Typography &
Type Specimens

D Gratz
Rte #2, Box 89
Bluffton, Ohio 45817
(419) 358-7431
Short Name: **D Gratz**
Comic Books; Geneaologies;
IlluminatedManuscripts;
Manuscripts, Medieval &
Illuminated; Mountaineering;
Mennonites

The Great Southwest Books
960 Santander
Santa Fe, N.Mex. 87501
(505) 983-1680
Short Name: **Grt So'west**
Southwestern America; First
Editions; Press Books & Fine
Printing; Art

Great Lake Bookman
P O Box 162
Houghton, Mich. 49931
Short Name: **Grt Lake**
History, American; Naval &
Marine; Out of Print, without
Stock

Great Northwest Book Company
338 Jarvis, At Carlton
Toronto, Ont. M4Y 2G6
Short Name: **Grt NO'West**
Canada & Canadiana; Arctica
& Antarctica; General; Out of
Print, with Stock; Canadian
Literature

Green Dolphin Bookshop
1300 SW Washington
Portland, Ore. 97205
(503) 224-3060
Short Name: **Green Dolphin**
Northwest; First Editions,
Modern; Naval & Marine

Green River Southern
P O Box 95
Plainsboro, N.J. 08536
Short Name: **Green River**
Railroads

Green Thought Booksellers
283 Lee Avenue
Yonkers, N.Y. 10705
(914) 423-3144
Short Name: **Green Thought**
Manuscripts; Autographed
Material & Autographs; First
Editions

Greenblatt Used Books
7771 Santa Monica Boulevard
Los Angeles, Calif. 90046
Short Name: **Greenblatt**
Drama; Science Fiction;
Paperbacks (early &
collectible); Childrens' Books;
Biography; Literature

Paulette Greene Rare Books
140 Princeton Road
Rockville Centre, N.Y. 11570
Short Name: **P Greene**
Childrens' Books; Detective
Fiction; First Editions, Modern;
19th Century Literature;
Science Fiction; Women &
Feminism

R D Greenlee
5490 Tenino
Boulder, Colo. 80302
Short Name: **R D Greenlee**
Books about Books; Press
Books & Fine Printing

Greenwich Books Ltd
127 Greenwich Avenue
New York, N.Y. 10014
Short Name: **Greenwich**
Art; First Editions, Modern;
Autographed Material &
Autographs

Ron Greenwood
3682a South Bristol
Santa Ana, Calif. 92704
(714) 549-9548
Short Name: **R Greenwood**
Revolutionary War; Western
Americana; Occult &
Metaphysics; Militaria; Search
Service, with Stock

Greetings & Readings
809 Taylor Avenue
Towson, Md. 21204
Short Name: **Greet & Read**
New Books; General; Gambling;
Paperbacks (new); Search
Service, without Stock; Out of
Print, without Stock

K Gregory (Appt Only)
222 East 71st Street
New York, N.Y. 10021
(212) 288-2119
Short Name: **K Gregory**
Botany; Childrens' Books; Color
Plate Books; Miniature Books;
Playing Cards; Prints

Griffin Books
3 Lois Lane
Poughkeepsie, N.Y. 12603
(914) 454-6765
Short Name: **Griffin**
Poetry; Biography; Childrens'
Books; Fiction; History,
American; Performing Arts

Young W Griffin
11 East 9th Street
New York, N.Y. 10003
Short Name: **Y W Griffin**
Russia & Eastern European
Region; Literature; Music;
Theatre

Arthur M Griffiths
6201 West Blackfoot Court
Sedalia, Colo. 80135
Short Name: **A M Griffiths**
Hunting, Fishing & Angling;
Western Americana; Colorado

Grolier Book Shop
6 Plympton Street
Cambridge, Mass. 02138
Short Name: **Grolier**
Poetry; Little Magazines &
Literary Small Presses;
Appraisals & Appraisal
Services

David Grossblatt Western Books
P O Box 3000i
Dallas, Tex. 75230
(214) 361-4320
Short Name: **D Grossblatt**
*Appraisals & Appraisal
Services; Civil War &
Confederacy; First Editions,
Modern; Outlaws & Rangers;
Search Service, with Stock;
Western Americana*

Grub Street-A Bookery
15038 MacK
Grosse Point Park, Mich. 48230
Short Name: **Grub St**
*First Editions; Photography;
Art; Rare Books; Scholarly
Books*

Klaus Grunewald-Bookdealer
807 West 87th Terrace
Kansas City, Mo. 64114
(816) 333-7799
Short Name: **K Grunewald**
*General; Philosophy; Rare
Books; Scholarly Books*

Gryphon's Lair
RFD #2, Moore Road
Windham, N.H. 03087
(603) 434-2616
Short Name: **Gryphon's Lair**
*Naval & Marine; Americana;
Childrens' Books; History,
American; Voyages, Travels, &
Exploration; Fine & Rare
Bindings*

Anton Gud
41-22 Judge
Elmhurst, N.Y. 11373
(212) 898-2316
Short Name: **A Gud**
*Americana; First Editions;
Press Books & Fine Printing;
Illustrated Books; Science
Fiction; Autographed Material
& Autographs*

Guerin Editeur Litee
4574 Rue Saint-Denis
Montreal, Que. H2J 2L3
(514) 843-6241
Short Name: **Guerin Editeur**
*Education; Childrens' Books;
Geography; History; General;
Literature*

Daniel E Guice
1116 North Milpas Street
Santa Barbara, Calif. 93103
(805) 965-8888
Short Name: **D E Guice**
*Rare Books; Incunabula &
Early Printing; STC & Wing
Books; Mathematics; Medicine
& Science; Continental Books*

Guidon Books
7117 Main Street
Scottsdale, Ariz. 85251
Short Name: **Guidon**
*Civil War & Confederacy;
Western Americana; Cowboy
and Western Art & Artists*

Gull Bookshop
1547 San Pablo Avenue
Oakland, Calif. 94612
(415) 834-8108
Short Name: **Gull**
*Foreign Languages; Fiction;
General; Ephemera; Rare
Books; Orientalia*

Gundy's Book World
1440 East Charleston
Las Vegas, Nev. 89104
(702) 385-6043
Short Name: **Gundy's**
*First Editions; Gambling; Out
of Print, with Stock;
Paperbacks (new); Rare Books;
Search Service, with Stock*

Gutenberg's Folly
627 East Guenther
San Antonio, Tex. 78210
(512) 222-8449
Short Name: **Gutenberg's**
*First Editions, Modern;
Childrens' Books; Dictionaries;
Books about Books; Appraisals
& Appraisal Services; Search
Service, with Stock*

Guthman Americana
P O Box 392
Westport, Conn. 06880
(203) 259-9763
Short Name: **Guthman**
*Americana; American Indians;
Documents; Militaria; History,
American; Naval & Marine*

Albert Gutkin
1133 Broadway
New York, N.Y. 10010
(212) 243-3600
Short Name: **A Gutkin**
*Color Plate Books; Natural
History; Maps, Atlases, &
Cartography; Voyages, Travels,
& Exploration; Sporting; Prints*

Arthur J Gutman
100 West Coldspring Lane
Baltimore, Md. 21210
(301) 433-6545
Short Name: **A J Gutman**
*H. L. Mencken; Maryland;
Maps, Atlases, & Cartography*

H

H W K Books
540 West 114th Street
New York, N.Y. 10025
(212) 685-6201
Short Name: **H W K**
*Art; Biography; Color Plate
Books; Natural History;
Voyages, Travels, &
Exploration*

Hacker Art Books Inc
54 West 57th Street
New York, N.Y. 10019
(212) 757-1450
Short Name: **Hacker Art**
*Art; Archaeology; Architecture;
Antiques; Illustrated Books;
Africa*

Carol Hacker-Books
5 Shagback Road
Rolling Meadows, Ill. 60008
(312) 397-3896
Short Name: **C Hacker**
*Out of Print, with Stock;
Philately & Philatelic
Literature*

**Donald E Hahn-Natural History
  Books**
P O Box 1004, 512 West Gila
Cottonwood, Ariz. 86326
(602) 634-5016
Short Name: **D E Hahn**
*Natural History; Ichthyology;
Herpetology; Mammalogy*

H Halbach-Bookseller
116 East De La Guerra, #3
Santa Barbara, Calif. 93101
Short Name: **H Halbach**
*Playing Cards; Poetry; Cookery
& Gastronomy; Detective
Fiction; Paperbacks (new);
Voyages, Travels, &
Exploration*

J H Hale
3117 Daulac Road
Montreal, Que. H3Y 2A1
(514) 932-0568
Short Name: **J H Hale**
*Arctica & Antarctica; Canada
& Canadiana; First Editions;
Illustrated Books; Maps,
Atlases, & Cartography;
Voyages, Travels, &
Exploration*

William F Hale Books
1208 31st Street, NW
Washington, D.C. 20007
(202) 338-8272
Short Name: **W F Hale**
*Travel; Art; Photography;
Science; Performing Arts;
Archaeology*

Half Price Book Shop
170 Portland Street
Rochester, N.H. 03867
Short Name: **Half Price**
General; Paperbacks (new)

George Hall, Jr
1441 Lincoln Way, East
Chambersburg, Penna. 17201
(717) 263-4388
Short Name: **G Hall, Jr**
*Americana; Hunting, Fishing &
Angling; Militaria; Out of Print,
with Stock; Technology*

Jonell Hall
Rte #2
Inola, Okla. 74036
(405) 543-8595
Short Name: **J Hall**
*Childrens' Books; Fiction;
General; Paperbacks (new)*

M T Hall Booksellers, Inc
9312 Second Avenue
Silver Spring, Md. 20910
(301) 585-9184
Short Name: **M T Hall**
Civil War & Confederacy

W D Hall
99 Maple Street
East Longmeadow, Mass. 01028
(413) 525-3064
Short Name: **W D Hall**
*Americana; Americana,
Regional; Ephemera; Naval &
Marine*

Hall's Nostalgia
21-25 Mystic Street
Arlington, Mass. 02174
Short Name: **Hall's Nostalg**
*Baseball; Sports; Ice Hockey;
Rock & Roll; Comic Books*

Walter E Hallberg
16 Hawthorn Street
Hartford, Conn. 06105
Short Name: **W E Hallberg**
*Americana; Connecticut; Maps,
Atlases, & Cartography; Prints*

D Halloran-Books
7629 Wydown Boulevard
St Louis, Mo. 63105
(314) 863-1690
Short Name: **D Halloran**
*Appraisals & Appraisal
Services; First Editions,
Modern; Hunting, Fishing &
Angling; Out of Print, with
Stock; Press Books & Fine
Printing; Sporting*

Frank M Halpern
6525 North 10th Street
Philadelphia, Penna. 19126
Short Name: **F M Halpern**
Fantasy; Science Fiction

Michael Halpern
67-32 136th Street
Flushing, N.Y. 11367
Short Name: **M Halpern**
*Illustrated Books; Drama;
Juveniles; General*

Renate Halpern Galleries, Inc
147 West 57th Street
New York, N.Y. 10019
Short Name: **R Halpern**
Textiles; Travel

Bernard Hamel
2326 Westwood Boulevard
Los Angeles, Calif. 90064
Short Name: **B Hamel**
Foreign Languages

Hamill & Barker
400 North Michigan Avenue
Chicago, Ill. 60611
(312) 644-5933
Short Name: **Hamill & Barker**
*Americana; First Editions;
General; Incunabula & Early
Printing; Medicine & Science;
Rare Books*

Charles Hamilton Galleries
25 East 77th Street
New York, N.Y. 10021
Short Name: **C Hamilton**
*Autographed Material &
Autographs; Manuscripts;
Inscribed Books*

Milton Hammer
819 Anacapa Street
Santa Barbara, Calif. 93101
Short Name: **M Hammer**
*General; Literature; Americana;
Voyages, Travels, &
Exploration; Maps, Atlases, &
Cartography; Illustrated Books*

Hammer Mountain Book Halls
771 State Street
Schenectady, N.Y. 12307
(518) 393-5266
Short Name: **Hammer Mtn**
*Scholarly Books; Political,
Social, & Cultural History &
Thought; Social Sciences;
Economics & Business; Foreign
Languages; European History*

Hampton Books
Rte #1, Box 202
Newberry, S.C. 29108
Short Name: **Hampton**
*Cinema & Mass Media;
Television; Aircraft &
Aerospace History; South
Carolina; First Editions;
Childrens' Books*

Charles F Hamsa
612 Alonda Drive
Lafayette, La. 70503
Short Name: **C F Hamsa**
Beverages; Wines; Photography

Hannelore Headley Books
71 Queen Street
St Catharines, Ont. L2R 5G9
(416) 684-6145
Short Name: **Hannelore**
*Canada & Canadiana; General;
Literature*

J & J Hanrahan
62 Marcy Street
Portsmouth, N.H. 03801
(603) 436-6234
Short Name: **J & J Hanrahan**
*Paintings; Prints; Rare Books;
New England; Naval & Marine;
Kenneth Roberts*

James Hansen
3514 Highland
Carlsbad, Calif. 92008
Short Name: **J Hansen**
*First Editions, Modern; Author
Collections; Detective Fiction;
Illustrated Books; Periodicals*

Richard Hansen
11245 Dry Creek Road
Auburn, Calif. 95603
(916) 885-4878
Short Name: **R Hansen**
*American Indians; Americana;
Americana, States; Americana,
Regional; Overland Narratives;
Geology*

Hanzel Galleries Inc
1120 South Michigan Avenue
Chicago, Ill. 60605
(312) 922-6234
Short Name: **Hanzel Gall**
Auctions & Auctioneers

The Happy Book Source
66 SE 15th Street
Pompano Beach, Fla. 33060
Short Name: **Happy Source**
*Americana; Natural History;
Psychiatry, Psychology, &
Psychonanalysis*

Harbor Hill Books, Inc
P O Box 407
Harrison, N.Y. 10528
Short Name: **Harbor Hill**
*New York Metropolitan Area;
New York*

Harcourt Bindery
9-11 Harcourt Street
Boston, Mass. 02116
Short Name: **Harcourt Bind**
*Bookbinders Services; Fine &
Rare Bindings; Bookbinding &
Restoration; Books about Books*

James Harder
124 Monte Vista Drive
Los Alamos, N.Mex. 87544
(505) 672-9152
Short Name: **J Harder**
*Americana; Arctica &
Antarctica; Maps, Atlases, &
Cartography; Militaria; Natural
History; Voyages, Travels, &
Exploration*

Douglas N Harding
35 East Pearl Street, Box 361
Nashua, N.H. 03060
Short Name: **D N Harding**
*Color Plate Books; Atlases;
Caribbean; Arctica &
Antarctica*

J W Harmand & Sons
8078 Caladesia Drive
Sarasota, Fla. 33580
Short Name: **J W Harmand**
*Art; General; Rare Books;
Prints*

Harold's Books
186 West 7th Street
St Paul, Minn. 55102
(612) 222-4524
Short Name: **Harold's**
Minnesota; War; General

Lathrop C Harper, Inc
300 Madison Avenue
New York, N.Y. 10017
(212) 490-3412
Short Name: **L C Harper**
*Incunabula & Early Printing;
IlluminatedManuscripts;
Illustrated Books; Fine & Rare
Bindings; Medicine & Science;
Voyages, Travels, &
Exploration*

Terry Harper
P O Box 103
Rouseville, Penna. 16344
(816) 676-6728
Short Name: **T Harper**
*Americana; Natural History;
Out of Print, with Stock; Rare
Books; Search Service, with
Stock; Voyages, Travels, &
Exploration*

Harrington's
333 Cognewaug Road
Cos Cob, Conn. 06807
(203) 869-1070
Short Name: **Harrington's**
Newspapers

Harris Auction Galleries
875 North Howard Street
Baltimore, Md. 21201
(301) 728-7040
Short Name: **Harris Auct**
Auctions & Auctioneers

Doris Harris Autographs
5410 Wilshire Boulevard
Los Angeles, Calif. 90036
(213) 939-4500
Short Name: **D Harris**
*Autographed Material &
Autographs; Documents;
Manuscripts; Presidents;
Association Books; Overland
Narratives*

Harris Search And Research
145 East 37th Street
New York, N.Y. 10016
Short Name: **Harris Srch**
*Childrens' Books; Art;
Illustrated Books; Out of Print,
without Stock; Performing Arts;
South America*

Winston R Harris
P O Box 634
Franklin, Mich. 48025
Short Name: **W R Harris**
*Numismatics; Philately &
Philatelic Literature; Rare
Books*

Hartfield Books
117 Dixboro Road
Ann Arbor, Mich. 48105
(313) 662-6035
Short Name: **Hartfield**
*Rare Books; Poetry; STC &
Wing Books; First Editions;
Books about Books*

Haslam's Book Store, Inc
2025 Central Avenue
St Petersburg, Fla. 33713
(813) 822-8616
Short Name: **Haslam's-St P**
*Americana, Regional; Civil War
& Confederacy; Religion &
Theology; Childrens' Books;
Americana, States; Comic
Books*

The Haunted Bookshop
822-1/2 Fort Street
Victoria, B.C. V8W 1H6
(604) 382-1427
Short Name: **Haunted Bksh**
*General; Literature; Out of
Print, with Stock; Canada &
Canadiana; Childrens' Books;
Rare Books*

Thomas N Haviland
P O Box 510
Cornwall, N.Y. 12518
(914) 534-7794
Short Name: **T N Haviland**
*Anthropology; Medical &
Medicine; Biography; Natural
History; Curiosa*

F Hawkins
404 Lincoln
Alpena, Mich. 49707
Short Name: **F Hawkins**
*Childrens' Books; Out of Print,
with Stock; Search Service, with
Stock*

John Donald Hawkins
54 Tisdale Road
Scarsdale, N.Y. 10583
Short Name: **J D Hawkins**
*Civil War & Confederacy;
Americana; Americana, States;
Americana, Regional*

Hawley's Island-Books
340 Amsterdam Road
Scotia, N.Y. 12302
Short Name: **Hawley's Island**
*Mathematics; Medicine &
Science; Natural History;
Technology*

Walter S Hay
2608 Baltic Avenue
Virginia Beach, Va. 23451
Short Name: **W S Hay**
*First Editions; First Editions,
Modern; Autographed Material
& Autographs; Orientalia;
Books about Books; Inscribed
Books*

Robert G Hayman
575 West Street
Carey, Ohio 43316
(419) 396-6933
Short Name: **R G Hayman**
*Americana; Americana, States;
Americana, Regional; History,
American; Political, Social, &
Cultural History & Thought;
Rare Books*

J M Hays (Aislinn Books)
121 Benmont Avenue
Bennington, Vt. 05201
Short Name: **J M Hays**
*Women & Feminism; Ireland &
The Irish; British Isles*

Heartwood Books
9 Elliewood
Charlottesville, Va. 22903
Short Name: **Heartwood**
*Southeastern America; Virginia;
Literature; 19th Century
Literature; Thomas Jefferson;
Books about Books*

**Barry J Hecht-Hectic
Enterprises**
510 Pine Street
Philadelphia, Penna. 19106
(215) 923-2226
Short Name: **B J Hecht**
*First Editions, Modern;
American Literature; Scholarly
Books; Sets; First Editions;
Illustrated Books*

John L Heflin, Jr
5708 Brentwood Trace
Brentwood, Tenn. 37027
(615) 373-2917
Short Name: **J L Heflin, Jr**
Civil War & Confederacy

Heinemann's Books
85 Princess Street
Kingston, Ont. K7G 1A5
(613) 542-8615
Short Name: **Heinemann's**
*General; Out of Print, with
Stock; Rare Books; Paperbacks
(new)*

W S Heinman
P O Box 926, Ansonia Station
New York, N.Y. 10023
(212) 787-3154
Short Name: **W S Heinman**
Dictionaries

Heinoldt Books
Central And Buffalo Avenues
South Egg Harbor, N.J. 08215
(609) 965-2284
Short Name: **Heinoldt**
*Americana; American Indians;
History, American; Americana,
States; Outlaws & Rangers;
Overland Narratives*

Helen E Heinrich
7 Palfrey Street
Stony Brook, N.Y. 11790
Short Name: **H E Heinrich**
*Sherlock Holmes & A. Conan
Doyle; Autographed Material &
Autographs; Childrens' Books;
Original Art of Book
Illustrations*

Claude Held
P O Box 140
Buffalo, N.Y. 14225
Short Name: **C Held**
*Comic Books; Detective Fiction;
Science Fiction*

W H Helfand
P O Box 702
Rahway, N.J. 07065
Short Name: **W H Helfand**
*History of Medicine & Science;
Ephemera; Cartoons &
Caricature*

F Thomas Heller
308 East 79th Street
New York, N.Y. 10021
Short Name: **F T Heller**
*Medicine & Science; Psychiatry,
Psychology, & Psychonanalysis*

Susan Heller Books
22611 Halburton Road
Beachwood, Ohio 44122
(216) 283-2665
Short Name: **S Heller**
*Americana; Inscribed Books;
Out of Print, with Stock;
Scholarly Books; Search
Service, with Stock; Sets*

**Judith S Helms, Doe Run Valley
Bks**
P O Box 255
Cochranville, Penna. 19330
(215) 593-6997
Short Name: **J S Helms**
*Illustrated Books; Press Books
& Fine Printing; Natural
History; Inscribed Books;
Autographed Material &
Autographs*

Hemlock Books
170 Beach 145th Street
Neponsit, N.Y. 11694
(212) 474-1372
Short Name: **Hemlock**
Medicine & Science

Paul Henderson
50 Berkeley Street
Nashua, N.H. 03060
(603) 883-8918
Short Name: **P Henderson**
*Geneaologies; Local History;
Americana, States; Americana,
Regional*

John F Hendsey
25 Middle Street
Newburyport, Mass. 01950
(617) 462-3434
Short Name: **J F Hendsey**
*Auctions & Auctioneers;
Appraisals & Appraisal
Services*

Hennessey And Ingalls Inc
10814 West Pico Boulevard
Los Angeles, Calif. 90064
(213) 474-2541
Short Name: **Henn & Ing**
Architecture; Art

The Hennesseys
Fourth & Woodlawn
Saratoga, N.Y. 12866
(518) 584-4921
Short Name: **Hennesseys**
General; Sporting

**Henry C Hensel, Memorablia
Corner**
P O Box 15052
Norfolk, Va. 23511
(804) 444-2414
Short Name: **H C Hensel**
*Americana; Civil War &
Confederacy; Maps, Atlases, &
Cartography; Naval & Marine;
Out of Print, with Stock; Search
Service, with Stock*

Dave Henson-Books
P O Box 11402
Santa Ana, Calif. 92711
Short Name: **D Henson**
*California; Western Americana;
Biography*

Heritage Books
3438 Sixth Streeet, SW
Calgary, Alb. T2S 2M4
Short Name: **Heritage-Cal**
Canada & Canadiana

Heritage Books & Coffee Mill
52 South Washington Street
Sonora, Calif. 95370
(209) 532-6261
Short Name: **Heritage-Son**
*Religion & Theology; Search
Service, without Stock; Out of
Print, with Stock; Out of Print,
without Stock; Americana;
Americana, Regional*

Heritage Bookshop
847 North La Cienega
Boulevard
Los Angeles, Calif. 90069
(213) 659-5738
Short Name: **Heritage-L A**
*First Editions; Rare Books;
Press Books & Fine Printing;
Illustrated Books; Fine & Rare
Bindings; Voyages, Travels, &
Exploration*

Heritage Books Inc
3602 Maureen
Bowie, Md. 20715
Short Name: **Heritage-Bow**
*Geneaologies; History,
American; Americana*

S L Heritage (Mail Only)
P O Box 3862
New Haven, Conn. 06511
Short Name: **S L Heritage**
Southwestern America;
Voyages, Travels, &
Exploration; Cattle & Range
Industry; Outlaws & Rangers;
Stereoviews; Western
Americana

J N Herlin, Inc
68 Thompson Street
New York, N.Y. 10012
Short Name: **J N Herlin**
Art; Cinema & Mass Media

The Hermeticus Book Shop
Main Street, Box 169
Mendocino, Calif. 95460
(707) 937-4555
Short Name: **Hermeticus**
Orientalia; Philosophy; Art; Out
of Print, with Stock; Rare
Books

The Hermit's Book House
R F D #3, Box 10
Wyoming, Penna. 18644
(717) 696-1474
Short Name: **Hermit's**
Search Service, with Stock

Hermitage Antiquarian
   Bookshop
2817 East Third Avenue
Denver, Colo. 80206
Short Name: **Hermitage**
Americana, States; Western
Americana; First Editions,
Modern; First Editions;
Scholarly Books; Literature

Larry Herndon Remember When
2431 Valwood Parkway
Dallas, Tex. 75234
Short Name: **L Herndon**
Cinema & Mass Media; Comic
Books; Graphic Arts; Science
Fiction

Herpetological Search &
   Exchange
117 East Santa Barbara Road
Lindenhurst, N.Y. 11757
(516) 226-2775
Short Name: **Herp Exch**
Natural History; Out of Print,
without Stock; General

G S Herron
P O Box 1442
Rome, Ga. 30161
(404) 232-1441
Short Name: **G S Herron**
Americana; Americana, States;
Americana, Regional; Fiction;
Geneaologies; General

Herman Herst, Jr
P O Box 1583
Boca Raton, Fla. 33432
(305) 391-3223
Short Name: **H Herst, Jr**
Philately & Philatelic
Literature; Counterfeit Stamps
& Coins

John A Hess
P O Box 62
Andover, Mass. 01810
Short Name: **J A Hess**
Photography; Civil War &
Confederacy

Ernest S Hickok
382 Springfield Avenue
Summit, N.J. 07901
(201) 277-1427
Short Name: **E S Hickok**
Hunting, Fishing & Angling;
Authors

High Ridge Corner
P O Box 286
Rye, N.Y. 10580
Short Name: **High Ridge**
Books about Books; Hunting,
Fishing & Angling; Maps,
Atlases, & Cartography; Naval
& Marine; Shooting &
Firearms; Whaling

Highway Book Shop
Cobalt, Ont.
Short Name: **Highway**
Canada & Canadiana

Highwood Books
P O Box 1246
Traverse City, Mich. 49684
(616) 271-3898
Short Name: **Highwood**
Hunting, Fishing & Angling;
Shooting & Firearms; Sporting;
Derrydale Press; Guns

W W Hildreth
P O Box 58852
Houston, Tex. 77058
(713) 333-2721
Short Name: **W W Hildreth**
Medicine & Science;
Americana, Regional; History,
American; Naval & Marine;
Stock Market & Wall Street

F M Hill
P O Box 1037
Kingsport, Tenn. 37662
Short Name: **F M Hill**
Tennessee; The South;
Bibliography; Books about
Books

Jonathan A Hill
P O Box 629
New York, N.Y. 10021
Short Name: **J A Hill**
Medicine & Science;
Bibliography; Printing &
Printing History; Voyages,
Travels, & Exploration

Louise Hill
24 Waterloo Row
Fredericton, N.B. E3B 1Y9
Short Name: **L Hill**
Loyalists

Austin Hills
311 California Street, Suite
   1000
San Francisco, Calif. 94104
Short Name: **A Hills**
Americana, States; Pacific
Region

Christopher Hinchliffe
815-1/2 Bank Street
Ottawa, Ont. K1S 3V7
(613) 232-3102
Short Name: **C Hinchliffe**
Arctica & Antarctica; Naval &
Marine; Voyages, Travels, &
Exploration; Whaling;
Manuscript Logbooks

Hinds Book Center
6462 North Oracle Road
Tucson, Ariz. 85704
Short Name: **Hinds**
Fine & Rare Bindings; Classics;
First Editions; Mathematics;
Medicine & Science; Search
Service, with Stock

Hingham Book House
112 North Street
Hingham, Mass. 02043
Short Name: **Hingham**
*New England; Natural History;
Cape Cod & Martha's
Vineyard; Documents*

C J Hinke-Venkatesa Books
Wickanninish Island
Tofino, B.C.
(604) 592-6137
Short Name: **Cj Hinke**
*Childrens' Books; Color Plate
Books; Appraisals & Appraisal
Services; Authors; Author
Collections; First Editions*

Daniel Hirsch-Books
P O Box 315
Hopewell Junction, N.Y. 12533
(914) 462-7404
Short Name: **D Hirsch**
*Childrens' Books; Illustrated
Books; Reference; Rare Books;
Literature; Original Art of Book
Illustrations*

Hirschtritt's 1712'
1712 Republic Road
Silver Springs, Md. 20902
(301) 649-5393
Short Name: **Hirschtritt's**
*Americana; Japan; Childrens'
Books; Illustrated Books; 19th
Century Literature; First
Editions, Modern*

Historic Newspapers
9850 Kedvale
Skokie, Ill. 60076
(312) 676-9850
Short Name: **Historic News**
*Civil War & Confederacy;
Documents; Maps, Atlases, &
Cartography; Newspapers;
Periodicals; Prints*

Historical Realia
1059 Douglas Drive
Wooster, Ohio 44691
Short Name: **Hist Real**
*American Indians; Americana;
Autographed Material &
Autographs; Civil War &
Confederacy; Rare Books;
Voyages, Travels, &
Exploration*

History House
P O Box 146
Ashley Falls, Mass. 01222
Short Name: **History House**
*Americana; Nautica; New York
Metropolitan Area*

Robert Hittel
3020 North Federal Highway,
  Bldg 6
Fort Lauderdale, Fla. 33306
(305) 563-1752
Short Name: **R Hittel**
*First Editions, Modern;
Hunting, Fishing & Angling;
Science Fiction; Western
Americana; Cookery &
Gastronomy; Press Books &
Fine Printing*

Hive Of Industry
P O Box 602
Easton, Penna. 18042
Short Name: **Hive**
*Political Science & Theory;
Technology*

Hobbit Antiquarian Books
102 Elm Street
Westfield, N.J. 07090
(201) 654-4115
Short Name: **Hobbit**
*Appraisals & Appraisal
Services; Bookbinding &
Restoration; Art; First Editions;
Illustrated Books; General*

Hobby Helpers
7369 East Main Street
Lima, N.Y. 14485
Short Name: **Hobby Helpers**
*Childrens' Books; Dogs;
Ephemera; Search Service, with
Stock; Authors; World's Fairs*

Hobby House Books
P O Box 692-A
Lewiston, Maine 04240
Short Name: **Hobby Hse**
*Out of Print, without Stock;
General; Detective Fiction;
Western Books*

Hobson's Choice
511 Runnymede Avenue
Jenkintown, Penna. 19046
(215) 884-4853
Short Name: **Hobson's Ch**
*Biography; Books about Books;
First Editions; Poetry; Press
Books & Fine Printing; Search
Service, without Stock*

Hock-Hocking Books
P O Box 114
Athens, Ohio 45701
Short Name: **Hock-Hocking**
*Americana; Rare Books; First
Editions; Poetry; Art;
Photography*

William Hoffer, Bookseller
570 Granville Street, Suite 104
Vancouver, B.C. V6C 1W6
(604) 683-3022
Short Name: **W Hoffer**
*Canada & Canadiana;
Literature; Pacific Region;
Poetry*

**Hoffman Lane Bks-Nicklas &
  Parker**
P O Box 711
Cooperstown, N.Y. 13326
Short Name: **Hoffman Lane**
*Golf; Archery; Hunting, Fishing
& Angling*

Richard J Hoffman
5732 Buffalo Avenue
Van Nuys, Calif. 91401
Short Name: **R J Hoffman**
*Printing & Printing History;
Typography & Type Specimens;
Papermaking & Marbling; Fine
& Rare Bindings*

Hoffman Research
P O Box 342
Rillton, Penna. 15678
Short Name: **Hoffman Resch**
*Americana; Criminology; Dogs;
Psychiatry, Psychology, &
Psychonanalysis; Scholarly
Books; Sporting*

Hofmann & Freeman
P O Box 207
Cambridge, Mass. 02138
Short Name: **Hofmann & Free**
*English Literature;
Manuscripts; Autographed
Material & Autographs;
Continental Books;
Manuscripts, Medieval &
Illuminated*

Nancy W Hofmann
1922 Heritage Road
Schenectady, N.Y. 12309
(518) 374-7455
Short Name: **N W Hoffman**
Voyages, Travels, &
Exploration; Cookery &
Gastronomy; Crafts & Trades;
Gardening & Horticulture

Holistic Health Resource Center
P O Box 20037
Seattle, Wash. 98102
(206) 325-9077
Short Name: **Holistic Health**
Health; Medicine & Science;
Astrology; Psychiatry,
Psychology, & Psychonanalysis;
Out of Print, with Stock

Michael S Hollander
P O Box 3678
San Rafael, Calif. 94902
Short Name: **M S Hollander**
Color Plate Books; Natural
History; Orientalia;
Photography; Voyages, Travels,
& Exploration; Technology

Hollands' Books
3522 SW Hawthorne
Portland, Ore. 97214
(503) 232-3596
Short Name: **Hollands'**
History; Literature; Political,
Social, & Cultural History &
Thought; Pacific Region;
Scholarly Books; Philosophy

Hollywood Book Shop
6613 Hollywood Boulevard
Hollywood, Calif. 90028
Short Name: **H'wood Bk Shop**
Americana; Archaeology;
Collection Development;
General; Geology; Out of Print,
with Stock

Hollywood Book City
6627 Hollywood Boulevard
Hollywood, Calif. 90028
Short Name: **H'wood Bk City**
Cinema & Mass Media; Art;
Photography; Illustrated Books;
Prints; Collecting & Collectibles

Holmes Book Company
274 14th Street
Oakland, Calif. 94612
(415) 893-6860
Short Name: **Holmes-Oak**
Americana; Western Americana;
Rare Books; Scholarly Books;
General; Out of Print, with
Stock

The Holmes Book Company
22 Third Street
San Francisco, Calif. 94103
(415) 362-3283
Short Name: **Holmes-S F**
Americana; Western Americana;
Rare Books; Scholarly Books;
General; Out of Print, with
Stock

The Holy Land
3041 Normanstone Terrace,
 NW
Washington, D.C. 20008
(202) 965-4831
Short Name: **Holy Land**
Israel; Maps, Atlases, &
Cartography; Judaica &
Hebraica; Voyages, Travels, &
Exploration; Illustrated Books;
Rare Books

Homestead Bookshop
Route 101, Box 90
Marlborough, N.H. 03455
(603) 876-4610
Short Name: **Homestead**
Childrens' Books; Americana,
Regional; Printing & Printing
History; Cookery &
Gastronomy; General; Naval &
Marine

Homesteader
4 South Wentachee Avenue
Wentachee, Wash. 98801
Short Name: **Homesteader**
Americana, Regional; Out of
Print, with Stock; Search
Service, without Stock; New
Books; Childrens' Books; Self-
Sufficiency

Linda Honan Art Books
49 Church Street
Westborough, Mass. 01581
(617) 366-0860
Short Name: **L Honan**
Antiques; Archaeology;
Architecture; Art; Out of Print,
with Stock; Scholarly Books

Dora Hood Book Room
34 Ross Street
Toronto, Ont. M5T 1Z9
(416) 979-2129
Short Name: **D Hood**
Arctica & Antarctica;
Bibliography; Canada &
Canadiana; Search Service, with
Stock; Rare Books; Voyages,
Travels, & Exploration

J Hood, Bookseller
1401 Massachusetts
Lawrence, Kan. 66044
(913) 841-4644
Short Name: **J Hood**
Scholarly Books; Search
Service, with Stock; Out of
Print, with Stock; Humanities;
Literary Criticism; Philosophy

Hooked On Books
1366 North Main Street
Walnut Creek, Calif. 94596
(415) 933-1025
Short Name: **Hooked On**
Paperbacks (new); Fiction;
Science Fiction; Pulps

A Hoosier Schoolmaster's Books
1228 Michigan Avenue
La Porte, Ind. 46350
Short Name: **Hoosier School**
Indiana; Americana;
Autographed Material &
Autographs; Inscribed Books;
First Editions; Presidents

Hoosier Bookshop
3820 East 61st Street
Indianapolis, Ind. 46220
Short Name: **Hoosier Bksh**
Americana, Regional; Civil War
& Confederacy; Appraisals &
Appraisal Services

Hope Farm Press And Bookshop
Strong Road
Cornwallville, N.Y. 12418
(518) 239-4745
Short Name: **Hope Farm**
Americana, Regional; Civil War
& Confederacy

Norman T Hopper
1142 Plymouth Drive
Sunnyvale, Calif. 94087
Short Name: **N T Hopper**
Juveniles; Pulps; Fiction;
General; Out of Print, with
Stock; Pacific Region

Horchow Book Society
201 East 16th Street
New York, N.Y. 10003
(212) 777-4529
Short Name: **Horchow**
Antiques; Art; Cookery &
Gastronomy; Crafts & Trades;
Graphic Arts; Performing Arts

Horizon Books
425 15th Avenue, East
Seattle, Wash. 98112
(206) 329-3586
Short Name: **Horizon**
Science Fiction; Literature;
Literary Criticism; Folklore

Glenn Horowitz, Bookseller
141 East 44th Street
New York, N.Y. 10017
(212) 557-1381
Short Name: **G Horowitz**
First Editions, Modern;
Manuscripts

Horse In The Attic Books
52 Boylston Street, Rte #9
Brookline Village, Mass. 02147
(617) 566-6070
Short Name: **Horse In Attic**
Childrens' Books; Poetry; Art;
Women & Feminism; History,
American; General

Horticultural Books, Inc
P O Box 107
Stuart, Fla. 33495
(305) 287-1091
Short Name: **Horticultural**
Horticulture; Natural History

Hortulus
101 Scollard Street
Toronto, Ont. M5T 1Z9
(416) 960-1775
Short Name: **Hortulus**
Architecture; Botany; Gardening
& Horticulture

Norman Houle
Pinecrest Lane
Durham, N.H. 03824
Short Name: **N Houle**
Aviation & Aeronautics

George Houle-Rare Books
2277 Westwood Boulevard
Los Angeles, Calif. 90064
(213) 474-1539
Short Name: **G Houle**
Autographed Material &
Autographs; Antiques; Art;
First Editions; Sets; Press
Books & Fine Printing

Hound Dog Press Book Shop
340 West Ponce De Leon
    Avenue, #230
Decatur, Ga. 30030
(404) 373-2291
Short Name: **Hound Dog**
Georgia; The South;
Appalachia

House Of Books Ltd
667 Madison Avenue
New York, N.Y. 10021
(212) 755-5998
Short Name: **Hse Of Bks Ltd**
Association Books; First
Editions, Modern; Inscribed
Books; Poetry; Autographed
Material & Autographs

House Of Books
1758 Gardenaire Lane
Anaheim, Calif. 92804
Short Name: **Hse Of Bks-Ana**
British Isles

House Of Fiction
688 East Walnut Street
Pasadena, Calif. 91101
(213) 449-9861
Short Name: **Hse Of Fict**
Fiction; Detective Fiction;
Literature; Paperbacks (new);
Continental Books; First
Editions, Modern

House Of El Dieff, Inc
139 East 63rd Street
New York, N.Y. 10021
(212) 838-4160
Short Name: **El Dieff**
Manuscripts; Rare Books

Household Words
P O Box 7231
Berkeley, Calif. 94707
(415) 524-8859
Short Name: **Hsehold Words**
Cookery & Gastronomy;
Beverages; Bibliography; Wines;
Ephemera

Gary Houseman
327 Dayton Street
Yellow Springs, Ohio 45387
Short Name: **G Houseman**
Science Fiction; Medical &
Medicine; Americana

Vernon Howard-Books
723 California Street
Burlingame, Calif. 94010
(415) 343-7428
Short Name: **V Howard**
Mountaineering; Western
Americana; Literary Criticism;
History; Voyages, Travels, &
Exploration; General

Paul Howard-Old Books
P O Box 82661
San Diego, Calif. 92138
Short Name: **P Howard**
Panama & Panama Canal;
California; Mammalogy;
Basketry; Costumes

Howe Books
16 Lakeview Avenue
Chester, Conn. 06412
Short Name: **Howe**
Authors; First Editions,
Modern; Literature

Edward Howe Rare Books
56 Lispenard Street
New York, N.Y. 10013
Short Name: **E Howe**
Architecture; Printing &
Printing History; Press Books
& Fine Printing; Graphic Arts;
Calligraphy; Ephemera

John Howell-Books
434 Post Street
San Francisco, Calif. 94102
Short Name: **J Howell**
Rare Books; Manuscripts;
Prints

Donald B Howes Antiques
Rte #6
Brewster, Mass. 02631
Short Name: **D B Howes**
Americana; Autographed
Material & Autographs;
Ephemera; Paintings;
Documents; Sporting

Howland & Company
100 Rockwood Street
Jamaica Plain, Mass. 02130
Short Name: **Howland**
*Yachts, Yachting, & Sailing;
Ships & The Sea; New
England; First Editions,
Modern*

George Hubert
2173-2 Ptarmigan Drive
Walnut Creek, Calif. 94595
Short Name: **G Hubert**
Shakespeare

John C Huckans-Books
P O Box 270
Cazenovia, N.Y. 13035
(315) 655-8499
Short Name: **J C Huckans**
*Rare Books; Manuscripts;
Arctica & Antarctica; Latin
America; Voyages, Travels, &
Exploration; Illustrated Books*

Murray Hudson-Book & Maps
Rte #1, Bruceville Road
Dyersburg, Tenn. 38024
(901) 285-0666
Short Name: **M Hudson**
*Maps, Atlases, & Cartography;
Americana; Voyages, Travels, &
Exploration; Literature;
Geography; Fiction*

Tim Hughes
2410 North Hills Drive
Williamsport, Penna. 17701
Short Name: **T Hughes**
*Newspapers; Civil War &
Confederacy; Documents;
Ephemera; Periodicals;
Americana*

Pauline C Hull Bookseller
529 Thompson Run Road
Pittsburgh, Penna. 15237
Short Name: **P C Hull**
*Americana; Heritage Press;
First Editions,
Modern; History, American*

Hummingbird Books
2400 Hannett, NE
Albuquerque, N.Mex. 87106
(505) 268-6277
Short Name: **Hummingbird**
*First Editions; Humanities;
Literature; Out of Print, with
Stock; Philosophy; Search
Service, with Stock*

Michael L Hunegs
2670 Quail Avenue, North
Minneapolis, Minn. 55422
(612) 588 3955
Short Name: **L Hunegs**
*Art; First Editions, Modern;
Literary Criticism; History;
Scholarly Books; Orientalia*

Hungry Eye Books
219 East Florida Avenue
Hemet, Calif. 92343
(714) 658-1412
Short Name: **Hungry Eye**
*Americana, Regional;
Automotive; Aviation &
Aeronautics; American Indians;
California*

Maxwell Hunley
634 Mission
South Pasadena, Calif. 91030
Short Name: **M Hunley**
*Rare Books; First Editions;
Childrens' Books; Western
Americana*

Paul Hunt
1063 North Spaulding Avenue
Los Angeles, Calif. 90046
(213) 650-0973
Short Name: **P Hunt**
*Cinema & Mass Media;
Detective Fiction; Militaria;
Paperbacks (new); Periodicals;
Railroads*

The Hunted Bookshop
516 North Euclid Avenue
Ontario, Calif. 91762
(714) 986-0523
Short Name: **Hunted**
*Search Service, with Stock;
Americana; Out of Print, with
Stock; First Editions; Sets*

Alan C Hunter-Books
Harriman Heights Road
Harriman, N.Y. 10926
(914) 783-1930
Short Name: **A C Hunter**
*Americana, States; Americana,
Regional; Out of Print, with
Stock; Search Service, with
Stock*

Huntley Bookstore
8th At Dartmouth
Claremont, Calif. 91711
(714) 621-8168
Short Name: **Huntley**
*Childrens' Books; Classics;
Literature; Philosophy; Political
Science & Theory; Religion &
Theology*

Keith Huntress
509 Ash Avenue
Ames, Iowa 50010
Short Name: **K Huntress**
*Naval & Marine; Voyages,
Travels, & Exploration*

Hurley Books
Rte #12
Westmoreland, N.H. 03467
Short Name: **Hurley**
*Agriculture; Gardening &
Horticulture; Imprints; Religion
& Theology; Books about
Books; Press Books & Fine
Printing*

Roger F Hutson
21 Osborne Terrace
Wayne, N.J. 07470
(201) 694-6781
Short Name: **R F Hutson**
*General; Search Service, with
Stock*

William M Hutter, Book Scout
Rte #3, Box 123
Ocean Springs, Miss. 39564
Short Name: **W M Hutter**
*Philosophy; Art; Civil War &
Confederacy; Rare Books;
Scholarly Books; Books about
Books*

Hyman & Son
38 Avenal Drive
Toronto, Ont.
Short Name: **Hyman & Son-Tor**
*Judaica & Hebraica; Bible &
Bible Studies; Israel*

Hyman & Sons Rare Books
2315 Westwood Boulevard,
  Suite 4
Los Angeles, Calif. 90064
(213) 474-8023
Short Name: **Hyman & Son-L A**
*Ancient Civilizations;
Archaeology*

I

I Am I Books
474 Orange Center
Orange, Conn. 06477
Short Name: **I Am I**
*Art; First Editions; General;
Out of Print, with Stock;
Paperbacks (new); Search
Service, with Stock*

John S Iavarone
7 Forest Avenue
Albany, N.Y. 12208
(518) 489-4508
Short Name: **J S Iavarone**
*Comic Books; Cartoons &
Caricature; Science Fiction*

Icart Vendor
8111 Melrose Avenue
Los Angeles, Calif. 90046
(213) 653-3190
Short Name: **Icart Vendor**
*Louis Icart; Posters; Avant
Garde, Experimental, &
Modern Art*

Illustrated Antiques
1557 33rd Street, NW
Washington, D.C. 20007
(202) 333-6359
Short Name: **Illustrated Ant**
*Illustrated Books; Childrens'
Books; Press Books & Fine
Printing; Color Plate Books;
Paintings; Miniature Books*

Imagine That Bookstore
58 Dalton Street
Pittsfield, Mass. 01201
(413) 445-5934
Short Name: **Imagine That**
*Comic Books; Paperbacks
(new); Reprints; Science Fiction;
Phonograph Records;
Remainders*

Orval J Imel
424 East Vermont
Indianapolis, Ind. 46202
(317) 638-2618
Short Name: **O J Imel**
National Geographic Magazine

In Our Time
P O Box 386
Cambridge, Mass. 02139
Short Name: **In Our Time**
*First Editions, Modern;
American Literature; British
Isles; Press Books & Fine
Printing; Americana*

Indian Head Books
3240 Knapp Road
Vestal, N.Y. 13850
Short Name: **Indian Head**
*History, American; Colonial
America & Revolutionary War
Era; American Indians*

The Indolent Antiquarian
P O Box 5644
Orange, Calif. 92667
Short Name: **Indolent Antiq**
*Books about Books; Maps,
Atlases, & Cartography;
Medicine & Science; Natural
History; Printing & Printing
History; Technology*

Info Books
P O Box 5200
San Angelo, Tex. 76902
Short Name: **Info**
*Americana; Americana,
Regional; Farming, Ranching,
& Livestock; Folklore; Pacific
Region; Commodities Trading*

Inland River Books
P O Box 87
Washington, W.Va. 26181
(304) 428-4948
Short Name: **Inland River**
*West Virginia; Civil War &
Confederacy; Steamships, River
Travel, & Steamboats; Prints;
Ephemera; History, American*

Inn Books Ltd
3430 Dodge Inn Plaza
Dubuque, Iowa 52001
(319) 556-4391
Short Name: **Inn**
*Search Service, without Stock;
Childrens' Books; Classics;
Cookery & Gastronomy;
Education; New Books*

Inprint
P O Box 426
Trinidad, Calif. 95570
Short Name: **Inprint**
*Out of Print, with Stock; First
Editions*

International Books
P O Box 6970
Washington, D.C. 20032
Short Name: **International**
*Tobacco & Smoking; Search
Service, with Stock; Performing
Arts; Black Literature & Black
Studies; Little Magazines &
Literary Small Presses; Women
& Feminism*

International Bookfinders
P O Box 1
Palisades, Calif. 90272
Short Name: **Int'l Bkfndrs**
*Bibliography; Americana;
American Literature*

International Hobbies
P O Box 963
Wilmington, Calif. 90748
Short Name: **Int'l Hobbies**
Whaling; Militaria; Nautica

**International University
Bookseller**
30 Irving Place
New York, N.Y. 10003
(212) 254-4100
Short Name: **Int Univ Bkslrs**
*Africa; Collection Development;
Economics & Business;
Medicine & Science;
Periodicals; Social Sciences*

Invisible Bookman
97 Franciscan Way
Berkeley, Calif. 94707
(415) 524-7823
Short Name: **Invisible**
*First Editions; Fiction;
Literature; Out of Print, with
Stock; Poetry; Rare Books*

Irene's Books
49 West Broadway
South Gardner, Mass. 01440
(617) 632-5574
Short Name: **Irene's**
Americana; Literature; General

Iroqrafts Ltd
R R #2
Ohskweken, Ont. N0A 1M0
(416) 765-4206
Short Name: **Iroqrafts**
American Indians

Deborah Isaacson
P O Box 607
Lewiston, Maine 04240
Short Name: **D Isaacson**
Maine; Art

Isaiah Thomas Books & Prints
980 Main Street
Worcester, Mass. 01603
(617) 754-0750
Short Name: **Isaiah Thomas**
*Appraisals & Appraisal
Services; Art; First Editions;
General; Out of Print, with
Stock; Rare Books*

David Ishii-Bookseller
212 First Avenue, South
Seattle, Wash. 98104
Short Name: **D Ishii**
Americana

Ishtar Books
318 Sherman Street
Canton, Mass. 02021
(617) 828-2753
Short Name: **Ishtar**
Horses; Desert

Ithaca House
108 North Plain Street
Ithaca, N.Y. 14850
Short Name: **Ithaca Hse**
Poetry; Fiction

Angelo Iuspa
474 North 7th Street
Newark, N.J. 07107
Short Name: **A Iuspa**
Olympic Games

Ivycrest Books
P O Box 745
Boulder, Colo. 80306
Short Name: **Ivycrest**
*Bibliography; Book Trade &
Catalogues; Books about Books;
Dictionaries; Press Books &
Fine Printing; Printing &
Printing History*

J

J & W Books
P O Box 277
Bernice, La. 71222
Short Name: **J & W**
General

J & C Book Farm
P O Box 723
Lake Forest, Ill. 60045
(312) 234-1173
Short Name: **J & C**
*Childrens' Books; Biography;
Philosophy; Sporting;
Illustrated Books; Cookery &
Gastronomy*

J D S Books
P O Box 67
Dayton, Ohio 45402
(513) 256-5957
Short Name: **J D S**
*Science Fiction; Asia; History;
Naval & Marine; Jesse Stuart;
Fiction*

J F F Autographs Inc
269-22f Grand Central Parkway
Queens, N.Y. 11005
(212) 631-5511
Short Name: **J F F**
*Presidents; Civil War &
Confederacy; Militaria; Naval
& Marine; History, American*

J & J House Booksellers
5694 Bounty Street
San Diego, Calif. 92120
(714) 265-1113
Short Name: **J & J House**
*Overland Narratives;
Philosophy; Voyages, Travels,
& Exploration; Scholarly
Books; Natural History;
Illustrated Books*

Jack London Bookstore
P O Box 337
Glen Ellen, Calif. 95442
Short Name: **Jack London**
*Jack London; First Editions;
Alaska; Hawaii; Western
Americana; 19th Century
Literature*

Jack's Used Books
718 East Northwest Highway
Mount Prospect, Ill. 60056
(312) 398-7767
Short Name: **Jack's Used**
*First Editions, Modern;
History; Detective Fiction;
Science Fiction; Americana;
Paperbacks (new)*

Ian Jackson
P O Box 9075
Berkeley, Calif. 94709
(415) 548-1431
Short Name: **I Jackson**
*Botany; Gardening &
Horticulture*

Peter L Jackson
23 Castle Green Crescent
Weston, Ont. M9R 1N5
Short Name: **P L Jackson**
Militaria; Napoleon

Arnold Jacobs
5038 Hazeltine Avenue
Sherman Oaks, Calif. 91423
(213) 789-6431
Short Name: **A Jacobs**
*Americana; American Indians;
Military (World War II); Out of
Print, with Stock; Search
Service, with Stock*

Douglas M Jacobs (Appt Only)
P O Box 363, Chestnut Ridge
Bethel, Conn. 06801
(203) 748-6222
Short Name: **D M Jacobs**
*Autographed Material &
Autographs; First Editions;
Rare Books*

David Jaffe
P O Box 4173
Arlington, Va. 22204
(703) 920-4943
Short Name: **D Jaffe**
*Humanities; Literary Criticism;
Literature; Pacific Region;
Scholarly Books; Whaling*

Elinor Jaksto, Bookmistress
4104 Archer Avenue
Chicago, Ill. 60632
Short Name: **E Jaksto**
*American Indians;
Parapsychology*

B A James-Books
P O Box 521
Brookline, Mass. 02147
(617) 566-6070
Short Name: **B A James**
*Rare Books; Americana; Naval
& Marine; Literature;
Manuscripts; Appraisals &
Appraisal Services*

V Janta (Appt Only)
88-28 43rd Avenue
Elmhurst, N.Y. 11373
(212) 898-6917
Short Name: **V Janta**
*Russia & Eastern European
Region*

Janus Books
36 Wyoming Drive
Huntington Station, N.Y. 11746
Short Name: **Janus-Hun**
*Birds & Ornithology; Science
Fiction; Voyages, Travels, &
Exploration; Cookery &
Gastronomy; Childrens' Books;
Illustrated Books*

Janus Books
P O Box 35040
Tucson, Ariz. 85740
(602) 297-2212
Short Name: **Janus-Tuc**
*Detective Fiction; First
Editions, Modern; Fiction;
Literature; Poetry; Mystery
Fiction*

Gregory Javitch
1589 Dr Penfield Avenue
Montreal, Que. H3G 1C6
Short Name: **G Javitch**
*Canada & Canadiana;
American Discovery; American
Indians; Americana; American
Indians; Dance*

Jay's Booktique
1 Canadian Woods
Marlboro, N.J. 07746
Short Name: **Jay's**
*First Editions, Modern; Rare
Books; Search Service, with
Stock; War; Drug Culture;
Computers*

Jean's Book Service
P O Box 264
Hatfield, Penna. 19440
Short Name: **Jean's**
*Ephemera; Trade Catalogues;
Juveniles; Books about Books;
Printing & Printing History*

Jehovah's Witnesses Books
P O Box 597
Clayton, Calif. 94517
Short Name: **Jehovah's**
*Watchtower Books & Jehovah's
Witnesses*

Jeltrups'-Books
51 ABC Company Street
Christiansted, St Croix, V.I.
00820
(809) 773-1018
Short Name: **Jeltrups'**
*Caribbean; New York
Metropolitan Area*

Jenison's Books
11 Judson Street
Canton, N.Y. 13617
Short Name: **Jenison's**
Adirondacks

Jenkins Company
P O Box 2085
Austin, Tex. 78768
Short Name: **Jenkins**
*Rare Books; Appraisals &
Appraisal Services;
Bookbinding & Restoration;
Literature; Americana;
Incunabula & Early Printing*

Pauline Jenkins
13313 Van Nuys Boulevard
Pacoima, Calif. 91331
Short Name: **P Jenkins**
*Cinema & Mass Media;
Americana; American Indians;
Archaeology; Color Plate
Books; Rare Books*

Jennies Book Nook
15 West Howell Avenue
Alexandria, Va. 22301
Short Name: **Jennies**
*History; Poetry; Biography;
Geneaologies; Fiction; Juveniles*

Jenny Lind Enterprises
1041 Washington Avenue
Sellersville, Penna. 18960
Short Name: **Jenny Lind**
*Opera; Sporting; Search
Service, with Stock;
Autographed Material &
Autographs*

R W Jimerson
7 Edward Avenue
San Raphael, Calif. 94903
Short Name: **R W Jimerson**
*General; California; Voyages,
Travels, & Exploration*

Johnny Appleseed Bookshop
Manchester, Vt. 05254
Short Name: **J Appleseed**
*Americana, Regional; Fine &
Rare Bindings; First Editions;
History, American; Hunting,
Fishing & Angling; Rare Books*

Johnson & Small Booksellers
45 Bastion Square
No. Vancouver, B.C. V8W 1J1
Short Name: **Johnson & Small**
*Voyages, Travels, &
Exploration; Paintings; Rare
Books; IlluminatedManuscripts;
Canada & Canadiana*

Harmer Johnson Books
667 Madison Avenue
New York, N.Y. 10021
Short Name: **H Johnson**
*Africa; American Indians;
Appraisals & Appraisal
Services; Archaeology; Art;
Orientalia*

Walter J Johnson Inc
355 Chestnut Street
Norwood, N.J. 07648
(201) 767-1303
Short Name: **W J Johnson**
*Medicine & Science;
Periodicals; Foreign Languages*

John Johnson
RFD #2
North Bennington, Vt. 05257
(802) 442-6738
Short Name: **J Johnson**
*Botany; Color Plate Books;
Natural History; Rare Books;
Voyages, Travels, &
Exploration; Whaling*

**Johnson & O'Donnell-Rare
  Bookd**
84 Bayberry Circle
Liverpool, N.Y. 13088
Short Name: **Johnson & O'D**
*First Editions; First Editions,
Modern; Author Collections;
Autographed Material &
Autographs; Rare Books; Fine
& Rare Bindings*

William S Johnson
829 East Dr Woodruff Place
Indianapolis, Ind. 46201
Short Name: **W S Johnson**
*Bibliography; Book Trade &
Catalogues; Literary Criticism;
Literature; Russia & Eastern
European Region*

William S Johnson, Books
P O Box 33
Indianapolis, Ind. 46206
(317) 639-1256
Short Name: **W S Johnson**
*Russia & Eastern European
Region; Orientalia; Book Trade
& Catalogues; Humanities*

Sam: Johnson's Bookshop
11552 Santa Monica Boulevard
Los Angeles, Calif. 90025
(213) 477-9247
Short Name: **S Johnson's**
General

Jokal Research
2953 Bainbridge Avenue
Bronx, N.Y. 10458
Short Name: **Jokal**
*Bibliography; Crafts & Trades;
Search Service, without Stock;
Reference; Technology*

Jolie's Books
2020 South Federal Highway U
S #1
Stuart, Fla. 33494
(305) 287-7575
Short Name: **Jolie's**
*Rare Books; Nautica; Comic
Books; Collection Development*

Jolly Roger Records & Books
190 Columbus Avenue
New York, N.Y. 10023
(212) 877-1836
Short Name: **Jolly Roger**
*Performing Arts; First Editions,
Modern; Literary Criticism;
Art; Poetry; Out of Print,
without Stock*

Richard T Jordan
225 Lafayette Street, Room 306
New York, N.Y. 10012
Short Name: **R T Jordan**
*Cinema & Mass Media; Art;
Reference; Theatre; Women &
Feminism; Phonograph Records*

Joseph The Provider
903 State Street
Santa Barbara, Calif. 93101
(805) 962-6862
Short Name: **Joseph Provider**
*Literature; 20th Century
Literature; American Literature;
English Literature;
Manuscripts; Association Books*

The Joyce Book Shops
P O Box 310
Martinez, Calif. 94553
(415) 834-8108
Short Name: **Joyce**
*Foreign Languages; Fiction;
General; Rare Books;
Orientalia; Detective Fiction*

Thomas J Joyce And Company
8 South Third Street, Box 561
Geneva, Ill. 60134
(312) 232-6383
Short Name: **T J Joyce**
*Americana; Appraisals &
Appraisal Services; First
Editions; Illustrated Books;
Press Books & Fine Printing;
Rare Books*

Judaica Book Agency
P O Box 385, Blythbourne
  Station
Brooklyn, N.Y. 11219
(212) 435-2280
Short Name: **Judaica Bk Agy**
Judaica & Hebraica

Junction Book Shop Inc
Junction City
Peoria, Ill. 61614
(309) 691-4633
Short Name: **Junction**
Art; Travel

Junius Book Distributors
P O Box 85
Fairview, N.J. 07022
Short Name: **Junius**
*Bibliography; Scholarly Books;
Medicine & Science*

**Janet Jurist-Bibliographic
  Research**
510 East 86th Street
New York, N.Y. 10028
Short Name: **J Jurist**
*Bibliographical Research
Services; Book Scouts*

J Juszyk
P O Box 3262
Thousand Oaks, Calif. 91359
Short Name: **J Juszyk**
Hunting, Fishing & Angling;
Natural History

K

K N Enterprises
P O Box 87397
Chicago, Ill. 60680
Short Name: **K N**
Search Service, with Stock

Helen R Kahn, Antiquarian
 Books
P O Box 323, Victoria Station
Montreal, Que. H3Z 2V8
(514) 844-5344
Short Name: **H R Kahn**
Voyages, Travels, &
Exploration; Americana;
Arctica & Antarctica; Canada
& Canadiana

L S Kaiser Books
1820 Graham Hill
Santa Cruz, Calif. 95060
Short Name: **L S Kaiser**
Search Service, with Stock;
Americana, Regional; Religion
& Theology; Childrens' Books

Robert J Kalanja
247 East Fairmont Avenue
Trafford, Penna. 15085
Short Name: **R J Kalanja**
Pennsylvania; Natural History;
Hunting, Fishing & Angling;
Kennedy Assasinations;
Nicola Tesla;
Ephemera

Kalonbooks
P O Box 16, Rte #114
Bradford, N.H. 03221
Short Name: **Kalonbooks**
History, American; European
History; Biography; Literature;
New England; Literary
Criticism

Kardy's Book Store
105-A West Main Street
Salisbury, Md. 21801
Short Name: **Kardy's**
Humor; Maryland; Local
History

Ken Karith
P O Box 1687
New York, N.Y. 10001
Short Name: **K Karith**
Photography; First Editions;
Rare Books; Illustrated Books;
Out of Print, with Stock; Art

Kenneth Karmiole-Bookseller
2255 Westwood Boulevard
Los Angeles, Calif. 90064
(213) 474-7305
Short Name: **K Karmiole**
Rare Books; Press Books &
Fine Printing; Printing &
Printing History; First Editions;
Art; Voyages, Travels, &
Exploration

Howard Karno-Books
P O Box 64608
Los Angeles, Calif. 90064
(213) 474-1551
Short Name: **H Karno**
Archaeology; Art; Caribbean;
Central America; Latin
America; South America

Kats Trading Post
P O Box 392
Park City, Utah 84060
Short Name: **Kats**
Utah; Mormons; Erotica

Elliot M Katt-Bookseller
P O Box 1455
Studio City, Calif. 91604
Short Name: **E M Katt**
Cinema & Mass Media; Comic
Books; First Editions, Modern;
Performing Arts; Circus &
Carnival; Bibliography

Samuel W Katz
10845 Lindbrook Drive, #6
Los Angeles, Calif. 90024
Short Name: **S W Katz**
Rare Books; Women &
Feminism; Law; Medicine &
Science; Illustrated Books;
IlluminatedManuscripts

Kay's Book & Magazine
 Supermarket
620 Prospect Avenue
Cleveland, Ohio 44115
Short Name: **Kay's**
Out of Print, with Stock;
History; Literature; Science
Fiction; Cinema & Mass Media

Edward J Kearin
P O Box 563
Goldens Bridge, N.Y. 10526
Short Name: **E J Kearin**
Americana

Irving Keats
280 Del Mesa Crm
Carmel, Calif. 93921
(408) 624-5428
Short Name: **I Keats**
Book Trade & Catalogues;
Color Plate Books; First
Editions; First Editions,
Modern; Illustrated Books;
Press Books & Fine Printing

Dorothy V Keck
1360 West Riverview
Decatur, Ill. 62522
(217) 428-5100
Short Name: **D V Keck**
*Fiction; General; Out of Print,
with Stock; Rare Books*

Joyce B Keeler (Appt Only)
Wilson Pond Road
North Monmouth, Maine 04265
Short Name: **J B Keeler**
*Childrens' Books; Out of Print,
with Stock; Science Fiction;
Americana; Natural History;
Maine Authors*

E F Keenan Books
P O Box 43
Lake Bluff, Ill. 60044
Short Name: **E F Keenan**
*Chicago; Wyoming;
Photography; Western
Americana; Prints*

Robert Keene-Books
38 Hampton Road
Southampton, N.Y. 11968
(516) 283-1612
Short Name: **R Keene**
*Whaling; Steamships, River
Travel, & Steamboats; Ships &
The Sea*

Keith & Martin Books
722 Pollock Street
New Bern, N.C. 28560
(919) 638-2797
Short Name: **Keith & Martin**
*Detective Fiction; Criminology;
Paperbacks (new); North
Carolina; Architecture; Out of
Print, with Stock*

J J Keleher
10 Baldry Bay
Winnipeg, Man. R3T 3C4
(204) 269-2875
Short Name: **J J Keleher**
*Arctica & Antarctica;
Biography; Canada &
Canadiana; Hunting, Fishing &
Angling; Natural History;
Voyages, Travels, &
Exploration*

Don Greame Kelley
2 Yolanda Drive
San Anselmo, Calif. 94960
(415) 453-2395
Short Name: **Greame Kelley**
*Miniature Books; Press Books
& Fine Printing*

Cesi Kellinger
735 Philadelphia Avenue
Chambersburg, Penna. 17201
Short Name: **C Kellinger**
*Americana; Art; Books about
Books; First Editions; Dance*

Bryce R Kemp
7430 Georgian Road, West Oak
   Lane
Philadelphia, Penna. 19138
Short Name: **B R Kemp**
*First Editions, Modern; Press
Books & Fine Printing; Out of
Print, with Stock*

Richard J Kempe
200 East 16th Street
New York, N.Y. 10003
Short Name: **R J Kempe**
*Art; Drawings; Graphic Arts;
Illustrated Books; Paintings;
Prints*

Ken-L-Questor
Rte #2, Box 279
Newberg, Ore. 97132
Short Name: **Ken-L-Questor**
Dogs; Horses; Mushrooms

Richard T Kennedy
1017 South 251st Street
Kent, Wash. 98031
(206) 824-2635
Short Name: **R T Kennedy**
National Geographic Magazine;
Search Service, without Stock;
Out of Print, without Stock;
Periodicals; Maps, Atlases, &
Cartography; Specialized
Publications

Kennedy's Bookshop
1911 Central Street, Box 191
Evanston, Ill. 60204
(312) 475-2481
Short Name: **Kennedy's**
*General; Out of Print, with
Stock; Rare Books; Technology*

Kent's Crossing Book Store
College At Linden
Normal, Ill. 61761
Short Name: **Kent's Crossing**
Childrens' Books

Peg & Don Kenyon Books
408 De Anza Heights Drive
San Dimas, Calif. 91773
Short Name: **P & D Kenyon**
*Aircraft & Aerospace History;
Rare Books; Puzzles, Contests,
& Games; Jesse Stuart;
Authors; Juveniles*

Keramos
P O Box 7500
Ann Arbor, Mich. 48107
(313) 429-7864
Short Name: **Keramos**
*Antiques; Art; Asia; Voyages,
Travels, & Exploration; Rare
Books; Orientalia*

The Keshcarrigan Bookshop
90 West Broadway
New York, N.Y. 10007
(212) 962-4237
Short Name: **Keshcarrigan**
Ireland & The Irish

Kestrel Books
1 West Carmel Valley Road,
   Box Q
Carmel Valley, Calif. 93924
(408) 659-4534
Short Name: **Kestrel**
*Press Books & Fine Printing;
Out of Print, with Stock; Rare
Books; Search Service, with
Stock*

Jocelyne Kidston
R R #1
Tarzwell, Ont. P0K 1V0
Short Name: **J Kidston**
*Arctica & Antarctica; Canada
& Canadiana; Geology; Out of
Print, without Stock; Search
Service, without Stock;
Voyages, Travels, &
Exploration*

M Kilen
5400 London Road
Duluth, Minn. 55804
(507) 525-4487
Short Name: **M Kilen**
*Logging; Hunting, Fishing &
Angling*

John K King-Books
P O Box 363
Detroit, Mich. 48232
Short Name: **J K King**
Illustrated Books; Civil War &
Confederacy; Literature;
Americana; Out of Print, with
Stock; First Editions

Rollin King
800 Umbarger
Muncie, Ind. 47304
Short Name: **R King**
Americana, States; Authors;
Dogs; Rare Books

The Kingfisher
Lake Watch Rte #1, Box 44
Eureka Springs, Ark. 72632
Short Name: **Kingfisher**
Marine Biology

Yoshio Kishi
165 West 66th Street
New York, N.Y. 10023
Short Name: **Y Kishi**
Americana, States; Asia; First
Editions, Modern; Orientalia;
Outlaws & Rangers

Elliot Klein Ltd
19 West 44th Street
New York, N.Y. 10036
(212) 840-6885
Short Name: **E Klein**
Folklore; Anthropology;
Religion & Theology; Foreign
Languages; Out of Print, with
Stock

Joyce Klein-Bookseller
177 South Oak Park Avenue
Oak Park, Ill. 60302
Short Name: **J Klein**
Childrens' Books; Cookery &
Gastronomy; Art; Mystery
Fiction; General

Gail Klemm-Books
P O Box 551
Ellicott City, Md. 21043
(301) 465-7414
Short Name: **G Klemm**
Childrens' Books; Illustrated
Books; Americana; Typography
& Type Specimens; Collection
Development

J & P Klemperer
400 Second Avenue
New York, N.Y. 10010
Short Name: **J & P Klemperer**
New York Metropolitan Area;
Ephemera; General; Postcards;
Posters

Terrence M Knaus
21601 Foster Lane
Fort Bragg, Calif. 95437
(707) 964-0681
Short Name: **T M Knaus**
Irish & Scottish History;
Fiction; History; Gardening &
Horticulture; Out of Print, with
Stock; Search Service, without
Stock

Kneedeep In Books
P O Box 1314
Manchester Center, Vt. 05255
(802) 362-3663
Short Name: **Kneedeep**
General; Hunting, Fishing &
Angling; Out of Print, with
Stock; Search Service, with
Stock; Crafts & Trades

Knights Book Service
11 Helena Avenue
Harwich Port, Mass. 02646
Short Name: **Knight's**
Americana; History, American;
Political, Social, & Cultural
History & Thought; Technology

Knutson's Fine Arts
606 Lloyd Building
Seattle, Wash. 98101
(206) 623-1410
Short Name: **Knutson's**
Western Americana

Benjamin Koenig's Country
  Bookshop
R F D #2
Plainfield, Vt. 05667
(802) 454-8439
Short Name: **B Koenig's**
Archaeology; Folklore; Out of
Print, with Stock; Search
Service, with Stock; Bells

Louis Kohrs, Books & Prints
3876 Belmont Avenue
San Diego, Calif. 92116
Short Name: **L Kohrs**
Magic; Gambling; Psychiatry,
Psychology, & Psychonanalysis;
Circus & Carnival

George Frederick Kolbe
23881 Via Fabricante #511
Mission Viejo, Calif. 92691
(714) 768-6854
Short Name: **G F Kolbe**
Numismatics

Vern Koppelman
R R #1
Moorhead, Minn. 56560
Short Name: **V Koppelman**
Dogs

Stephen Koschal
P O Box 201
Verona, N.J. 07044
Short Name: **S Koschal**
Association Books;
Autographed Material &
Autographs; Inscribed Books;
Manuscripts; Presidents; Rare
Books

Koths Speciality Co
P O Box 310
Morton, Wash. 98356
Short Name: **Koths**
Law; Authors; Bible & Bible
Studies

Frank L Kovacs-Archaeology
  Books
422 Post Street
San Francisco, Calif. 94102
(415) 982-4072
Short Name: **F L Kovacs**
Archaeology; Numismatics

Valerie Kraft, Fine Books &
  Prints
309 North Elmhurst Road
Prospect Heights, Ill. 60070
(312) 253-1419
Short Name: **V Kraft**
Rare Books; First Editions;
Color Plate Books; Childrens'
Books; Sporting; Prints

Dr Eugene F Kramer (Appt
  Only)
2804 Downing Street
Jacksonville, Fla. 32205
(904) 388-1123
Short Name: **E F Kramer**
Americana

Philip Krapp
Monee, Ill. 60449
(312) 534-2918
Short Name: **P Krapp**
*Americana, Regional; Cinema
& Mass Media; Detective
Fiction; First Editions, Modern;
Middle Ages; Typography &
Type Specimens*

H P Kraus
16 East 46th Street
New York, N.Y. 10017
(212) 687-4808
Short Name: **H P Kraus**
*Incunabula & Early Printing;
Maps, Atlases, & Cartography;
Americana; Manuscripts,
Medieval & Illuminated*

Milton M Kraus
10 Grosvenor Place
Great Neck, N.Y. 11021
Short Name: **M M Kraus**
*Education; Foreign Languages;
Humanities; Paperbacks (new);
Psychiatry, Psychology, &
Psychonanalysis; Erotica*

Edgar Krebs
5849 North Talman Avenue
Chicago, Ill. 60659
Short Name: **E Krebs**
*History, American; History;
Literature; Out of Print, with
Stock*

Kregel's Bookstore
525 Eastern Avenue, Se, Box
  2607
Grand Rapids, Mich. 49501
(616) 459-9444
Short Name: **Kregel's**
*Religion & Theology; Reprints;
Classics*

Ralph Kristiansen
P O Box 524, Kenmore Station
Boston, Mass. 02215
(617) 424-1527
Short Name: **R Kristiansen**
*Detective Fiction; First
Editions; Science Fiction;
Illustrated Books; Literature*

Dr Milton Kronovet
881-C Balmoral Court
Lakewood, N.J. 08701
Short Name: **M Kronovet**
*Autographed Material &
Autographs*

Krown & Speelman Booksellers
1975-1/2 Westwood Boulevard
Los Angeles, Calif. 90025
(213) 474-1745
Short Name: **Krown & S'man**
*Classics; Middle Ages;
Renaissance; Rare Books;
Scholarly Books; STC & Wing
Books*

Daniel & Maybelle Krueger
Rte #2, Milo Center
Penn Yan, N.Y. 14527
(315) 536-8964
Short Name: **D & M Krueger**
*Out of Print, with Stock; First
Editions; Literature; Rare
Books*

Gen Krueger-Books
7840 McGroarty Street
Sunland, Calif. 91040
Short Name: **G Krueger**
Childrens' Books

Patricia Kufus
Allan At Marriott
Portland, Tex. 78374
(512) 643-2341
Short Name: **P Kufus**
*Childrens' Books; Cookery &
Gastronomy; Fiction; Comic
Books; Magazines; Automotive*

**Jeanne Kuwalsky-Books (Appt
  Only)**
518 Flora Street
Laguna Beach, Calif. 92651
(714) 494-8927
Short Name: **J Kuwalsky**
*Cinema & Mass Media;
General; Inscribed Books; Out
of Print, with Stock; Poetry;
Rare Books*

P & L Kwasniewski
P O Box 248
Arlington, Vt. 05250
(802) 375-2255
Short Name: **Kwasniewski**
*Photography; Technology;
Ephemera; Cinema & Mass
Media; Crafts & Trades;
Search Service, with Stock*

American Book Collector has computerized all the names, addresses, and book specialties for the 3,000 dealers found in this directory and for a growing list of dealers who will appear in subsequent editions. We can provide mailing labels for these dealers, selected by specialty if you wish, at reasonable cost. Write for our price schedule. *ABC*, 274 Madison Avenue, New York, N.Y. 10016.

L

L'estampe Originale
P O Box 897
Saratoga, Calif. 95070
(408) 867-0833
Short Name: **L'estampe**
Art; Color Plate Books;
Illustrated Books; Prints; Press
Books & Fine Printing; Graphic
Arts

Lionel La Berge
S Ange-Gardien, 8905 Ave
  Royale
Montmorency, Que.
Short Name: **L La Berge**
Americana, Regional; Antiques;
Incunabula & Early Printing;
Illustrated Books; Manuscripts;
Rare Books

La Cite Des Livres
2306 Westwood Boulevard
Los Angeles, Calif. 90064
Short Name: **La Cite-L A**
Foreign Languages; Maps,
Atlases, & Cartography

La Galeria De Los Artesanos
P O Box 1657
Las Vegas, N.Mex. 87701
(505) 425-8331
Short Name: **Los Artesanos**
American Indians;
Southwestern America; Outlaws
& Rangers; Folklore; General;
Cattle & Range Industry

La Mesa Bookstore
8209 La Mesa Boulevard
La Mesa, Calif. 92041
Short Name: **La Mesa**
Science Fiction; Fiction; New
Books; First Editions

La Scala Autographs, Inc
P O Box 268
Plainsboro, N.J. 08536
Short Name: **La Scala**
Opera; Music; Theatre; Dance;
Cinema & Mass Media

La Valois Books
P O Box 386
New York, N.Y. 10028
(212) 722-1877
Short Name: **La Valois**
French Books & Literature;
Documents; Ephemera; History;
Rare Books

Donald LaChance
1032 Bay Oaks Drive
Los Osos, Calif. 93402
(805) 528-7383
Short Name: **D LaChance**
Search Service, with Stock

David Ladner
P O Box 6179
Whitneyville, Conn. 06517
Short Name: **D Ladner**
Architecture; Classics; Foreign
Languages; Printing & Printing
History; Russia & Eastern
European Region; Scholarly
Books

N L Laird, Bookseller
1240 West Jarvis
Chicago, Ill. 60626
(312) 761-4380
Short Name: **N L Laird**
Art; Illustrated Books;
Detective Fiction

D & E Lake Ltd
106 Berkeley Street
Toronto, Ont. M5A 2W7
(416) 863-9930
Short Name: **D & E Lake**
Philosophy; Economics &
Business; Canada & Canadiana;
Law; Voyages, Travels, &
Exploration; Rare Books

Lake Law Books
142 McAllister Street
San Francisco, Calif. 94102
Short Name: **Lake Law**
Law; Appraisals & Appraisal
Services

Lambda Rising, Inc
2014 South Street, NW
Washington, D.C. 20009
(202) 462-6969
Short Name: **Lambda Rising**
Homosexual & Gay Literature;
Autographed Material &
Autographs; First Editions; Out
of Print, with Stock;
Paperbacks (new); Ephemera

M S Lambeth
221 South Broadway
San Antonio, Tex. 78205
(512) 226-6049
Short Name: **M S Lambeth**
Texas; Southwestern America;
Mexico; Primitive & Pre-
Columbian; American Indians;
Book Scouts

The Lamp (William G Mayer,
  Jr)
204 Auburn Street
Pittsburgh, Penna. 15206
Short Name: **Lamp**
Americana, States; Maps,
Atlases, & Cartography; Prints

Landau Book Company
272 West Park
Long Beach, N.Y. 11561
Short Name: **Landau**
Art; Dictionaries; Archery;
Chess, Checkers, & Draughts;
Self Help

Jan Landau
Rte #2, Box 293
New Castle, Va. 24127
(703) 864-6288
Short Name: **J Landau**
Science Fiction; Paperbacks
(new); Out of Print, with Stock;
Autographed Material &
Autographs; Detective Fiction;
Search Service, with Stock

Dr Lawrence M Lande
4870 Cedar Crescent
Montreal, Que. H3W 2H9
Short Name: **Dr L M Lande**
Canada & Canadiana

Landmark Book Company
119 West 57th Street
New York, N.Y. 10019
(212) 765-5252
Short Name: **Landmark**
Art; Reference; Scholarly Books

Jules Landry
124 Martina Street
Point Richmond, Calif. 94801
Short Name: **J Landry**
Authors

Landscape Books
P O Box 483
Exeter, N.H. 03833
Short Name: **Landscape**
*Landscape Architecture;
General*

Kenneth Lang
105 Avon Place
Amityville, N.Y. 11701
Short Name: **K Lang**
General; Publishing History

Gerald Lange, Bookseller
P O Box 3856
St Paul, Minn. 55165
Short Name: **G Lange**
*Books about Books; Graphic
Arts; Press Books & Fine
Printing; Printing & Printing
History; Rare Books;
Typography & Type Specimens*

Lange's Book Shop
Casper, Wyom. 82601
Short Name: **Lange's**
Childrens' Books

Lantern Book Shop
24 East Oceanside
Pompano Beach, Fla. 33062
Short Name: **Lantern**
*Fiction; New Books; Cookery &
Gastronomy; Juveniles;
Paperbacks (new); Rare Books*

Carl Larson
24411 Woodmere
North Olmsted, Ohio 44070
(216) 734-3575
Short Name: **C Larson**
*Scandinavia; Out of Print, with
Stock; Search Service, without
Stock*

David L Larson
221 North Reading Avenue
Boyertown, Penna. 19512
Short Name: **D L Larson**
Prints

Las Lenguas Book Store
12215 Coit Road, #264
Dallas, Tex. 75251
Short Name: **Las Lenguas**
*Search Service, with Stock;
Poetry; Illustrated Books;
American Indians*

Rose Lasley
5827 Burr Oak
Berkeley, Ill. 60163
(312) 547-6239
Short Name: **R Lasley**
*Americana; Out of Print, with
Stock; Search Service, with
Stock; Childrens' Books;
General; Rare Books*

Latin American Books
P O Box 39090
Washington, D.C. 20016
(202) 362-2973
Short Name: **Latin Amer**
*Collection Development;
Foreign Languages; Latin
America; Out of Print, with
Stock; Scholarly Books; Iberia*

Alexander Lauberts
1073 West Broad
Falls Church, Va. 22046
Short Name: **A Lauberts**
*Armed Forces Editions;
Bookplates & Ex Libris;
Virginia; Russia & Eastern
European Region*

**James & Mary Laurie,
   Booksellers**
251 South Snelling
St Paul, Minn. 55105
Short Name: **J & M Laurie**
*Books about Books; Press
Books & Fine Printing;
American Literature; English
Literature; Minnesota*

Clarence E Law
Rte #1, Box 144
Farmland, Ind. 47340
(317) 468-8258
Short Name: **C E Law**
Civil War & Confederacy

Larry Laws
831 Cornelia
Chicago, Ill. 60657
(312) 477-9247
Short Name: **L Laws**
*Cinema & Mass Media;
Periodicals; Performing Arts;
Chicago; World's Fairs*

David A Lawyer, Bookseller
Plains, Mont. 59859
Short Name: **D A Lawyer**
*Agriculture; Botany; Logging;
Foreign Languages; History*

Josephine Lazarus, Inc
Grace Lane
Ossining, N.Y. 10562
Short Name: **J Lazarus**
*Presidents; Autographed
Material & Autographs;
Americana*

Philip G Le Van
2443 Liberty Street
Allentown, Penna. 18104
(215) 432-6147
Short Name: **P G Le Van**
Golf

Kenneth Leach
P O Box 78
Brattleboro, Vt. 05301
(802) 257-7918
Short Name: **K Leach**
*Americana; Ephemera;
Literature; History, American;
Rare Books*

Leaves Of Grass
2433 Whitmore Lake Road
Ann Arbor, Mich. 48103
(313) 995-2300
Short Name: **Leaves Of Grass**
*Americana; Appraisals &
Appraisal Services; Books
about Books; First Editions;
Press Books & Fine Printing;
Rare Books*

Shirley B Lebo
221 E' Street, SE
Washington, D.C. 20003
(202) 546-9102
Short Name: **S B Lebo**
*Appraisals & Appraisal
Services*

Patricia Ledlie-Bookseller
P O Box 46
Buckfield, Maine 04220
(207) 336-2969
Short Name: **P Ledlie**
*Birds & Ornithology; Natural
History*

Lee & Lee Booksellers, Inc
424 Broome Street
New York, N.Y. 10013
(212) 226-3460
Short Name: **Lee & Lee**
Art; Architecture; Illustrated Books; Graphic Arts; Archaeology; Photography

Helen B Leech-Fine Books
Harrisburg, Penna. 17112
Short Name: **H B Leech**
Maps, Atlases, & Cartography; History, American; Farming, Ranching, & Livestock; Search Service, without Stock; Steamships, River Travel, & Steamboats; History

James P Leeds
2470 East 116th Street
Carmel, Ind. 46032
Short Name: **J P Leeds**
Optics

Leekley Book Search
711 Sheriden Road, Box 337
Winthrop Harbor, Ill. 60096
(312) 872-2311
Short Name: **Leekley Srch**
Out of Print, with Stock; Search Service, with Stock; Americana, Regional; Collection Development; Illinois; Scholarly Books

Jean-Jacques Lefebvre
3540 Rue Durocher, #15
Montreal, Que. H2X 2E5
(514) 844-6091
Short Name: **J J Lefebvre**
Biography; Canada & Canadiana; Dictionaries; Geneaologies; History; Political, Social, & Cultural History & Thought

Edward J Lefkowicz
P O Box 630
Fairhaven, Mass. 02719
(617) 997-6839
Short Name: **E J Lefkowicz**
Arctica & Antarctica; Maps, Atlases, & Cartography; Naval & Marine; Pacific Region; Voyages, Travels, & Exploration; Whaling

Legacy Books
P O Box 494
Hatboro, Penna. 19040
Short Name: **Legacy**
Folklore; Popular Culture

Janet Lehr, Inc (Appt Only)
P O Box 617
New York, N.Y. 10028
(212) 288-1802
Short Name: **J Lehr**
Photography; Autographed Material & Autographs; Illustrated Books

Edward A Lehwald
3509 North Calvert Street
Baltimore, Md. 21218
Short Name: **E A Lehwald**
Paperbacks (new); Detective Fiction; Automotive

Barbara Leibowits Graphics, Ltd
80 Central Park West
New York, N.Y. 10023
(212) 799-0570
Short Name: **B Leibowits**
Drawings; Illustrated Books; Posters

The Leiden Gallery
1045 Morrison Lane
Northbrook, Ill. 60062
Short Name: **Leiden**
Photography

James G Leishman
P O Box A
Menlo Park, Calif. 94025
(415) 322-7034
Short Name: **J G Leishman**
Americana, Regional; Appraisals & Appraisal Services; First Editions; Geology; Natural History; Voyages, Travels, & Exploration

Lennies Book Nook
8125 West 3rd Street
Los Angeles, Calif. 90048
Short Name: **Lennies**
History; Biography; Theatre; Civil War & Confederacy; Out of Print, with Stock; General

Joseph L Lepczyk
P O Box 751
East Lansing, Mich. 48823
Short Name: **J L Lepczyk**
Numismatics; Medals (books on)

Jack R Levien
Rte #1, Box 18
Mc Dowell, Va. 24458
Short Name: **J R Levien**
Miniature Books; Mathematics; Medicine & Science

Barry R Levin Science Fiction
2253 Westwood Boulevard
Los Angeles, Calif. 90064
(213) 474-5611
Short Name: **B R Levin**
Science Fiction; Fantasy; First Editions; First Editions, Modern

Jacqueline Levine
107 East Oglethorpe Avenue
Savannah, Ga. 31401
(912) 233-8519
Short Name: **J Levine**
Naval & Marine; Fore-Edge Painting; Americana; Books about Books; Press Books & Fine Printing

Harry A Levinson-Rare Books
P O Box 534
Beverly Hills, Calif. 90213
(213) 276-9311
Short Name: **H A Levinson**
STC & Wing Books; Incunabula & Early Printing; Manuscripts, Medieval & Illuminated; Medicine & Science; Illustrated Books; Bibliography

Lester S Levy
2 Slade Avenue
Baltimore, Md. 21208
(301) 486-3095
Short Name: **L S Levy**
Sheet Music

Dorothy A Lewis
116 Pinehurst Avenue, #21f
New York, N.Y. 10033
Short Name: **D A Lewis**
Medical & Medicine; Health

R E Lewis, Inc
P O Box 1108
San Rafael, Calif. 94915
Short Name: **R E Lewis**
Prints; Sets

Liberty Lore Antiques, F L Frazier
215 Main Street
Santuit, Mass. 02635
Short Name: **Liberty Lore**
America's Cup; Joseph C. Lincoln

Liberty Rock Book Shoppe
55 Orange Turnpike
Sloatsburg, N.Y. 10974
(914) 753-2012
Short Name: **Liberty Rock**
Americana, Regional; Architecture; Literature; Out of Print, with Stock; Rare Books; Religion & Theology

Libra Books
18563 Sherman Way
Reseda, Calif. 91335
(213) 344-5400
Short Name: **Libra**
Out of Print, with Stock; General; Fiction; Literature; Biography; Performing Arts

La Librairie Quebecoise
1417 Rue Amherst
Montreal, Que. H2L 3L2
(514) 523-3305
Short Name: **Lib Quebecoise**
Rare Books; History; Voyages, Travels, & Exploration; Canada & Canadiana; French Books & Literature

Librarium
R D #190, Blackbridge Road
East Chatham, N.Y. 12060
(518) 392-5209
Short Name: **Librarium**
General; Childrens' Books; Art; Americana; Science; Literature

Librarius
P O Box 11
Glendora, Calif. 91740
Short Name: **Librarius**
Writing Instruction; Church Records

Library Books
P O Box 7240
Dallas, Tex. 75209
Short Name: **Library-Dal**
Bibliography; Author Collections; First Editions, Modern; Literary Criticism; Poetry; Reference

The Library Ltd
7538 Forsyth Street
Clayton, Mo. 63105
Short Name: **Library Ltd**
General

Libros Latinos
P O Box 1103
Redlands, Calif. 92373
(714) 793-8423
Short Name: **Libros Latinos**
American Indians; Archaeology; Art; Caribbean; Latin America; Central America

William B Liebmann (Appt Only)
211 East 70th Street
New York, N.Y. 10021
(212) 879-0669
Short Name: **W B Liebmann**
Autographed Material & Autographs; Manuscripts; Press Books & Fine Printing; Rare Books; Appraisals & Appraisal Services

Leland N Lien, Bookseller
413 South 4th Street
Minneapolis, Minn. 55415
(612) 332-7081
Short Name: **L N Lien**
American Indians; Civil War & Confederacy; Literature; History, American; Rare Books; Voyages, Travels, & Exploration

Lift Bridge Books
124 Village Landing
Fairport, N.Y. 14450
Short Name: **Lift Bridge-Fai**
Ephemera; Authors; English Literature

Lift Bridge Bookshop
71 Main Street
Brockport, N.Y. 14420
Short Name: **Lift Bridge-Bro**
New Books; Western New York State; Americana, Regional; First Editions, Modern

Lighthouse Books
148 Central Avenue
St Petersburg, Fla. 33701
(813) 822-3278
Short Name: **Lighthse**
Florida; Southeastern America; Caribbean; Ephemera; Literature; Out of Print, with Stock

Lilac Hedge Bookshop
P O Box 222
Putney, Vt. 05346
(802) 387-4445
Short Name: **Lilac Hedge**
General; Literature; Search Service, with Stock; Out of Print, with Stock

Wade Lillywhite
2302 East Franzen
Santa Ana, Calif. 92705
(714) 543-6820
Short Name: **W Lillywhite**
Americana; Out of Print, with Stock; Reference; Religion & Theology; Mormons

Limestone Hills Book Shop
P O Box 1125
Glen Rose, Tex. 76043
Short Name: **Limestone Hills**
19th Century Literature; 20th Century Literature; Natural History; Detective Fiction; Books about Books

Lincoln Hill Books
163 Delaware Avenue
Delmar, N.Y. 12054
Short Name: **Lincoln Hill**
Gardening & Horticulture

Lincoln Out-Of-Print Book Search
Mt Hygela Road, Box 47
Foster, R.I. 02825
(401) 647-2825
Short Name: **Lincoln-O P**
Search Service, with Stock; Literary Criticism; Social Sciences; Economics & Business; Political Science & Theory; History

Ernest E Lindh
12060 McKee Road
North Huntington, Penna. 15642
Short Name: **E E Lindh**
Western Pennsylvania; Surveying & Surveys; Waterfowl & Shore Birds

Robert Loren Link
P O Box 70
Cool, Calif. 95614
Short Name: **R L Link**
First Editions, Modern; Literature; Press Books & Fine Printing; Poetry; Fiction; Detective Fiction

Lion Enterprises
R R #3, Box 127
Walkerton, Ind. 46574
(219) 369-9394
Short Name: **Lion Ent**
Political Science & Theory;
Philosophy; Foreign Affairs;
Art; Poetry; Humanities

Lion Heart Autographs
12 West 37th Street
New York, N.Y. 10018
(212) 695-1310
Short Name: **Lion Heart**
Autographed Material &
Autographs; Documents;
Manuscripts

Lion's Head Books
Academy Street
Salisbury, Conn. 06068
(203) 435-9328
Short Name: **Lion's Head**
Books about Books; Gardening
& Horticulture; Natural
History; New Books; Out of
Print, with Stock; First
Editions, Modern

Literary Seal (Mail Only)
1448 Rogwin, SW
North Canton, Ohio 44720
Short Name: **Literary Seal**
Book Scouts; Out of Print, with
Stock; Search Service, with
Stock

Little Hundred Gallery
6028 Bentway Drive
Charlotte, N.C. 28211
Short Name: **Little Hundred**
Maps, Atlases, & Cartography;
Manuscripts; Americana;
Ephemera; Prints; Law

Little Professor Book Center
8 York Ridge Shop Center
Timonium, Md. 21093
Short Name: **Little Prof**
Childrens' Books; Cookery &
Gastronomy; Fiction;
Periodicals; Reference; Science
Fiction

Little Read Book Shop
118 Hayward
Ames, Iowa 50010
(515) 292-7651
Short Name: **Little Read**
American Indians; Humanities;
Literature; Paperbacks (new);
Science Fiction; Women &
Feminism

Littwin & Feiden
124 East Prospect Avenue
Mamaroneck, N.Y. 10543
(914) 698-6504
Short Name: **Littwin & Fel**
Art; Illustrated Books;
Literature

E Llewellyn-Bookseller
4510 State Line
Kansas City, Kan. 66103
(913) 677--118
Short Name: **E Llewellyn**
Childrens' Books; Illustrated
Books; Architecture; Books
about Books; General; Rare
Books

Lobster Lane Bookshop
Spruce Head, Maine 04859
Short Name: **Lobster Lane**
General

Leo Loewenthal
4 North Elk Avenue
Dover, N.J. 07801
(201) 328-7196
Short Name: **L Loewenthal**
Architecture; Art; Cinema &
Mass Media; Dance;
Photography; Poetry

William Loewy Books
25 West Maple Avenue
Monsey, N.Y. 10952
Short Name: **W Loewy**
Judaica & Hebraica;
IlluminatedManuscripts;
Illustrated Books; Broadsides;
Ephemera; Photography

Loft Bookstore
4901 39th Avenue
Minneapolis, Minn. 55417
Short Name: **Loft**
Literature; History; Theology;
Reference; General

Log Cabin Books
Rte #2, Box 281
Harrisonburg, Va. 22801
Short Name: **Log Cabin**
Victorian Literature

London Bookshop
127 Madison Avenue
Albany, N.Y. 12202
Short Name: **London-Alb**
Americana; Local History; First
Editions

London Bookshop
79 West Monroe Street, #1122
Chicago, Ill. 60603
(312) 782-2261
Short Name: **London-Chi**
Fine & Rare Bindings;
Biography; First Editions;
History; Literature; Political,
Social, & Cultural History &
Thought

Judith R Long
P O Box 443
New Albany, Ind. 47150
(812) 944-6672
Short Name: **J R Long**
Indiana

Long's Book Store
905 O' Street, Box 81704
Lincoln, Neb. 68501
Short Name: **Long's-Lin**
Americana; Americana,
Regional; General

Long's Books
711 West Lakeview Avenue
Pensacola, Fla. 32501
Short Name: **Long's-Pen**
First Editions

Longhorn Book Distributors Inc
5002 North Lamar
Austin, Tex. 78751
(512) 454-4197
Short Name: **Longhorn**
Science Fiction; Fantasy;
Cinema & Mass Media;
Paperbacks (new); Comic
Books; Magazines

William D Longo Auctioneers
16 West Natick Road
Warwick, R.I. 02886
(401) 737-8160
Short Name: **Longo Auct**
Auctions & Auctioneers

Looking Glass
5584 Morning Street
Worthington, Ohio 43085
Short Name: **Looking Glass**
*Canada & Canadiana; First
Editions, Modern; Illustrated
Books; Out of Print, with Stock;
Poetry; General*

L S Loomer
P O Box 878
Windsor, N.S. B0N 2T0
Short Name: **L S Loomer**
*Rare Books; Ephemera;
Periodicals; Prints*

Ken Lopez
156 East Hamilton
Englewood, N.J. 07631
Short Name: **K Lopez**
*First Editions, Modern;
Literature; Latin America;
American Indians*

**Natasha & Stephen Halpert
   Lorenz**
46-B Lincoln Avenue
Marblehead, Mass. 01945
(617) 631-8293
Short Name: **Lorenz Books**
*First Editions, Modern;
Americana; General*

James Lorson
305 North Harbor Boulevard,
   #a-9
Fullerton, Calif. 92632
Short Name: **J Lorson**
*Miniature Books; Americana;
Bibliography; Press Books &
Fine Printing; First Editions;
First Editions, Modern*

Derek M H Lowe
254 228th Avenue, NE
Redmond, Wash. 98052
Short Name: **D M H Lowe**
*Fine & Rare Bindings;
Bibliography;
IlluminatedManuscripts;
Literature; Bookbinding &
Restoration; Authors*

James Lowe Autographs, Ltd
667 Madison Avenue
New York, N.Y. 10021
(212) 889-8204
Short Name: **J Lowe**
*Appraisals & Appraisal
Services; Autographed Material
& Autographs; Documents;
Manuscripts; Photography*

**Samuel L Lowe, Jr, Antiques,
   Inc**
80 Charles Street
Boston, Mass. 02114
(617) 742-0845
Short Name: **Lowe Antiques**
*Naval & Marine; Whaling;
Voyages, Travels, &
Exploration; History, American*

Carlton Lowenberg
737 St Mary's Road
Lafayette, Calif. 94549
(415) 284-4988
Short Name: **C Lowenberg**
*Autographed Material &
Autographs; Cookery &
Gastronomy; Literature; Women
& Feminism; Authors*

Richard A Lowenstein
Geymer Drive, R F D #7
Mahopac, N.Y. 10541
(914) 628-3325
Short Name: **R A Lowenstein**
*Mark Twain; World War II
Battlefield Art; First Editions;
First Editions, Modern; Out of
Print, without Stock; Prints*

Philip Lozinski, Scholarly Books
1504 Drift Road
Westport, Mass. 02790
(617) 636-2044
Short Name: **P Lozinski**
*Russia & Eastern European
Region; Orientalia; Reprints;
Out of Print, with Stock*

Ernest Lubbe-Books
280 Golden Gate Avenue
San Francisco, Calif. 94102
(415) 441-5682
Short Name: **E Lubbe**
Western Americana

J & J Lubrano
P O Box 47, Main Street
South Lee, Mass. 01260
(413) 243-2218
Short Name: **J & J Lubrano**
*Music; Dance; Autographed
Material & Autographs;
Performing Arts; Rare Books;
Scholarly Books*

Lubrecht & Cramer
R F D #1, Box 227
Monticello, N.Y. 12701
(914) 794-8539
Short Name: **Lubrecht & Cram**
Botany

Robert F Lucas
P O Box 63
Blandford, Mass. 01008
(413) 848-2061
Short Name: **R F Lucas**
*Americana; Naval & Marine;
Pacific Region; Voyages,
Travels, & Exploration;
Whaling; American Diaries &
Narratives*

Herbert A Luft
69-11 229th Street
Oakland Gardens, N.Y. 11364
Short Name: **H A Luft**
Astronomy; Optics

Phyllis M Lumb
11725 Larry Road
Fairfax, Va. 22030
Short Name: **P M Lumb**
*Search Service, with Stock; Out
of Print, with Stock; Biography;
Natural History; Americana,
Regional; General*

Stephen C Lunsford
P O Box 86773
No. Vancouver, B.C. V7L 4L3
Short Name: **S C Lunsford**
*American Indians; Pacific
Region; Americana; Overland
Narratives; Arctica &
Antarctica; Canada &
Canadiana*

Stephen Lupack
2860 Creston Avenue
Bronx, N.Y. 10468
Short Name: **S Lupack**
*First Editions; First Editions,
Modern; Poetry*

Lust Auction Service
Mount Horeb, Wisc. 53572
Short Name: **Lust Auct**
Auctions & Auctioneers

Talmage N Luther
P O Box 6083
Shawnee Mission, Kan. 66206
Short Name: **T N Luther**
*Western Americana; American
Indians*

Abbot Lutz
1270 Avenue Of The Americas
New York, N.Y. 10020
(212) 582-2232
Short Name: **A Lutz**
*Philately & Philatelic
Literature*

B Lynch Book Finder
8840 Debra Avenue
Sepulveda, Calif. 91343
(213) 892-8491
Short Name: **B Lynch**
*General; Out of Print, with
Stock; Search Service, with
Stock*

Nevin E Lyon
11552 Hartsook Street
North Hollywood, Calif. 91601
Short Name: **N E Lyon**
Dogs

Lyrical Ballad Books
7 Phila Street
Saratoga Springs, N.Y. 12866
(518) 584-8779
Short Name: **Lyrical Ballad**
*Childrens' Books; General;
Dance; Horses; Illustrated
Books; Sporting*

Burton Lysecki-Books
527 Osborne Street
Winnipeg, Man. R3B 2B2
(204) 284-4546
Short Name: **B Lysecki**
*Biography; Canada &
Canadiana; Fiction; General;
Out of Print, with Stock;
Paperbacks (new)*

M

M & M Books
21 Perth Place
East Northport, N.Y. 11731
(516) 368-4858
Short Name: **M & M**
*Childrens' Books; Fiction; First
Editions; First Editions,
Modern; Literature; Out of
Print, without Stock*

M & S Rare Books, Inc
P O Box 311, 45 Colpitts Road
Weston, Mass. 02193
(617) 891-5650
Short Name: **M & S**
*Color Plate Books; First
Editions; Literature; Medicine
& Science; Political, Social, &
Cultural History & Thought;
Rare Books*

**Thomas MacAluso, Rare & Fine
Books**
P O Box 133
Kennett Square, Penna. 19348
(215) 444-1063
Short Name: **T MacAluso**
*Americana; Architecture; Art;
First Editions; General;
Illustrated Books*

**MacDonald's Military
Memorabilia**
Eustis, Maine 04936
Short Name: **MacDonald's Mil**
*Civil War & Confederacy;
Ephemera; Photography*

Ray MacDougall
Rte #1, Box 278, RFD #2
Wells, Maine 04090
Short Name: **R MacDougall**
National Geographic Magazine

**Andrew B W MacEwen,
Bookseller**
Victorian House
Stockton Springs, Maine 04981
Short Name: **A B W MacEwen**
*Americana; Maine; Detective
Fiction; Mystery Fiction*

M A MacIntosh
996 Camino Del Retiro
Santa Barbara, Calif. 93110
Short Name: **M A MacIntosh**
*Middle East; Americana;
History; Iberia; Russia &
Eastern European Region*

Rod & Anne MacKay
P O Box 793
Sussex, N.B. E0E 1P0
Short Name: **R & A MacKay**
*Canada & Canadiana;
Ephemera; Fiction; General;
Prints; Postcards*

R MacKendrick-Books
P O Box 390
Manchester, Conn. 06040
Short Name: **R MacKendrick**
*Psychiatry, Psychology, &
Psychonanalysis*

Isobel MacKenzie, Rare Books
900 Sherbrooke Street, West,
#23
Montreal, Que. H3A 1G3
(514) 843-6200
Short Name: **I MacKenzie**
*Napoleon; Fishing & Angling;
Prints; Color Plate Books;
Maps, Atlases, & Cartography*

Richard A MacKsey
107 St Martins Road
Baltimore, Md. 21218
(301) 235-6237
Short Name: **R A MacKsey**
*Americana; Author Collections;
First Editions; Foreign
Languages; Little Magazines &
Literary Small Presses;
Scholarly Books*

George S MacManus
1317 Irving Street
Philadelphia, Penna. 19107
Short Name: **G S MacManus**
*Americana; Americana,
Regional; Manuscripts; First
Editions; Literature;
Association Books*

William Madden-Books
Carlton Road
Harwinton, Conn. 06791
Short Name: **W Madden**
*Art; Archaeology; Americana;
Hunting, Fishing & Angling;
Natural History; Shakespeare*

Madonna House Bookshop
Combermere, Ont. K0J 1L0
(613) 756-2252
Short Name: **Madonna Hse**
*Americana; Canada &
Canadiana; Religion &
Theology; General; Catholica*

Maelstrom
572 Valencia
San Francisco, Calif. 94110
Short Name: **Maelstrom**
*Fiction; Literature; Art;
Illustrated Books; Out of Print,
with Stock; General*

Maestro
P O Box 848
Bayport, N.Y. 11705
(516) 472-1222
Short Name: **Maestro**
*Violins; Dance; Childrens'
Books; First Editions, Modern;
Paintings; Performing Arts*

Magazine Center
1133 Broadway
New York, N.Y. 10010
Short Name: **Magazine Center**
*Art; Little Magazines &
Literary Small Presses;
Periodicals; Search Service,
with Stock; Specialized
Publications*

The Magazine
839 Larkin Street
San Francisco, Calif. 94109
Short Name: **Magazine**
*Ephemera; Magazines;
Periodicals; Search Service,
with Stock; Pacific Region;
Sporting*

Claire Magee
16840 Elm Lane Drive
Tinley Park, Ill. 60477
Short Name: **C Magee**
*Out of Print, without Stock;
General; Technology; Fiction;
Political, Social, & Cultural
History & Thought; Medicine
& Science*

Magic Mountain Books
8-04 Fox Run Drive
Plainsboro, N.J. 08536
(609) 799-9279
Short Name: **Magic Mtn**
*Search Service, with Stock;
Women & Feminism; First
Editions, Modern; Literature;
Press Books & Fine Printing;
Childrens' Books*

Magnalia Americana
P O Box M
North Amherst, Mass. 01059
Short Name: **Magnalia**
*Americana, Regional; Arctica &
Antarctica; History, American;
Law; Maps, Atlases, &
Cartography; Naval & Marine*

**Geoffrey H Mahfuz-Paper
Cinema**
P O Box 40, Prudential Center
Sta
Boston, Mass. 02199
(617) 267-0012
Short Name: **G H Mahfuz**
*Americana; Cinema & Mass
Media; Ephemera; Fiction;
Paperbacks (new); Performing
Arts*

Marie Mahoney
P O Box 587
Oregon House, Calif. 95962
Short Name: **M Mahoney**
Classics

Thomas D Mahoney
513 Virginia Street
Buffalo, N.Y. 14202
(716) 856-6024
Short Name: **T D Mahoney**
*Americana; Appraisals &
Appraisal Services; Art;
Literature; Prints; Rare Books*

**Maiden Voyage-Gordon
Robotham**
1 Fifth Avenue
New York, N.Y. 10003
(212) 260-5131
Short Name: **Maiden Voy**
*Literature; First Editions,
Modern; Rare Books; Black
Literature & Black Studies*

Main Street Booksellers
P O Box 103
Brooklyn, N.Y. 11210
Short Name: **Main St**
*Biography; Fiction; First
Editions, Modern; Literature;
Out of Print, with Stock*

Anthony Maita
813 Greenwood Road
Glenview, Ill. 60025
(312) 724-6534
Short Name: **A Maita**
*Militaria; Out of Print, with
Stock*

Joseph Majer
307 West 79th Street, #219
New York, N.Y. 10024
(212) 787-6600
Short Name: **J Majer**
*Americana; Color Plate Books;
First Editions; Illustrated
Books; Prints; Voyages, Travels,
& Exploration*

Major's Book Store
221 Hale Street
Charlestown, W.Va. 25301
Short Name: **Major's**
West Virginia

John Makarewich Books
P O Box 7032
Van Nuys, Calif. 91409
Short Name: **J Makarewich**
*Americana; Art; Books about
Books; Illustrated Books;
Literature; Pacific Region*

Jan & Larry Malis
P O Box 211
New Caanan, Conn. 06840
(203) 966-8510
Short Name: **J & L Mallis**
*Americana; Ephemera;
Political, Social, & Cultural
History & Thought; Rare
Books; Voyages, Travels, &
Exploration; Trade Catalogues*

P T Mallahan-Bookseller
307 130th, SE
Bellevue, Wash. 98005
(206) 454-1663
Short Name: **P T Mallahan**
*World Wars; Russia & Eastern
European Region*

G B Manaser, Inc
P O Box 909
Chesterton, Ind. 46304
Short Name: **G B Manasek**
*Astronomy;
IlluminatedManuscripts; Maps,
Atlases, & Cartography;
Medicine & Science;
Manuscripts, Medieval &
Illuminated; Prints*

Jeffrey Mancevice
P O Box 413, West Side Station
Worcester, Mass. 01602
(617) 757-7042
Short Name: **J Mancevice**
*Continental Books; Emblem
Books; Illustrated Books;
Renaissance; STC & Wing
Books*

Mandeville Price Guide
525 Kenmore Station
Kenmore, Wash. 98028
Short Name: **Mandeville**
*Useful Publications for
Bookdealers*

Mandrake Book Store
8 Story Street
Cambridge, Mass. 02138
Short Name: **Mandrake**
*Psychiatry, Psychology, &
Psychonanalysis; Architecture;
Design; Philosophy; Art*

Manning's Fine Books
1255 Post Street, #609
San Francisco, Calif. 94109
Short Name: **Manning's**
*Atlases; Photography;
Illustrated Books; California*

Mansfield Book Mart
2065 Mansfield Street
Montreal, Que. H3A 1Y7
Short Name: **Mansfield**
*Canada & Canadiana; First
Editions; Art; Illustrated Books*

The Manuscript
223 High Street Northeast
Salem, Ore. 97301
Short Name: **Manuscript**
*Americana, Regional;
Appraisals & Appraisal
Services; First Editions; Out of
Print, with Stock; Press Books
& Fine Printing; Search Service,
with Stock*

Maps & Books
88 Pleasant Street
St Johns, N.F. A1E 1L4
(709) 722-3148
Short Name: **Maps & Bks**
*Maps, Atlases, & Cartography;
Prints; Canada & Canadiana;
Arctica & Antarctica; Voyages,
Travels, & Exploration*

John R Mara-Law Books
5628 Richmond Avenue
Dallas, Tex. 75206
(214) 821-1979
Short Name: **J R Mara**
Law

Melvin Marcher
6204 North Vermont
Oklahoma Citgy, Okla. 73112
(405) 946-6270
Short Name: **M Marcher**
*Shooting & Firearms; Hunting,
Fishing & Angling; Natural
History*

Margolis & Moss
Santa Fe, N.Mex. 87501
(505) 982-1028
Short Name: **Marg & Moss**
*Americana; Ephemera; Graphic
Arts; Illustrated Books;
Photography; Prints*

Mariner's Unlimited
1522 West Washington
   Boulevard
Venice, Calif. 90291
(213) 392-5705
Short Name: **Mariner's Unltd**
*Naval & Marine; Periodicals;
Nautica*

Marion Antique Librarian
3668 Shimmons Circle, South
Auburn Heights, Mich. 48057
(313) 373-8414
Short Name: **Marion Antiq**
*First Editions; General; Out of
Print, with Stock; Search
Service, with Stock*

Markey & Asplund
131 Washington Street
Providence, R.I. 02903
(401) 421-9277
Short Name: **Markey & Asp**
Bookbinders Services

Marlil Book Service
5101 South Birch
Tempe, Ariz. 85282
Short Name: **Marlil**
History

Marple Apicultural Library
320 62nd Street
Oakland, Calif. 94618
Short Name: **Marple**
Apiculture

Marsh Farm Publications
14232 Brookhurst Street
Garden Grove, Calif. 92643
Short Name: **Marsh Farm**
*Farming, Ranching, &
Livestock; Education*

Marshall Field & Co
111 North State Street
Chicago, Ill. 60690
(312) 781-3339
Short Name: **Marshall Field**
*First Editions; Fine & Rare
Bindings; Prints; Maps, Atlases,
& Cartography; Autographed
Material & Autographs*

C G Martignette
P O Box 9292
Boston, Mass. 02114
Short Name: **C G Martignette**
*Erotica; American Illustrative
Art; Illustrated Books*

John Wm Martin-Bookseller
436 South 7th Avenue
La Grange, Ill. 60525
(312) 352-8115
Short Name: **J W Martin**
*Books about Books; First
Editions; Literary Criticism;
Literature; Rare Books;
Scholarly Books*

Martin's Bookshop
162 West 4th Street
New York, N.Y. 10014
(212) 243-2886
Short Name: **Martin's**
Art; Poetry; Literary Criticism

Marvelous Books
P O Box 9138
St Louis, Mo. 63117
Short Name: **Marvelous**
*Childrens' Books; Color Plate
Books; Illustrated Books*

Stan Marx
15 Sinclair Martin Drive
Roslyn, N.Y. 11576
(516) 621-8382
Short Name: **S Marx**
*Childrens' Books; First
Editions; General; Out of Print,
with Stock; Search Service, with
Stock*

Jan Mashman
Saunders Lane
Ridgefield, Conn. 06877
Short Name: **J Mashman**
*Neurosciences; Medicine &
Science; Psychiatry, Psychology,
& Psychonanalysis; Calligraphy*

David Mason Books
638 Church Street
Toronto, Ont. M4Y 2G3
(416) 922-1712
Short Name: **D Mason**
*Canada & Canadiana; First
Editions; First Editions,
Modern; Literature; Classics;
History*

Harold J Mason, Inc
25 Van Zant Street
Norwalk, Conn. 06855
(203) 838-6809
Short Name: **H J Mason**
*Economics & Business;
Humanities; Periodicals;
Political, Social, & Cultural
History & Thought; Social
Sciences; Stock Market & Wall
Street*

Mason's Books
264 South Wabash
Wabash, Ind. 46992
Short Name: **Mason's-Wab**
*American Indians; Americana,
Regional; Farming, Ranching,
& Livestock; Militaria; General;
Search Service, with Stock*

Mason's Bookshop
789 Lexington Avenue
New York, N.Y. 10021
Short Name: **Mason's**
*Astrology; Numerology &
Tarot; Parapsychology;
Metaphysics*

F A L Mathewson
283 Yale Avenue
Winnipeg, Man. R3M 0L4
(204) 475-4600
Short Name: **F A L Mathewson**
Canada & Canadiana

Robert W Mattila Bookseller
P O Box 4040, Pioneer Square
  Sta
Seattle, Wash. 98104
(206) 622-9455
Short Name: **R W Mattila**
*Arctica & Antarctica;
Northwest; Chess, Checkers, &
Draughts; Literature; Voyages,
Travels, & Exploration*

Maverick Publications
Drawer 5007
Bend, Ore. 97701
(503) 382-6978
Short Name: **Maverick**
*Americana; New Books;
Geneaologies; First Editions;
Poetry; Science Fiction*

F Mavis
P O Box 211
Bethpage, N.Y. 11714
Short Name: **F Mavis**
*Americana, Regional; Arctica &
Antarctica; History, American;
Pacific Region; Voyages,
Travels, & Exploration*

Timothy Mawson
134 West 92nd Street
New York, N.Y. 10025
(212) 874-6839
Short Name: **T Mawson**
*Out of Print, with Stock; Search
Service, with Stock; Gardening
& Horticulture; Illustrated
Books; Cookery & Gastronomy;
Beverages*

A E Maxted
P O Box 276
Cohasset, Mass. 02025
Short Name: **A E Maxted**
*Out of Print, with Stock;
Scholarly Books*

M M Einhorn Maxwell
80 East 11th Street
New York, N.Y. 10003
(212) 228-6767
Short Name: **M M E Maxwell**
*Beverages; Cinema & Mass
Media; Cookery & Gastronomy;
Shakespeare; Theatre; Puppetry
& Marionettes*

Maxwell Scientific International
Division Of Pergamon Press Inc
Elmsford, N.Y. 10523
Short Name: **Maxwell Sci**
*Mathematics; Science; Physics;
Medical & Medicine;
Economics & Business; Social
Sciences*

Maxwell's Books
914 North Yosemite Street
Stockton, Calif. 95203
Short Name: **Maxwell's**
*Bookbinding & Restoration;
Farming, Ranching, &
Livestock; Fiction; General; Out
of Print, with Stock; Pacific
Region*

Ronald W Mayer
1920 Taraval Street
San Francisco, Calif. 94116
(415) 664-3111
Short Name: **R W Mayer**
*Psychiatry, Psychology, &
Psychonanalysis; Philosophy;
General*

Mayflower Bookshop
23136 North Woodward
Ferndale, Mich. 48220
Short Name: **Mayflower**
*Astrology; Metaphysics; Health;
Philosophy; Numerology &
Tarot*

McBlain Books
P O Box 971
Des Moines, Iowa 50304
Short Name: **McBlain**
*Africa; Black Literature &
Black Studies; South America;
Middle East; Orientalia; Russia
& Eastern European Region*

Bill McBride
157 Sisson Avenue
Hartford, Conn. 06105
Short Name: **B McBride**
*First Editions, Modern; First
Editions; Fiction; Graphic Arts;
Naval & Marine; Periodicals*

Ruth McCarthy
29 Hawthorne Street
Belmont, Mass. 02178
Short Name: **R McCarthy**
Childrens' Books

Boyce E McCaslin
16 Country Club Hills Drive
Ironton, Mo. 63650
Short Name: **B E McCaslin**
*Americana; Americana,
Regional; First Editions;
Inscribed Books; Presidents;
Press Books & Fine Printing*

McClintock Books
P O Box 3111
Warren, Ohio 44485
Short Name: **McClintock**
*First Editions; Detective
Fiction; Science Fiction;
Paperbacks (new); General;
Rare Books*

Thomas L McCook, Jr
2464 Cravey Drive, NE
Atlanta, Ga. 30345
Short Name: **T L McCook**
*Autographed Material &
Autographs; Performing Arts;
Music*

Melvin McCosh, Bookseller
26500 Edgewood Road
Excelsior, Minn. 55331
Short Name: **M McCosh**
*Literature; History, American;
Scholarly Books; Literature in
English Translation; First
Editions; Reference*

William McDonnell
R D #1, Box 4az, Glenwood
    Road
Pine Island, N.Y. 10969
Short Name: **W McDonnell**
*Collection Development; Crafts
& Trades; Medicine & Science;
First Editions, Modern*

McDuffies Books
P O Box 14557
Opportunity, Wash. 99214
Short Name: **McDuffies**
*Medicine & Science;
Technology; Architecture;
Western Americana; Trade
Catalogues; Comic Books*

J Patrick McGahern
783 Bank Street
Ottawa, Ont. K1S 3V5
(613) 233-2215
Short Name: **J P McGahern**
*Arctica & Antarctica; Canada
& Canadiana; First Editions;
Rare Books; Voyages, Travels,
& Exploration; Ireland & The
Irish*

L H McGill-Rare Books
41 Third Street
New City, N.Y. 10956
(914) 634-0729
Short Name: **L H McGill**
*Rare Books; Scholarly Books;
Out of Print, with Stock;
Literature; Graphic Arts;
General*

Laurence McGilvery
P O Box 852
La Jolla, Calif. 92038
Short Name: **L McGilvery**
*Art; Fine Arts; Art Catalogues,
Periodicals, & Books;
Collection Development;
Architecture; Illustrated Books*

J McGovern, Books
516 Washington Boulevard
Oak Park, Ill. 60302
Short Name: **J McGovern**
*Science Fiction; Sporting;
General; Fiction; Search
Service, with Stock*

Stephen McIntyre
201-319 West Pender Street
Vancouver, B.C. V6B 1T4
Short Name: **S McIntyre**
Naval & Marine; Railroads

Harper McKee, Bookseller
224 West 7th Street
St Paul, Minn. 55102
(612) 292-1434
Short Name: **H McKee**
*Childrens' Books; General; Out
of Print, with Stock; Religion &
Theology*

Jean S McKenna-Books
131 Dodge Street, Box 397
Beverly, Mass. 01905
(617) 927-3067
Short Name: **J S McKenna**
*Childrens' Books; Illustrated
Books; Fiction; General; Search
Service, with Stock*

Bruce McKittrick
Philadelphia, Penna. 19130
(215) 235-3209
Short Name: **B McKittrick**
*Renaissance; Incunabula &
Early Printing; Medicine &
Science; Continental Books;
Appraisals & Appraisal
Services; Rare Books*

McLean Books
6631 Old Dominion
Mclean, Va. 22101
(703) 356-1994
Short Name: **McLean**
*General; Search Service, with
Stock; Childrens' Books*

D W McLennan
209 Main Street, East
Grimsby, Ont.
Short Name: **D W McLennan**
*Sir Winston Churchill; Aircraft
& Aerospace History; Yachts,
Yachting, & Sailing*

McMahon Books, Inc
101 Christiana Mall
Newark, Del. 19702
Short Name: **McMahon**
General

Bob McMaster Book Bin
121 West First Avenue
Albany, Ore. 97321
(503) 926-6869
Short Name: **B McMaster**
General

James O McMeans
P O Box 5251
Atlanta, Ga. 30307
Short Name: **J O McMeans**
*Americana; Literature; The
South; Natural History; First
Editions; Search Service, with
Stock*

Harlow McMillen
131 Manor Road
Staten Island, N.Y. 10310
Short Name: **H McMillen**
General

**Mary Noble McQuerry-Orchid
    Books**
5700 Salerno Road, West
Jacksonville, Fla. 32210
Short Name: **M N McQuerry**
*Natural History; Gardening &
Horticulture; Horticulture*

G T McWhorter
1425 St James Court
Louisville, Ken. 40208
(502) 636-5926
Short Name: **G T McWhorter**
Edgar Rice Burroughs

B L Means (Mail Only)
5935 Creola Road
Charlotte, N.C. 28211
(704) 364-0636
Short Name: **B L Means**
*Botany; Geology; Gardening &
Horticulture; Illustrated Books*

Medical Book Service
P O Box 447
Brewer, Maine 04412
Short Name: **Medical**
Medical & Medicine

Medical Manor Books,
8 Fox Pavillion, Box 647
Jenkintown, Penna. 19046
(215) 824-1476
Short Name: **Medical Manor**
Medicine & Science

Susan & Herbert Meller
1435 Broadway
New York, N.Y. 10018
Short Name: **S & H Meller**
Textiles

Memorabilia Americana
1211 Avenue I'
Brooklyn, N.Y. 11230
Short Name: **Memor Amer**
*Autographed Material &
Autographs; Judaica &
Hebraica; Presidents; Civil War
& Confederacy; Women &
Feminism; Black Literature &
Black Studies*

Memorabilia, Ltd
7624 El Camino Real
Carlsbad, Calif. 92008
(714) 436-2321
Short Name: **Memorabilia**
*History, American; Judaica &
Hebraica*

Memorable Books
3317 Piedmont Road, NE
Atlanta, Ga. 30305
(404) 261-0256
Short Name: **Memorable**
*General; Scholarly Books;
Political, Social, & Cultural
History & Thought; Biography;
Social Sciences; Bookbinding &
Restoration*

Memory Aisle Books
207 West Columbia
Battle Creek, Mich. 49015
Short Name: **Memory Aisle**
*Local History; Michigan;
Americana; Western Americana;
Hunting, Fishing & Angling*

**The Memory Box (Sandy
  Freeman)**
519 Jasmine Avenue
Corona Del Mar, Calif. 92625
(714) 644-1053
Short Name: **Memory Box**
*Calligraphy; Childrens' Books;
Ephemera; Graphic Arts;
Illustrated Books; Prints*

Isaac Mendoza Book Co
15 Ann Street
New York, N.Y. 10038
(212) 227-8777
Short Name: **I Mendoza**
*Science Fiction; First Editions,
Modern; Detective Fiction*

Merlin's Bookshop
6543 Pardall Road
Isla Vista, Calif. 93117
Short Name: **Merlin's**
*Science Fiction; Mathematics;
Biography; Computers;
Economics & Business*

Merlin's Closet
355 South Main Street, Lower
Level
Providence, R.I. 02903
(401) 351-9272
Short Name: **Merlin's Closet**
*Out of Print, with Stock; First
Editions; Illustrated Books;
Science Fiction; Childrens'
Books; Literature*

The Mermaid Books & Records
3 School Street
Marblehead, Mass. 01945
(617) 631-5817
Short Name: **Mermaid**
*Voyages, Travels, &
Exploration; First Editions,
Modern; Paperbacks (new);
Detective Fiction; Search
Service, without Stock;
Phonograph Records*

Robert L Merriam
New Hall Road
Conway, Mass. 01341
(413) 369-4052
Short Name: **R L Merriam**
*Books about Books;
Bibliography; Americana;
Antiques; Miniature Books*

Metacomet Book Shop
905 Westminster Street
Providence, R.I. 02903
(401) 331-0932
Short Name: **Metacomet**
General; Childrens' Books

Metaphysical Book Store
721 Chautaqua Avenue
Portsmouth, Va. 23707
(804) 399-6365
Short Name: **Metaphysic-Por**
*Search Service, without Stock;
Out of Print, with Stock; New
Books; Scholarly Books;
Philosophy; Religion &
Theology*

Metaphysical Bookfinders
438-1/2 North Gardner
Los Angeles, Calif. 90036
(213) 653-1471
Short Name: **Metaphsic-L A**
*Metaphysics; Self Help;
Astrology; Search Service, with
Stock*

Fran Metcalf
734 Millard Avenue
Conneaut, Ohio 44030
Short Name: **F Metcalf**
*City & Urban Planning;
Education; Newspapers;
Philosophy; Scholarly Books;
Women & Feminism*

Methodist Book Collectors
1715 East Woodland Street
Nashville, Tenn. 37206
(615) 226-5477
Short Name: **Methodist**
*Books about Books;
Methodism; Graphic Arts; 19th
Century Periodicals*

Mexican Book Service
St Peters, Penna. 19470
Short Name: **Mexbooks**
*Latin America; Search Service,
without Stock; Paperbacks
(new)*

Meyer Boswell-Books
982 Hayes Street
San Francisco, Calif. 94117
(415) 346-1839
Short Name: **Meyer Boswell**
*Law; Rare Books; STC & Wing
Books; Scholarly Books*

Meyerbooks
235 West Main Street, Box 427
Glenwood, Ill. 60425
Short Name: **Meyerbks**
*Magic; Circus & Carnival;
Puppetry & Marionettes;
Games & Pasttimes; Show
Business; Gambling*

Jeff Meyerson
50 First Place
Brooklyn, N.Y. 11231
(212) 596-7739
Short Name: **J Meyerson**
*Detective Fiction; Paperbacks
(new); Out of Print, with Stock;
Search Service, with Stock*

R A Mezoff, Bookseller
1302 Bay Street
Bellingham, Wash. 98225
(206) 671-3358
Short Name: **R A Mezoff**
*Literature; First Editions,
Modern; History; Pacific
Region; Hunting, Fishing &
Angling; Childrens' Books*

Michael's Old Books
3636 North Western
Oklahoma City, Okla. 73118
Short Name: **Michael's**
*General; Paperbacks (new);
Western Americana; Oklahoma
(& Indian Territory); Out of
Print, with Stock; Authors*

J Michaels
101 West Seventh Avenue
Eugene, Ore. 97401
(503) 342-2002
Short Name: **J Michaels**
*Art; First Editions, Modern;
Out of Print, with Stock;
Photography; Search Service,
with Stock; Illustrated Books*

Frank Michelli Books
45 Halsey Street
Newark, N.J. 07102
(201) 623-4289
Short Name: **F Michelli-Nwk**
*Search Service, with Stock;
Poetry; Out of Print, with
Stock; Detective Fiction;
Childrens' Books*

Frank Michelli-Books
P O Box 627
Ogunquit, Maine 03907
(207) 646-3275
Short Name: **F Michelli-Ogu**
*General; Out of Print, with
Stock; Poetry; Search Service,
with Stock; Detective Fiction*

Mickler's Floridiana
P O Box 38
Chuluota, Fla. 32766
(305) 365-3636
Short Name: **Mickler's**
Florida

Midnight Book Company
3929 Ebeneezer Road
Marietta, Ga. 30066
Short Name: **Midnight-Mar**
*Science Fiction; Fantasy; First
Editions; Sets; Art*

Midnight Bookman
237 Schilling
West Lafayette, Ind. 47906
Short Name: **Midnight-West**
*Books about Books; Press
Books & Fine Printing;
Typography & Type Specimens;
Bookplates & Ex Libris;
Papermaking & Marbling;
Bibliography*

Midvale Books
155 SW Midvale Road
Portland, Ore. 97218
(503) 636-7952
Short Name: **Midvale**
*Sporting; New Books; Out of
Print, with Stock; Out of Print,
without Stock; Rare Books;
Search Service, with Stock*

Midway Book Store, Inc
1579 University Avenue
St Paul, Minn. 55104
Short Name: **Midway**
*Childrens' Books; Comic Books;
Out of Print, with Stock;
Illustrated Books; Literature;
Science Fiction*

Mil-Air Photos & Books
P O Box U
Norwalk, Calif. 90654
(213) 863-5028
Short Name: **Mil-Air**
*Aviation & Aeronautics;
Autographed Material &
Autographs; Civil War &
Confederacy; Militaria; Naval
& Marine*

Milestone Autobooks
3435 West Magnolia
Burbank, Calif. 91505
Short Name: **Milestone Auto**
Automotive

Milestone Books Inc
256 Fifth Avenue
New York, N.Y. 10001
(212) 679-6332
Short Name: **Milestone-NYC**
*Illustrated Books; Natural
History; Rare Books*

The Military Bookman Ltd
29 East 93rd Street
New York, N.Y. 10028
(212) 348-1280
Short Name: **Military**
*Militaria; Naval & Marine;
Americana; Civil War &
Confederacy; History; History,
American*

Allan R Milkerit
715 Calmar
Oakland, Calif. 94610
Short Name: **A R Milkerit**
*First Editions, Modern; First
Editions; Fiction*

Miller & Miller
295 Madison Avenue
New York, N.Y. 10017
Short Name: **Miller & Miller**
Humor

C E Miller
736 North Frazier Street
Baldwin Park, Calif. 91706
Short Name: **C E Miller**
*Americana; Documents;
Ephemera; Railroads; Tobacco
& Smoking; Stock Market &
Wall Street*

Ernest C Miller
P O Box 1
Warren, Penna. 16365
(814) 723-8335
Short Name: **E C Miller**
Petroleum

Evangelene Miller
30 South Prospect Street
Norwalk, Ohio 44857
Short Name: **E Miller**
*Americana; Art; Childrens'
Books; Out of Print, with Stock;
Search Service, with Stock;
Search Service, without Stock*

Hugh Miller, Bookseller
216 Crown Street, #506
New Haven, Conn. 06510
(203) 776-7076
Short Name: **H Miller**
*Poetry; Little Magazines &
Literary Small Presses; First
Editions, Modern*

Paul F Miller
4365 Belmar
Vienna, Ohio 44473
Short Name: **P F Miller**
*Periodicals; Horatio Alger;
Frank L. Munsey*

Peter Miller Books
1909 First Avenue
Seattle, Wash. 98101
Short Name: **P Miller**
Architecture; Design

Miller-Fruchart
1655 Jones Street
San Francisco, Calif. 94109
Short Name: **Miller-Fruchart**
Foreign Languages

Miller's Book Company
1355 Spring Street, NW
Atlanta, Ga. 30309
Short Name: **Miller's**
*New Books; Paperbacks (new);
Childrens' Books; Maps,
Atlases, & Cartography*

Million Year Picnic
99 Mt Auburn
Cambridge, Mass. 02138
(617) 492-6763
Short Name: **Million Year**
*Comic Books; Science Fiction;
Paperbacks (new); Bookbinding
& Restoration; First Editions;
Autographed Material &
Autographs*

S Millman
P O Box 23
Brooklyn, N.Y. 11208
Short Name: **S Millman**
*Economics & Business; History;
History, American; Social
Sciences; Industry & Labor;
Stock Market & Wall Street*

Thomas Minckler
111 North 30th, Room 221-222
Billings, Mont. 59101
Short Name: **T Minckler**
Montana; Western Books

George R Minkoff
P O Box 147, R F D #3
Great Barrington, Mass. 01230
(413) 528-4575
Short Name: **G R Minkoff**
*Science Fiction; First Editions,
Modern; Autographed Material
& Autographs; Press Books &
Fine Printing; Illustrated
Books; Drawings*

Harry Minkoff
28 Wildwood Drive
Kings Point, N.Y. 11024
Short Name: **H Minkoff**
Haggadot & Prayer Books

Arthur H Minters
84 University Place
New York, N.Y. 10003
Short Name: **A H Minters**
*Architecture; Art; Ephemera;
Literature; Periodicals;
Photography*

Daniel Miranda
P O Box 145
Brookline, Mass. 02146
Short Name: **D Miranda**
*Avant Garde, Experimental, &
Modern Art; Suffrage;
Childrens' Books; Illustrated
Books; Ephemera; Postcards*

Mitch's Archives
155 Yale Road
Menlo Park, Calif. 91608
Short Name: **Mitch's**
*Ephemera; Autographed
Material & Autographs;
Americana, States; Documents;
Overland Narratives*

Ken Mitchell
760 Ash Street
Winnipeg, Man. R3N 0R6
Short Name: **K Mitchell**
*Comic Books; Paperbacks
(new); Out of Print, with Stock;
Rare Books; Reference;
Specialized Publications*

Mitchell's Book Shop
17 Washington Street
Santa Clara, Calif. 95050
(408) 243-2672
Short Name: **Mitchell's-San**
*Americana, Regional; Farming,
Ranching, & Livestock; Outlaws
& Rangers; Search Service,
with Stock; Western Americana;
California*

Mithras Books
7458 La Jolla Boulevard
La Jolla, Calif. 92037
(714) 459-4343
Short Name: **Mithras**
*Childrens' Books; Color Plate
Books; Illustrated Books;
Detective Fiction*

William Frost Mobley
P O Box 333
Wilbraham, Mass. 01095
(413) 596-9516
Short Name: **W F Mobley**
*Ephemera; Prints; Appraisals &
Appraisal Services; Trade
Cards; Posters; Broadsides*

Moe's Books
2476 Telegraph Avenue
Berkeley, Calif. 94704
(415) 849-2087
Short Name: **Moe's**
*Art; Illustrated Books; Out of
Print, with Stock; Color Plate
Books*

Thomas T Moebs
3095-D Colonial Way
Atlanta, Ga. 30341
(404) 455-1872
Short Name: **T T Moebs**
*Americana; Art; Civil War &
Confederacy; Ephemera; Color
Plate Books; Voyages, Travels,
& Exploration*

**Edward Monarski Antiquarian
  Books**
1050 Wadsworth Street
Syracuse, N.Y. 13208
(315) 455-1716
Short Name: **E Monarski**
*New York; Out of Print, with
Stock; Rare Books*

Willis Monie, Books
R D #1, Box 335
Cooperstown, N.Y. 13326
(607) 547-8363
Short Name: **W Monie**
*Americana; Literature;
Ephemera; Presidents; Religion
& Theology; General*

Monroe Books
809 East Olive
Fresno, Calif. 93728
(209) 441-1282
Short Name: **Monroe**
*Americana; Fiction; Out of
Print, with Stock; Search
Service, with Stock; Rare
Books; First Editions*

Montgomery Bookstore
384 Queen Street, East
Toronto, Ont. M5A 1T1
(416) 363-7648
Short Name: **Montgomery**
*Canada & Canadiana; Crafts &
Trades; Rare Books; General*

Montrose Book Shop
P O Box 66265
Houston, Tex. 77006
(713) 522-1713
Short Name: **Montrose**
*First Editions; Cookery &
Gastronomy; Literature; Rare
Books; Press Books & Fine
Printing; Out of Print, with
Stock*

Elizabeth Moody
P O Box 327
Windham, Conn. 06280
Short Name: **E Moody**
Childrens' Books

Mooers Mail Auction
11910 Lafayette Drive
Wheaton, Md. 20902
(301) 949-4029
Short Name: **Mooers**
*Maps, Atlases, & Cartography;
Civil War & Confederacy;
Newspapers; Americana, States;
Prints; Rare Books*

Dale Moore, Books
960 North Bever
Wooster, Ohio 44691
(216) 264-7313
Short Name: **D Moore**
*Fiction; Reference; Classics;
First Editions, Modern;
History; Poetry*

Earl Moore
P O Box 243
Wynnewood, Penna. 19096
(215) 649-1549
Short Name: **E Moore**
*Americana; Appraisals &
Appraisal Services;
Autographed Material &
Autographs; Naval & Marine;
Railroads; Whaling*

Lee A Moore Sr
730 St John's Avenue
Lima, Ohio 45804
(419) 228-0885
Short Name: **L A Moore, Sr**
*Civil War & Confederacy;
History, American; Search
Service, with Stock; Americana;
Search Service, without Stock*

Ed Moran
P O Box 1231
Rocky Point, N.Y. 11778
Short Name: **E Moran**
*Aviation & Aeronautics; Ships
& The Sea; Rare Books;
Natural History; Sporting;
Transportation*

J C Morel
241 Central Park West
New York, N.Y. 10024
(212) 580-9140
Short Name: **J C Morel**
*First Editions, Modern; Fiction;
Poetry*

Constance Morelle
1282 Broadway
Haverhill, Mass. 01830
(617) 374-7256
Short Name: **C Morelle**
*Biography; Childrens' Books;
Fiction; Out of Print, with
Stock; General; Search Service,
with Stock*

Moriah Antique Judaica
699 Madison Avenue
New York, N.Y. 10021
Short Name: **Moriah**
*Haggadot & Prayer Books;
IlluminatedManuscripts;
Judaica & Hebraica*

Morningside Bookshop
P O Box 1087
Dayton, Ohio 45401
Short Name: **Morningside-Pob**
Civil War & Confederacy

Morningside Bookshop
260 Oak Street
Dayton, Ohio 45410
(513) 461-6736
Short Name: **Morningside-Oak**
*Black Literature & Black
Studies; Civil War &
Confederacy; History,
American; Out of Print, with
Stock*

Morrell's Book Service
50 Broadway
Ocean Grove, N.J. 07756
Short Name: **Morrell's**
*Bibliography; Childrens' Books;
Literary Criticism; Armed
Forces Editions; American
Mercury Magazine; Religion &
Theology*

Edward Morrill & Son, Inc
25 Kingston Street
Boston, Mass. 02111
Short Name: **E Morrill**
Americana; Voyages, Travels, &
Exploration; Militaria; First
Editions; Ephemera; Naval &
Marine

J W Morritt
3 Colgate Street
Warwick, R.I. 02888
Short Name: **J W Morritt**
Joseph C. Lincoln

Bradford Morrow Bookseller
  Ltd
P O Box 4725
Santa Barbara, Calif. 93103
(805) 687-9877
Short Name: **B Morrow**
First Editions, Modern;
Manuscripts; Bibliography;
Books about Books; Press
Books & Fine Printing; Rare
Books

Mosaic Books
1420 St Paul Street
Kelowna, B.C. V1Y 2E6
(604) 763-4418
Short Name: **Mosaic**
General

Mostly Books
222 Main Street
Farmington, Conn. 06032
Short Name: **Mostly-Farm**
Science Fiction; Fantasy; Comic
Books; New Books; Periodicals

Mostly Books
3141 Farnam
Omaha, Neb. 68131
Short Name: **Mostly-Oma**
Americana; Nebraska;
Americana, Regional; First
Editions; Literature; Out of
Print, with Stock

Mostly Books
645 South Oxford Avenue
Los Angeles, Calif. 90005
(213) 388-1989
Short Name: **Mostly-L A**
Christian Science; General

Mother Tongue Books
1227 15th Avenue
San Francisco, Calif. 94122
Short Name: **Mother Tongue**
General; Cookery &
Gastronomy

Howard S Mott, Inc
South Main Street
Sheffield, Mass. 01257
Short Name: **H S Mott**
Americana; Autographed
Material & Autographs;
Childrens' Books; Caribbean;
Literature; Drawings

Mount Falcon Books
926 Ninth Avenue
Greeley, Colo. 80631
(303) 356-9211
Short Name: **Mt Falcon**
Americana, Regional;
Education; Farming, Ranching,
& Livestock; Civil War &
Confederacy; Typography &
Type Specimens

Mountain Travel Inc
1398 Solano Avenue
Albany, Calif. 94706
(415) 527-8100
Short Name: **Mtn Travel**
Mountaineering; Voyages,
Travels, & Exploration; Arctica
& Antarctica; Asia

Barb Mraz
2255 Par Lane
Willoughby Hills, Ohio 44094
Short Name: **B Mraz**
First Editions, Modern; First
Editions; Natural History

Much Loved Books
P O Box 801
Royal Oak, Mich. 48068
(313) 549-2755
Short Name: **Much Loved**
Americana; First Editions;
Illustrated Books; Press Books
& Fine Printing; Bibliography;
Books about Books

A Mueller-Rare Books Maps &
  Prints
P O Box 3005
St Augustine, Fla. 32084
Short Name: **A Mueller**
Rare Books; Prints; Maps,
Atlases, & Cartography

Donald S Mull
1706 Girard Drive
Louisville, Ken. 40222
(502) 426-2947
Short Name: **D S Mull**
Civil War & Confederacy;
Americana, Regional

J B Muns
1162 Shattuck Avenue
Berkeley, Calif. 94707
(415) 525-2420
Short Name: **J B Muns**
Art; Architecture; Photography;
Music

Murray Books
473-477 Main Street
Wilbraham, Mass. 01095
(413) 596-3801
Short Name: **Murray**
Appraisals & Appraisal
Services; Ephemera; General;
Rare Books

Murray's Bookfinding Service
115 State
Springfield, Mass. 01101
Short Name: **Murray's**
Fiction; General; Childrens'
Books; Detective Fiction; Out of
Print, with Stock; Search
Service, with Stock

Museum Gallery Book Shop
363 Pequot Street
Southport, Conn. 06490
(203) 259-7114
Short Name: **Museum Gall**
Paintings (books about); Fine
Arts; Decorative Arts; Graphic
Arts; Architecture; Sculpture

E Musial
53 Idlewood Drive
Tonawanda, N.Y. 14150
Short Name: **E Musial**
Western New York State;
Travel Guides; Thomas
Jefferson

Mystery House
P O Box 4235
Reading, Penna. 19606
Short Name: **Mystery Hse**
Detective Fiction; Mystery
Fiction

Mystery Manor Books
P O Box 135
Huntingdon Valley, Penna.
 19006
(215) 824-1476
Short Name: **Mystery Manor**
*First Editions; Detective
Fiction; Mystery Fiction*

N

N R S Books
1181 Amsterdam Avenue
New York, N.Y. 10027
Short Name: **N R S**
*Sets; Modern Library
(Publishers); Fiction;
Biography; New Books*

Julian J Nadolny
121 Hickory Hill Road
Kensington, Conn. 06037
(203) 225-5353
Short Name: **J J Nadolny**
*Natural History; Geology;
Botany; Zoology; Paleontology;
Gardening & Horticulture*

S & C Najarian
852 Milmar Road
Newtown Square, Penna. 19073
Short Name: **S & C Najarian**
*Americana; Ephemera;
Newspapers*

National Library Publications
P O Box 73
Brooklyn, N.Y. 11234
Short Name: **N'tl Libry**
*Puzzles, Contests, & Games;
Reference*

Nationwide Book Service
150 Manhattan Avenue
Brooklyn, N.Y. 11206
(212) 782-4328
Short Name: **Nationwide**
*Fiction; First Editions, Modern;
Reprints; Out of Print, without
Stock; Rare Books; Americana*

Nautica Booksellers
1579 Dresden Row
Halifax, N.S. B3J 2K4
(902) 429-2741
Short Name: **Nautica**
*Naval & Marine; Arctica &
Antarctica; Voyages, Travels, &
Exploration; Whaling; Search
Service, with Stock; Out of
Print, with Stock*

'neath The Elms
235 Washington Street
Marblehead, Mass. 01945
Short Name: **'neath The Elms**
*Maps, Atlases, & Cartography;
Naval & Marine; Out of Print,
with Stock; Rare Books; Search
Service, with Stock*

Kenneth Nebenzahl, Inc
333 North Michigan Avenue
Chicago, Ill. 60601
(312) 641-2711
Short Name: **K Nebenzahl**
*Americana; Illustrated Books;
Maps, Atlases, & Cartography;
Natural History; Rare Books;
Voyages, Travels, &
Exploration*

Needham Book Finders P O B 469/040
~~2317 Westwood Boulevard~~ L.A.
~~Los Angeles, Calif. 90064~~ 90049
Short Name: **Needham**
*General; Search Service, with
Stock*

Neikrug Gallery
224 East 68th Street
New York, N.Y. 10021
(212) 288-7741
Short Name: **Neikrug**
*Art; Civil War & Confederacy;
Photography*

B Nelson Alaska Books
1633 Beaver Place
Anchorage, Alas. 99504
Short Name: **B Nelson**
Alaska; Arctica & Antarctica

**D R Nelson & Company,
 Booksellers**
P O Box B-954
New Bedford, Mass. 02740
(617) 997-1704
Short Name: **D R Nelson**
*Americana; Childrens' Books;
First Editions; Illustrated
Books; Naval & Marine;
Science Fiction*

W D Nelson, Bookseller
4226 Atlantic Avenue
Long Beach, Calif. 90807
Short Name: **W D Nelson**
*History; Biography; Voyages,
Travels, & Exploration;
Construction, Building
Materials, & Materials Science;
Literature; Search Service, with
Stock*

William Nelson-Books
P O Box 469, Station C
Toronto, Ont. M6J 3P5
Short Name: **W Nelson**
*Canadian Literature; Literary
Criticism; Little Magazines &
Literary Small Presses*

Nemaha Booksellers
Goff, Kan. 66428
(913) 939-2130
Short Name: **Nemaha**
Kansas; Americana, Regional;
Civil War & Confederacy; Out
of Print, with Stock; Outlaws &
Rangers; Search Service, with
Stock

H Nestler (Appt Only)
13 Pennington Avenue
Waldwick, N.J. 07463
(201) 444-7413
Short Name: **H Nestler**
New Jersey; Crafts & Trades;
Technology; Shakers; Trade
Catalogues; Revolutionary War

Susan Netgzorg Halas-Prints
  Pacific
R R #1, Box 276
Wailuku Maui, Haw. 96793
Short Name: **S N Halas**
Pacific Region; Voyages,
Travels, & Exploration;
Graphic Arts; Prints; Maps,
Atlases, & Cartography;
Photography

Maurice F Neville Rare Books
Santa Barbara, Calif. 93101
Short Name: **M F Neville**
First Editions, Modern;
Autographed Material &
Autographs; Inscribed Books

New Albion
P O Box 636
Concord, Mass. 01742
(617) 369-1038
Short Name: **New Albion**
Maps, Atlases, & Cartography

New Canaan Book Shop
59 Elm Street
New Canaan, Conn. 06840
Short Name: **New Canaan**
New Books; Cookery &
Gastronomy; Art; Juveniles

New Englandiana
P O Box 589
Bennington, Vt. 05201
Short Name: **New Engl-Benn**
Americana; Biography;
Geneaologies; History; Religion
& Theology; Social Sciences

New England Press (G Dorset)
45 Tudor City, Prospect Tower
#1903
New York, N.Y. 10017
Short Name: **New Engl-NYC**
Poetry; Literature; Rare Books;
Press Books & Fine Printing

New Jersey Books
167 University Avenue
Newark, N.J. 07102
Short Name: **New Jersey**
Law

New Steamship Consultants
P O Box 508
Fresh Meadows, N.Y. 11365
Short Name: **New Steamship**
Natural History; Voyages,
Travels, & Exploration;
Ephemera; Naval & Marine

New York Bound Bookshop
43 West 54th Street
New York, N.Y. 10019
Short Name: **N Y Bound**
New York Metropolitan Area;
New York; Americana

Newcomb Hall Bookstore
University Of Virginia
Charlottesville, Va. 22901
Short Name: **Newcomb Hall**
Foreign Languages; History,
American; Literary Criticism;
Literature; Poetry; Scholarly
Books

R G Newman, Inc
175 East Delaware Place
Chicago, Ill. 60611
Short Name: **R G Newman**
Appraisals & Appraisal
Services; Americana; Civil War
& Confederacy; History,
American; Manuscripts;
Presidents

Nickelodeon
13826 Ventura
Sherman Oaks, Calif. 91423
Short Name: **Nickelodeon**
Music; Physical Education;
Collecting & Collectibles; Sheet
Music; Games & Pasttimes

Kenneth W Nims Inc
P O Box 184
Winter Haven, Fla. 33880
(813) 294-1772
Short Name: **K W Nims**
Auctions & Auctioneers; Law

Nimue Books & Prints
P O Box 325
Orono, Maine 04473
(207) 947-8016
Short Name: **Nimue**
Americana, Regional;
Architecture; Color Plate
Books; Illustrated Books;
Natural History; Prints

19th Century Photographs
P O Box 211
North Haven, Conn. 06473
Short Name: **19th Cent Photo**
Photography; Surveying &
Surveys

Noah's Ark Book Attic
Stony Point, Rte #2
Greenwood, S.C. 29646
(803) 374-3013
Short Name: **Noahs Ark**
Religion & Theology;
Collection Development

H Noble, Jr
35 West 81st Street, #9a-621
New York, N.Y. 10024
Short Name: **H Noble Jr**
Illustrated Books; Literature;
Autographed Material &
Autographs; Books about
Books; Civil War &
Confederacy; Fiction

John B Nomland Booksellers
404 South Benton Way
Los Angeles, Calif. 90057
(213) 389-9745
Short Name: **J B Nomland**
Mexico; Poetry; Spain & The
Spanish; 20th Century
Literature

Charles A Noon-Bookseller
127 Newcastle Avenue
Portsmouth, N.H. 03801
(603) 436-5886
Short Name: **C A Noon**
First Editions; History,
American; Political, Social, &
Cultural History & Thought;
General; Immigration; Loyalists

Jeremy Norman & Co, Inc
442 Post Street
San Francisco, Calif. 94102
(415) 781-6402
Short Name: **J Norman**
Economics & Business;
Medicine & Science; Natural
History; Press Books & Fine
Printing; Rare Books; Voyages,
Travels, & Exploration

James Normile
6888 Alta Loma Terrace
Los Angeles, Calif. 90068
Short Name: **J Normile**
Primitive & Pre-Columbian;
Pacific Region; Archaeology;
First Editions

John E Norris
P O Box 442
Paoli, Penna. 19301
Short Name: **J E Norris**
Birds & Ornithology; Waterfowl
& Shore Birds; Cock Fighting

North Conway Bookshop
P O Box 898
North Conway, N.H. 03860
Short Name: **No Conway**
New England; General;
Literature

Paul H North, Jr
81 Bullitt Park Place
Columbus, Ohio 43209
(614) 252-1826
Short Name: **P H North, Jr**
History, American; Ohio; First
Editions; Manuscripts;
Paintings

North Shore Books, Ltd
8 Green Street
Huntington, N.Y. 11743
(516) 271-5558
Short Name: **North Shore**
Autographed Material &
Autographs; First Editions,
Modern; Foreign Languages;
Inscribed Books; Performing
Arts; Scholarly Books

Northeast Books
Hubbardton Battlefield Road
Castleton, Vt. 05735
Short Name: **Northeast**
First Editions; Antiques

Northern Lights Book Shop
112 First Avenue, SW
Rochester, Minn. 55901
(507) 282-1246
Short Name: **Northern Lights**
Western Americana; Minnesota;
Ephemera; Rare Books; Search
Service, with Stock; Mississippi
River

William P Northrop
5700 West Olympia Boulevard,
#223
Los Angeles, Calif. 90036
Short Name: **W P Northrop**
U.S. Government Publications;
Newspapers;
Nicola Tesla; Western
Americana; Revolutionary War;
Childrens' Books

Northwest Book Auction
231 Burlington
Clarendon Hills, Ill. 60514
Short Name: **NO'West Auct**
Auctions & Auctioneers

Northwest Books
3814 Lyon Avenue
Oakland, Calif. 94601
(415) 532-5227
Short Name: **NO'West**
Western Americana; Fine Arts

Northwoods Funnies
Main Street, Rte #201, Box 506
Bingham, Maine 04920
(207) 672-4888
Short Name: **N'Woods Funnies**
Pulps; Comic Books; Detective
Fiction; Illustrated Books;
Paperbacks (new); Science
Fiction

Northwoods Search Center
Severance, N.Y. 12782
(518) 532-7985
Short Name: **Northwoods**
Adirondacks; Olympic Games;
Postcards; Revolutionary War

Russell Norton, Old Book &
Photo
P O Box 1070
New Haven, Conn. 06504
(203) 562-7800
Short Name: **R Norton**
Photography

Norumbega Books
P O Box 25246
Houston, Tex. 77005
(713) 667-7601
Short Name: **Norumbega**
Rare Books; First Editions;
Literature; Inscribed Books;
Africa; Law

Nostalgia Books
P O Box 1442
Guelph, Ont. N1H 6N9
(519) 836-0170
Short Name: **Nostalgia**
Canada & Canadiana; Science
Fiction

Sal Noto-Bookscout
21995 McClellan Road
Cupertino, Calif. 95014
Short Name: **S Noto**
Jack London; California; John
Muir; John Steinbeck; Authors

Nouveau
5005 Meadow Oaks Park
Jackson, Miss. 39211
Short Name: **Nouveau**
Autographed Material &
Autographs; First Editions,
Modern; Fiction; Inscribed
Books; Literature; Prints

Novel Experience
778 Marsh Street
San Luis Obispo, Calif. 93401
Short Name: **Novel Exper**
Literature; Out of Print, with
Stock; Search Service, with
Stock

Noyes Art Books
Mill Road
Park Ridge, N.J. 07656
(201) 391-8484
Short Name: **Noyes**
Art

Nugent & Associates, Inc
170 10th Street, North
Naples, Fla. 33940
(813) 262-7562
Short Name: **Nugent & Assoc**
Appraisals & Appraisal
Services; New Books;
Paperbacks (new); Out of Print,
with Stock; First Editions;
Autographed Material &
Autographs

Nutmeg Books
5 Water Street
Torrington, Conn. 06790
(203) 482-8870
Short Name: **Nutmeg**
General; Out of Print, with
Stock; Search Service, with
Stock; Maps, Atlases, &
Cartography; Ephemera

O

F M O'Brien
34 & 36 High Street
Portland, Maine 04101
Short Name: **F M O'Brien**
Americana; Maine; Literature

O'Connell's Yesteryear
828 Orange Street
New Haven, Conn. 06511
(203) 777-3786
Short Name: **O'Conn Y'year**
General

John C O'Connor
54 Norman Place
Tenafly, N.J. 07670
(201) 568-0717
Short Name: **J C O'Connor**
Periodicals

J & J O'Donoghue-Books
1926 Second Avenue, South
Anoka, Minn. 55303
Short Name: **J & J O'Donoghue**
Mystery Fiction; Science
Fiction; Ireland & The Irish

Joseph O'Gara-Bookseller
1311 East 57th Street
Chicago, Ill. 60637
(312) 363-0993
Short Name: **J O'Gara**
History; Religion & Theology;
European History; American
Literature; English Literature

O'Leary's Books
10575 Gravelly Lake
Tacoma, Wash. 98499
(206) 588-2503
Short Name: **O'Leary's**
Comic Books; Cookery &
Gastronomy; Science Fiction

William T O'Malley
55 Linden Drive
Kingston, R.I. 02881
(401) 789-0355
Short Name: **W T O'Malley**
First Editions, Modern; Books
about Books; Press Books &
Fine Printing; Ireland & The
Irish; Bibliography

David L O'Neal
Sharon Road, Box 13, R F D
#1
Peterborough, N.H. 03458
(603) 924-7489
Short Name: **D L O'Neal**
Typography & Type Specimens;
Printing & Printing History;
First Editions; Press Books &
Fine Printing; Rare Books;
Americana

W B O'Neill-Old & Rare Books
11609 Hunters Green Court
Reston, Va. 22091
(703) 860-0782
Short Name: **W B O'Neill**
Greece & Turkey; Voyages,
Travels, & Exploration; Travel
Guides; Middle East; Rare
Books; History

O'Neills Book Shop
R F D #1, Box 74
Warner, N.H. 03278
Short Name: **O'Neills**
Paintings; Prints; Art

June O'Shea
6222 San Vincente
Los Angeles, Calif. 90048
(213) 935-7872
Short Name: **J O'Shea**
Criminology; Psychiatry,
Psychology, & Psychonanalysis

Oak Knoll Books
414 Delaware Street
New Castle, Del. 19720
(302) 328-7232
Short Name: **Oak Knoll**
Books about Books;
Bibliography; Bookbinding &
Restoration; Printing &
Printing History; Typography &
Type Specimens; Press Books &
Fine Printing

S T Oakley, Jr
Rte #2
Woodstock, Conn. 06281
Short Name: **S T Oakley, Jr**
Americana; Biography; Out of
Print, with Stock

Oblong Books & Records
P O Box 495
Millerton, N.Y. 12546
Short Name: **Oblong**
Conservation; General; Women
& Feminism; Paperbacks (new);
Maps, Atlases, & Cartography

The Observatory
P O Box 377
Sitka, Alas. 99835
(907) 747-3033
Short Name: **Observatory**
*Arctica & Antarctica; Rare
Books; Out of Print, with Stock;
Search Service, with Stock;
Voyages, Travels, &
Exploration; Maps, Atlases, &
Cartography*

Obsolescence
24 Chambersburg Street
Gettysburg, Penna. 17325
Short Name: **Obsolescence**
*German Books & Literature;
Church History; Pennsylvania;
Civil War & Confederacy;
Folklore; Out of Print, with
Stock*

Oceanic Primitive Arts
88 East 10th Street
New York, N.Y. 10003
(212) 982-8060
Short Name: **Oceanic Primitive**
*Primitive & Pre-Columbian;
Africa; Pacific Region;
American Indians; Out of Print,
with Stock; Art Catalogues,
Periodicals, & Books*

**Oceanside Books Unltd (Appt
Only)**
2856 St John Road
Oceanside, N.Y. 11572
(516) 764-3378
Short Name: **Oceanside**
*Detective Fiction; Mystery
Fiction; Illustrated Books*

Moll Ockett-Antiques
Rte #26
Bryant Pond, Maine 04219
Short Name: **M Ockett**
*Maine; Maine Authors;
Voyages, Travels, &
Exploration*

October Farm (Barbara Cole)
Rte #2, Box 183-C
Raleigh, N.C. 27610
(919) 772-0482
Short Name: **October Farm**
Horses

The Odd Book
8 Front Street
Wolfville, N.S.
Short Name: **Odd Bk**
Canada & Canadiana; Nautica

Odds & Eads
1127 Prospect
Indianapolis, Ind. 46203
Short Name: **Odds & Eads**
General

The Odyssey
1743 South Union
Alliance, Ohio 44601
(216) 821-9958
Short Name: **Odyssey**
*Mystery Fiction; Science
Fiction; Fantasy*

Isaac J Oelgart
177 Bentley Circle
Goshen, Conn. 06756
Short Name: **I J Oelgart**
*Natural History; Hunting,
Fishing & Angling; Shooting &
Firearms*

Emil Offenbacher
84-50 Austin Terrace
Kew Gardens, N.Y. 11415
Short Name: **E Offenbacher**
*Medicine & Science;
Technology; Rare Books;
Continental Books; Printing &
Printing History; Bibliography*

Ohio Bookhunter
564 East Townview Circle
Mansfield, Ohio 44907
(419) 756-0655
Short Name: **Ohio Bkhntr**
*Americana; First Editions;
American Indians; Western
Americana; Press Books & Fine
Printing; Signed, Limited
Editions*

**Richard E Oinonen Book
Auctions**
P O Box 470
Sunderland, Mass. 01375
(413) 665-3253
Short Name: **Oinonen Auct**
*Auctions & Auctioneers;
Ephemera; Manuscripts; Rare
Books*

Okanagan Bookman
2942 Pandosy Street
Kelowna, B.C. V1Y 2E6
(604) 763-4567
Short Name: **Okanagan**
*Arctica & Antarctica; Canada
& Canadiana; Pacific Region;
Voyages, Travels, &
Exploration*

Okman's Happy Endings
20418 Califa Street
Woodland Hills, Calif. 91367
(213) 346-8934
Short Name: **Okman's**
*Cinema & Mass Media;
Biography; Performing Arts;
First Editions, Modern;
Criminology; Detective Fiction*

Olana Gallery
P O Drawer 9
Brewster, N.Y. 10509
(914) 279-8077
Short Name: **Olana**
*Paintings (books about); Folk
Art; Sculpture*

Elizabeth Olcott
Quincy Road
Rumney, N.H. 03266
(603) 786-3962
Short Name: **E Olcott**
*First Editions, Modern; First
Editions; Cookery &
Gastronomy; Detective Fiction;
Gardening & Horticulture*

Old Block Books
240 West 10th Street
New York, N.Y. 10014
(212) 255-0416
Short Name: **Old Block**
*Illustrated Books; Art;
Childrens' Books*

Old Book Shop
75 Spring Street
Morristown, N.J. 07960
(201) 538-1210
Short Name: **Old Bk Sh-Morr**
*Arctica & Antarctica; New
Jersey; General; Ephemera;
Scholarly Books; Postcards*

Old Book Shop
1104 Sutter Street
San Francisco, Calif. 94109
Short Name: **Old Bk Sh-S F**
*General; California; Prints;
Maps, Atlases, & Cartography*

Old Book Store
2040 Lafayette Road
Portsmouth, N.H. 03801
Short Name: **Old Bk St-Port**
Magazines; Erotica; General

**Old Book And Curiosity
  Company**
5430 Chinmey Rock Road
Houston, Tex. 77081
Short Name: **Old Bk & Cur**
General

Old Book Room
111 Grand Street
Croton-On-Hudson, N.Y. 10520
Short Name: **Old Bk Rm-Cro**
*New York; Hudson River
Valley; Cookery & Gastronomy;
New York Metropolitan Area;
Juveniles*

Old Books
136 Maine Street
Brunswick, Maine 04011
(207) 725-4524
Short Name: **Old Bks-Brun**
*General; Maine; Literature; Out
of Print, with Stock; Women &
Feminism; Basketry*

Old Books & Collectables
103 Central Street
Wellesley, Mass. 02181
Short Name: **Old Bks & Coll**
*Childrens' Books; Natural
History; Illustrated Books;
Medicine & Science; Religion &
Theology; Fiction*

Old Bookshed
5910 California Avenue
Altoona, Penna. 16602
Short Name: **Old Bkshed**
*Natural History; Pennsylvania;
Hunting, Fishing & Angling;
Americana; Physical Education*

Old Bookshelf
2125 39th Street
Galveston, Tex. 77550
(713) 763-8652
Short Name: **Old Bkshelf**
*Texas; Civil War &
Confederacy; American Indians;
Photography*

Old Book Shop
61 York Street, Rte #1
Kennebunk, Maine 04043
Short Name: **Old Bk Sh-Ken**
*Kenneth Roberts; Maine; Maine
Authors; Childrens' Books;
Horatio Alger*

Old Corner Bookshop
237 Walnut
Fort Collins, Colo. 80524
(303) 484-6186
Short Name: **Old Corner**
*Classics; Out of Print, with
Stock; Paperbacks (new);
Science Fiction; Colorado;
Western Americana*

Old Curiosity Shop
619 Packard Avenue
Ann Arbor, Mich. 48104
Short Name: **Old Curiosity**
*Ephemera; Out of Print,
without Stock; Search Service,
without Stock*

Old Delavan Book Co
P O Box 511, 67 East Walworth
Delavan, Wisc. 53115
(414) 728-6988
Short Name: **Old Delavan**
*Out of Print, with Stock; Search
Service, with Stock;
Photography; Art; General;
History*

Old Dragon's Book Den
P O Box 186
Barrington, Ill. 60010
Short Name: **Old Dragon's**
*Dogs; Horses; Sporting;
Hunting, Fishing & Angling*

Old Editions Bookshop
23 Allen Street
Buffalo, N.Y. 14202
(716) 885-6473
Short Name: **Old Edtns**
*General; Chess, Checkers, &
Draughts; Travel; History;
Americana; Religion &
Theology*

Old Favorites Bookshop
250 Adelaide, West
Toronto, Ont. M5H 1X8
(416) 977-2944
Short Name: **Old Favorites**
*Canada & Canadiana; Fiction;
Horses; General; Out of Print,
with Stock; Search Service, with
Stock*

Old Galen's Books
P O Box 3044
West Durham, N.C. 27705
Short Name: **Old Galen's**
*Medicine & Science; Psychiatry,
Psychology, & Psychonanalysis;
Bibliography; Botany*

Old Glory Trading Post
P O Box 1327, Gracie Station
New York, N.Y. 10028
Short Name: **Old Glory**
*Childrens' Books; Illustrated
Books; Art; Fantasy; Science
Fiction*

Old Harbor Books
233 Lincoln Avenue, Box 1827
Sitka, Alas. 99835
(907) 747-8808
Short Name: **Old Harbor**
*Alaska; Arctica & Antarctica;
Voyages, Travels, &
Exploration; Search Service,
without Stock*

Old Hickory Bookshop
Brinklow, Md. 20727
Short Name: **Old Hickory**
Medical & Medicine

Old Louisville Books
426 West Oak Street
Louisville, Ken. 40203
(502) 637-6411
Short Name: **Old Lou Books**
*Americana; Civil War &
Confederacy; General; History,
American; Rare Books;
Voyages, Travels, &
Exploration*

Old Mill Books
P O Box 12353
Charleston, S.C. 29412
(803) 795-7177
Short Name: **Old Mill**
*Appraisals & Appraisal
Services; Asia; Childrens'
Books; Pacific Region; Voyages,
Travels, & Exploration; South
Carolina*

Old Monterey Book Co
Monterey, Calif. 93940
(408) 372-3111
Short Name: **Old Monterey**
*Out of Print, with Stock; Rare
Books; First Editions; Authors;
Americana, States*

Old Mystic Bookshop
58 Main Street
Old Mystic, Conn. 06372
(203) 536-6932
Short Name: **Old Mystic**
*Americana; Canada &
Canadiana; Naval & Marine;
Sporting*

Old New York Book
1069 Juniper Street, NE
Atlanta, Ga. 30309
Short Name: **Old New York**
First Editions

The Old Book Room, Ernest J Kionke
115 Buffalo Street
Gowanda, N.Y. 14070
(607) 532-3714
Short Name: **Old Bk Rm-Gow**
Americana; Appraisals & Appraisal Services; Childrens' Books; Crafts & Trades; Fiction; Criminology

The Old Book Store
210 East Cuyahoga Falls Avenue
Akron, Ohio 44310
(216) 253-5025
Short Name: **Old Bk St-Akr**
Americana; First Editions; Literature; Science Fiction; Comic Books; Ephemera

The Old Print Shop, Inc
150 Lexington Avenue
New York, N.Y. 10016
(212) 683-3950
Short Name: **Old Print Sh**
Maps, Atlases, & Cartography; Prints

Old Oregon Book Store
525 SW Twelfth Avenue
Portland, Ore. 97205
(503) 227-2742
Short Name: **Old Oregon**
Northwest; General; Rare Books; Scholarly Books

Old Print Gallery
1212 31st Street, NW
Washington, D.C. 20007
(202) 965-3777
Short Name: **Old Print Gall**
Prints; Maps, Atlases, & Cartography; Conservation; Appraisals & Appraisal Services; Americana

Old Printed Word
5017 Connecticut Avenue, NW
Washington, D.C. 20008
(202) 363-5809
Short Name: **Old Prntd Word**
Rare Books; Documents; Maps, Atlases, & Cartography; Ephemera; Photography; Prints

Old Quenzel Store
P O Box 326
Port Tobacco, Md. 20677
Short Name: **Old Quenzel**
Maryland; Lincoln & Lincoln Assassination; Civil War & Confederacy

Old South Books
352 Grandview Street
Memphis, Tenn. 38111
(901) 323-6585
Short Name: **Old South**
Medicine & Science

Old Verities Books (Mail Only)
P O Box 222
Olympia Fields, Ill. 60461
(312) 747-2211
Short Name: **Old Verities**
Criminology; General; Literature; Out of Print, with Stock

Olde Tyme Music Scene
915 Main Street
Boonton, N.J. 07005
Short Name: **Old Tyme**
Phonograph Records; Music

Ollies Books
3218 Boxdale Street
Memphis, Tenn. 38118
(901) 363-1996
Short Name: **Ollies**
Astrology; Out of Print, with Stock; Religion & Theology; Search Service, with Stock

Olympia Books
1807 Chestnut Street
Philadelphia, Penna. 19103
Short Name: **Olympia**
Color Plate Books; Illustrated Books

Omega Books
213 Main Street
Northampton, Mass. 01060
Short Name: **Omega**
Illustrated Books; Magazines; Comic Books; Posters

On Paper
5942 Broadway
San Antonio, Tex. 78209
(512) 828-4856
Short Name: **On Paper**
Performing Arts; Latin America; Scholarly Books

Once Read
629 South Front
Mankato, Minn. 56001
Short Name: **Once Read**
Minnesota; American Indians

Open Creel (Mail Order Only)
25 Breton Street
Palmer, Mass. 01069
(413) 283-3960
Short Name: **Open Creel**
Hunting, Fishing & Angling

Opera Box
P O Box 48
Brooklyn, N.Y. 11229
(212) 627-0477
Short Name: **Opera Box**
Opera

Orange Cat Goes To Market
442 Church Street
Garberville, Calif. 95440
(707) 923-9960
Short Name: **Orange Cat**
Architecture; Botany; Childrens' Books; Cookery & Gastronomy; Gardening & Horticulture; Pacific Region

William R Orbello, Duels & Dueling
912 Garraty
San Antonio, Tex. 78209
Short Name: **W R Orbelo**
Militaria

The Organ Literature Foundation
45 Norfolk Street
Braintree, Mass. 02184
(617) 848-1388
Short Name: **Organ Lit**
Musical Instruments

Rena & Merwin L Orner, Book Dealers
39 North Browning Avenue
Tenafly, N.J. 07670
Short Name: **R & M Orner**
Search Service, with Stock; Left Wing; Kennedy Assasinations

Orpheus Books
204 E' Street
Davis, Calif. 95616
Short Name: **Orpheus**
Metaphysics; Science Fiction; Holistic Health & Nutrition

Sidney Orr
P O Box 107, 308 Westwood
  Plaza
Los Angeles, Calif. 90024
Short Name: **S Orr**
*Illustrated Books; Voyages,
Travels, & Exploration;
Reference; Graphic Arts;
Author Collections;
Architecture*

Orsay Books
86-32 Eliot Avenue
Rego Park, N.Y. 11374
Short Name: **Orsay**
*Out of Print, with Stock;
General*

Ed Orth
1436 Killarney
Los Angeles, Calif. 90065
Short Name: **E Orth**
*World's Fairs; Americana;
Architecture; Ephemera*

G R Osgood, Jr
126 Dexter Street
Malden, Mass. 02148
(617) 324-1271
Short Name: **G R Osgood, Jr**
*Americana, States; Book Trade
& Catalogues; Classics;
Reference; General; Political,
Social, & Cultural History &
Thought*

Ostby's Americana
P O Box 89
Bellflower, Calif. 90706
Short Name: **Ostby's**
*Civil War & Confederacy;
Geneaologies; History,
American; Naval & Marine;
Overland Narratives; Pacific
Region*

Other Books
483 Bloor Street, West
Toronto, Ont. M5S 1Y2
(416) 961-5227
Short Name: **Other**
*Calligraphy; Cookery &
Gastronomy; Crafts & Trades;
Dictionaries; Performing Arts*

Hal N Ottaway, Bookseller
P O Box 18282
Wichita, Kan. 67218
Short Name: **H N Ottaway**
*Western Americana; Postcards;
Local History*

Ottenberg Books
717 Pike Street
Seattle, Wash. 98101
(206) 682-5363
Short Name: **Ottenberg Bks**
*First Editions, Modern;
Illustrated Books; Literary
Criticism; Literature;
Mountaineering; Voyages,
Travels, & Exploration*

Simon Ottenberg
P O Box 15509
Seattle, Wash. 98115
(206) 322-5398
Short Name: **S Ottenberg**
*Africa; Out of Print, with
Stock; Art*

Otzinachson Book Shop
Allenwood, Penna. 17810
Short Name: **Otzinachson**
*General; First Editions,
Modern; Pennsylvania*

Orville Oughtred
35992 South Gratiot
Mount Clemens, Mich. 48043
Short Name: **O Oughtred**
Canada & Canadiana

**Our Heritage Collectables &
  Books**
P O Box 42
Malverne, N.Y. 11565
Short Name: **Our Heritage**
*Fiction; First Editions; History;
Maps, Atlases, & Cartography;
Rare Books; Religion &
Theology*

Out Of Print Books
P O Box 6112, Perry Annex
Whittier, Calif. 90609
Short Name: **Out Of Prnt-Whi**
*Press Books & Fine Printing;
Illustrated Books; Color Plate
Books; Books about Books; Out
of Print, without Stock*

Out-Of-Print Book Center
P O Box 229
New York, N.Y. 10276
Short Name: **Out-Of-Prnt-NYC**
*Art; First Editions, Modern;
Literature; History; Science;
Rare Books*

Overstock Book Company
120 Secatogue Avenue
Farmingdale, N.Y. 11735
Short Name: **Overstock**
Scholarly Books

Jack Owen
113 North County Road
Palm Beach, Fla. 33480
(305) 833-3920
Short Name: **J Owen**
*Americana; Biography; Naval &
Marine; Out of Print, with
Stock; Search Service, with
Stock; First Editions*

Maurice E Owen
R F D #2, Bowdoin Center
  Road
Litchfield, Maine 04350
(207) 268-4206
Short Name: **M E Owen**
*Childrens' Books; Fiction;
General*

Vernon Owens Books
1621 Phyllis Avenue
Louisville, Ken. 40215
Short Name: **V Owens**
Kentucky; Authors; Jesse Stuart

**K C Owings, Jr-Antiques
  Americana**
P O Box 19
North Abington, Mass. 02351
(617) 587-6441
Short Name: **K C Owings Jr**
*Americana; Antiques;
Autographed Material &
Autographs; Manuscripts;
Maps, Atlases, & Cartography;
Photography*

Owl Creek Books
309 West Vine Street
Mount Vernon, Ohio 43050
(614) 397-9337
Short Name: **Owl Creek**
*Americana; Authors;
Biography; Childrens' Books;
First Editions; Religion &
Theology*

Owl Pen Books
Rte 2, Box 202
Greenwich, N.Y. 12834
Short Name: **Owl Pen**
*General; Americana; Childrens'
Books; Fiction; Gardening &
Horticulture*

Oxford Book Store
2345 Peachtree Road, NE
Atlanta, Ga. 30305
(404) 262-3332
Short Name: **Oxford**
General; New Books; Literature;
Periodicals; Search Service,
without Stock

Oz And Ends Book Shoppe
14 Dorset Drive
Kenilworth, N.J. 07033
Short Name: **Oz & Ends**
Juveniles; L. Frank Baum &
Oziana

Ozark Books
P O Box 488
Warsaw, Mo. 65355
Short Name: **Ozark**
Americana, States; Americana,
Regional; Out of Print, with
Stock; Search Service, with
Stock; History, American;
Fiction

P

P & H Books
619 North Estelle
Wichita, Kan. 67214
Short Name: **P & H**
First Editions; Harold Bell
Wight; Zane Grey; Authors

P M Book Shop
321 Park Avenue
Plainfield, N.J. 07060
(201) 754-3900
Short Name: **P M**
Art; Biography; Horses;
Hunting, Fishing & Angling

Pacific Book House
1016 Kapahulu, Kilohana
   Square
Honolulu, Haw. 96816
Short Name: **Pacific Bk Hse**
Hawaii; 18th Century
Literature; First Editions;
General; Pacific Region

Pacific Law Books Inc
305 North Main Street
Santa Ana, Calif. 92701
Short Name: **Pacific Law**
Law

Pacific Writers Corporation
P O Box 1042
Honolulu, Haw. 96808
(808) 988-7402
Short Name: **Pacific Writers**
Hawaii; Pacific Region;
Mountaineering; Voyages,
Travels, & Exploration;
Authors; Natural History

Pacificana
P O Box 398
Jamestown, N.C. 27282
(919) 454-4938
Short Name: **Pacificana**
Pacific Region; Voyages,
Travels, & Exploration; Search
Service, with Stock

J Packard
1329 Masonic Avenue
San Francisco, Calif. 94117
(415) 621-4799
Short Name: **J Packard**
Travel Guides

T C Packard
3775 Laurel Canyon
Studio City, Calif. 91604
(213) 766-4000
Short Name: **T C Packard**
American Indians; Americana;
Fiction; Paperbacks (new);
Railroads; Automobiles, Classic

Page One Books
114 Central Avenue
Albany, N.Y. 12206
(518) 434-3860
Short Name: **Page One**
Farming, Ranching, &
Livestock; Natural History;
General; Americana; Civil War
& Confederacy; Periodicals

Page 2
84 Donegani
Pointe Claire, Que. H9R 2V4
(514) 695-2297
Short Name: **Page 2**
General

Pageant Book & Print Shop
109 East 9th Street
New York, N.Y. 10003
(212) 674-5296
Short Name: **Pageant**
First Editions; Prints; Maps,
Atlases, & Cartography;
Literature; Americana; Rare
Books

Pages
R F D #1, Box 198
Bedford, N.Y. 10506
(914) 941-1334
Short Name: **Pages**
Hudson River Valley;
Ephemera; Out of Print, with
Stock; Prints

Alfred W Paine
Wolfpits Road
Bethel, Conn. 06801
Short Name: **A W Paine**
Naval & Marine; Voyages,
Travels, & Exploration; Arctica
& Antarctica; Printing in
Canada; Caribbean; Pacific
Region

Palinurus Rare Books
P O Box 15923
Philadelphia, Penna. 19103
(215) 735-2970
Short Name: **Palinurus**
Medicine & Science

R A Palket
P O Box 629
Aliquippa, Penna. 15001
Short Name: **R A Palket**
Classics; Cookery &
Gastronomy; Incunabula &
Early Printing

Palma Book Service
P O Box 602, 120 West 19th
  Street
Wilmington, Del. 19899
(301) 656-8629
Short Name: **Palma**
Biography; History; Literary
Criticism

Pan Books And Graphics-Copy
  Store
398 Main Street
Catskill, N.Y. 12414
(518) 943-4771
Short Name: **Pan**
Illustrated Books; Photography;
Authors; First Editions

Pan-American Books
P O Box 270
Cazenovia, N.Y. 13035
Short Name: **Pan-Amer**
Latin America

Pangloss Bookshop
1284 Massachusetts Avenue
Cambridge, Mass. 02138
(617) 354-4003
Short Name: **Pangloss**
Scholarly Books; Literature;
History; Social Sciences

Ellie Panos-Yesterdays Books
402 Bedford Street
Whitman, Mass. 02382
(617) 447-2730
Short Name: **E Panos**
Cookery & Gastronomy;
Fiction; Americana; Childrens'
Books; Crafts & Trades;
Illustrated Books

Pansy Patch (June-Sept Only)
59 Carleton Street
St Andrews, N.B. E0G 2X0
Short Name: **Pansy Patch**
Art; Canada & Canadiana;
Childrens' Books; Graphic Arts;
Prints; Illustrated Books

Paper & Ink
44 Beech Avenue
Berkeley Heights, N.J. 07922
Short Name: **Paper & Ink**
New Jersey; Documents;
Postcards; Ephemera; Folklore

Paper Chase Search Service
P O Box 665
Center Moriches, N.Y. 11934
Short Name: **Paper Chase Sch**
Out of Print, with Stock; Search
Service, with Stock

Paper Peddlers
4425 Mayfield Road
South Euclid, Ohio 44121
(216) 561-1242
Short Name: **Paper Peddlers**
Ephemera; Out of Print, with
Stock

Paper Person
P O Box 281
Oxford, N.Y. 13830
Short Name: **Paper Person**
Sheet Music; Broadsides;
American Illustrative Art;
Music

Paperback Exchange
355 East 86th Street
New York, N.Y. 10028
Short Name: **P'back Exch**
Americana, Regional; Antiques;
Autographed Material &
Autographs; Detective Fiction;
Illustrated Books; Paperbacks
(new)

Paperback Jack Bookshop
1063 North Spaulding Avenue
Los Angeles, Calif. 90046
Short Name: **Paperback Jack**
Paperbacks (new); Periodicals;
Comic Books

Paperback Paradise
468 Centre Street
Jamaica Plain, Mass. 02130
(617) 522-5313
Short Name: **P'back Paradise**
Paperbacks (new); General; Out
of Print, with Stock; Search
Service, with Stock; Science
Fiction; Literature

Paperbacks Plus
2307 Abrams Road
Dallas, Tex. 75214
Short Name: **P'backs Plus**
General; New Books

Papermill
P O Box 6556
Santa Rosa, Calif. 95406
(707) 544-3455
Short Name: **Papermill**
Collecting & Collectibles; Art;
Antiques; Out of Print, with
Stock

Paragon Book Gallery
14 East 38th Street
New York, N.Y. 10016
(212) 532-4920
Short Name: **Paragon Gall**
Africa; Asia; Orientalia; Out of
Print, with Stock; Middle East;
Search Service, with Stock

John L Parker
315 North Willow
Prescott, Ariz. 86301
Short Name: **J L Parker**
History; Rare Books;
Economics & Business;
Detective Fiction; Civil War &
Confederacy

Parker's Books
1465 Main Street
Sarasota, Fla. 33577
(813) 366-2898
Short Name: **Parker's**
Americana; Color Plate Books;
Press Books & Fine Printing;
Illustrated Books; Maps,
Atlases, & Cartography; Rare
Books

M R Parks
P O Box 11
Renton, Wash. 98055
Short Name: **M R Parks**
Out of Print, with Stock;
Americana; Biography;
Childrens' Books; Fiction;
Search Service, with Stock

Parnassus Book Service
Rte #6a
Yarmouth Port, Mass. 02675
Short Name: **Parnassus Svce**
Caribbean; Search Service, with
Stock; Naval & Marine;
Antiques; Birds & Ornithology;
Cape Cod & Martha's Vineyard

B Parrington
Star Route Box 132
Staples, Minn. 56479
Short Name: **B Parrington**
Orientalia; Needlework;
Herbology & Herbs;
Automotive; Crafts & Trades;
Art

Eleanor Pasotti Books
5939 Evanston Avenue
Indianapolis, Ind. 46220
(317) 255-2079
Short Name: **E Pasoti**
Out of Print, with Stock; Search
Service, with Stock

Passaic Book Center
594 Main Street
Passaic, N.J. 07055
Short Name: **Passaic**
Science Fiction; Comic Books;
General; Mystery Fiction

Past History
136 Parkview Terrace
Lincroft, N.J. 07738
Short Name: **Past History**
Americana; New Jersey

Opal Patterson
P O Box 1382
Cocoa, Fla. 32922
Short Name: **O Patterson**
Autographed Material &
Autographs; Dictionaries;
Documents; Paperbacks (new);
Reference; Search Service,
without Stock

Paul's Books
6691 Delmar Boulevard
University City, Mo. 63130
Short Name: **Paul's**
Childrens' Books; Judaica &
Hebraica; Science Fiction

Robert A Paulson
37 West Street
Englewood, N.J. 07631
(201) 871-1552
Short Name: **R A Paulson**
Adirondacks; Industry & Labor;
Literary Criticism; General

N & N Pavlov
37 Oakdale Drive
Dobbs Ferry, N.Y. 10522
(914) 693-1776
Short Name: **N & N Pavlov**
Prints; Maps, Atlases, &
Cartography; Color Plate
Books; Hudson River Valley;
Typography & Type Specimens;
Rare Books

Nathaniel Mason Pawlett,
   Antiquary
Box O, University Station
Charlottesville, Va. 22903
Short Name: **N M Pawlett**
Americana; Architecture;
Biography; Geneaologies;
History; Technology

Felix Paws
2 Stonecrop Road
Norwalk, Conn. 06851
Short Name: **F Paws**
Childrens' Books

Crystal Payton Antiques
P O Box 1666
Sedalia, Mo. 65301
Short Name: **C Payton**
Missouri; Arkansas; Oklahoma
(& Indian Territory); Ozarks

Peacock Papers
P O Box 533
Fairview, N.J. 07022
Short Name: **Peacock**
Childrens' Books; Illustrated
Books

J E Pearson Bookseller
P O Box 446
Chicago, Ill. 60690
(312) 523-8713
Short Name: **J E Pearson**
Railroads; Militaria

Peggatty Books Inc
609 Maple Street
Clarkston, Wash. 99403
(509) 758-9517
Short Name: **Peggatty**
New Books; Out of Print, with
Stock; Paperbacks (new); Rare
Books; Search Service, with
Stock

Pel's Books
2411 North Federal Highway
Delray Beach, Fla. 33444
(305) 272-1210
Short Name: **Pel's**
Paperbacks (new)

Pendleton Publications
5093 Paradise Drive
Tiburon, Calif. 94920
(415) 435-3325
Short Name: **Pendleton Publ**
Juveniles; Zane Grey;
Childrens' Books; Aviation &
Aeronautics

Pendragon Books
P O Box 265, Canal Street
   Station
New York, N.Y. 10013
(212) 362-8593
Short Name: **Pendragon**
Americana; Autographed
Material & Autographs; Books
about Books; Civil War &
Confederacy; Sporting; Fine &
Rare Bindings

Peninsula Antiquarian Books
506-1/2 West Balboa
Balboa, Calif. 92661
(714) 675-1990
Short Name: **Peninsula Antiq**
Fine & Rare Bindings;
Childrens' Books; Color Plate
Books; General; Naval &
Marine; Out of Print, with
Stock

Peninsula Booksearch
P O Box 1305
Burlingame, Calif. 94010
Short Name: **Peninsula Bksch**
Search Service, without Stock;
Out of Print, without Stock

S Penner
255-15 Walden Place
Great Neck, N.Y. 11020
Short Name: **S Penner**
First Editions, Modern; Press
Books & Fine Printing; Art;
Illustrated Books; Literature

Pennyroyal Books
2538 Cox Mill Road
Hopkinsville, Ken. 42240
Short Name: **Pennyroyal**
Kentucky; Geology; Agriculture;
Railroads; Ephemera

The People's Bookshop
117 Broad Street, Bunyan
   Village
Flemington, N.J. 08822
Short Name: **People's**
*Illustrated Books; General; Art;
Fiction; Nostalgic Fiction*

Robert Perata-Books
3170 Robinson Drive
Oakland, Calif. 94602
(415) 482-0101
Short Name: **R Perata**
*Illustrated Books; Press Books
& Fine Printing; Fine & Rare
Bindings*

Perception Plus
P O Box 283
Arlington, Mass. 02174
Short Name: **Perception Plus**
*Art; Cinema & Mass Media;
Out of Print, with Stock; Search
Service, with Stock; Performing
Arts; Photography*

Performing Arts Books
90 East 10th Street
New York, N.Y. 10003
(212) 982-9440
Short Name: **Performing Arts**
*Appraisals & Appraisal
Services; Cinema & Mass
Media; Ephemera; Out of Print,
with Stock; Performing Arts;
Rare Books*

Peri Lithon Books
5372 Van Nuys Court, Box
   9996
San Diego, Calif. 92109
(714) 488-6904
Short Name: **Peri Lithon**
*Appraisals & Appraisal
Services; Geology; Mining &
Metallurgy; Jewelry*

Dick Perier
704 NW 76th Street
Vancouver, Wash. 98665
(206) 696-2033
Short Name: **D Perier**
*American Indians; Americana,
Regional; Farming, Ranching,
& Livestock; Cookery &
Gastronomy; General;
Northwest*

Periodica Ludwig
3801 East Kleindale Road
Tucson, Ariz. 85716
Short Name: **Period Ludw**
*Periodicals; Archaeology; Art;
Humanities; Out of Print, with
Stock; Prints*

R F Perotti
P O Box 589
State College, Penna. 16801
Short Name: **R F Perotti**
*First Editions; Rare Books;
Americana; Literature;
Bibliography*

Perry's Antiques & Books
1863 West San Carlos
San Jose, Calif. 95128
(408) 286-0426
Short Name: **Perry's Antiq**
*Edgar Rice Burroughs; Jack
London; Childrens' Books;
Biography; Americana*

Perryman-Books
P O Box 333
Temple, Ga. 30179
(404) 562-3084
Short Name: **Perryman**
*Out of Print, without Stock;
Search Service, without Stock;
Collection Development*

Personal Bookshop
18523 Sherman Way
Reseda, Calif. 91335
Short Name: **Personal**
General

Peterson Book Co
P O Box 966
Davenport, Iowa 52805
Short Name: **Peterson Bk Co**
*Natural History; Botany;
Conservation; Hunting, Fishing
& Angling; Search Service, with
Stock*

Diane Peterson-Booklady
P O Box 2544
Atherton, Calif. 94025
(415) 324-1201
Short Name: **D Peterson**
*John Steinbeck; John Muir;
First Editions; Science Fiction;
Miniature Books; Pacific
Region*

Petrilla/Kane
P O Box 65
Doylestown, Penna. 18901
(215) 766-0233
Short Name: **Petrilla/Kane**
Auctions & Auctioneers

Gerald Pettinger Arms Books
Rte #2
Russell, Iowa 50238
(515) 535-2239
Short Name: **G Pettinger**
*Africa; Conservation; Hunting,
Fishing & Angling; Shooting &
Firearms; Sporting; Voyages,
Travels, & Exploration*

**Pettler & Lieberman,
   Booksellers**
8119 Melrose Avenue
Los Angeles, Calif. 90046
(213) 651-1568
Short Name: **Pett & Lieber**
*First Editions, Modern;
Detective Fiction; Cinema &
Mass Media; Fiction;
Literature; Poetry*

Joe Petty-Books
1704 Park
Victoria, Tex. 77907
(512) 573-3320
Short Name: **J Petty**
*West Virginia; Books about
Books; 20th Century Literature*

Donald V Pfeifer
Rte #49, Stoneledge
Pittsfield, Mass. 01201
Short Name: **D V Pfeifer**
*Search Service, with Stock; Out
of Print, with Stock; General*

Elsie Phalen
4510 North Troy
Chicago, Ill. 60625
Short Name: **E Phalen**
*First Editions; Childrens'
Books; Americana*

Pharos Books
282 York Street, Box 17
New Haven, Conn. 06511
Short Name: **Pharos**
*Appraisals & Appraisal
Services; Childrens' Books;
First Editions, Modern;
Photography; Poetry; Foreign
Languages*

Ted Phelps Books
230 Brewer
Winter Park, Fla. 32789
Short Name: **T Phelps**
Detective Fiction; Foreign
Affairs; History, American;
Political Science & Theory;
Political, Social, & Cultural
History & Thought

Albert J Phiebig, Inc
P O Box 352
White Plains, N.Y. 10602
(914) 948-2951
Short Name: **A J Phiebig**
Collection Development; Search
Service, with Stock; Foreign
Languages; Continental Books;
Orientalia; Periodicals

Philatelic Bibliopole
P O Box 21397
Louisville, Ken. 40221
(502) 451-0317
Short Name: **Philatelic**
Philately & Philatelic
Literature

Phillips Auctioneers-Book Dept
525 East 72nd Street, Attn M
  Rutter
New York, N.Y. 10021
(212) 570-4851
Short Name: **Phillips**
Auctions & Auctioneers

Philosophical Book Service, Ltd
P O Box 1181
Grand Rapids, Mich. 49501
(616) 949-7307
Short Name: **Philos Bk Ser**
Philosophy; Religion &
Theology; Astrology;
Psychiatry, Psychology, &
Psychonanalysis; Manuscripts,
Medieval & Illuminated

Philosophical Library
200 West 57th Street
New York, N.Y. 10019
Short Name: **Philosophical**
Philosophy; Religion &
Theology; Psychiatry,
Psychology, & Psychonanalysis;
Literature; History; Social
Sciences

Arlen Philpott
39 Merwin Avenue
Fairfax, Calif. 94930
Short Name: **A Philpott**
American Indians; Americana,
Regional; Natural History;
Press Books & Fine Printing;
Poetry

Phoenix Book Shop
22 Jones Street
New York, N.Y. 10014
Short Name: **Phoenix**
First Editions, Modern; Poetry;
Periodicals

A Photographer's Place
71 Greene Street
New York, N.Y. 10012
(212) 431-9358
Short Name: **Photog's Place**
Photography

Pier Books Inc
P O Box 5
Piermont, N.Y. 10968
(914) 359-4993
Short Name: **Pier**
Naval & Marine; Hobbies

Wayne Pierce
Rte #1, Box 240-C
Oroville, Calif. 95965
(916) 533-2131
Short Name: **W Pierce**
Childrens' Books; Fiction; Out
of Print, with Stock; Search
Service, with Stock; Western
Books; Sporting

Bronson A Pinchot
56 Hobart Street
New Haven, Conn. 06511
Short Name: **B A Pinchot**
Childrens' Books; L. Frank
Baum & Oziana

Ben E Pingenot
P O Box 848
Eagle Pass, Tex. 78852
Short Name: **B E Pingenot**
Southwestern America; Texas;
War; Militaria; Railroads;
Cattle & Range Industry

Wm & Lois Pinkney
240 North Granby Road
Granby, Conn. 06035
(203) 653-7710
Short Name: **W & L Pinkney**
New York; Western Americana;
Ephemera; First Editions,
Modern; Arctica & Antarctica;
Canada & Canadiana

Pinocchio's Books & Toys
124 High Street
Morgantown, W.Va. 26505
(304) 296-2332
Short Name: **Pinocchio's**
Childrens' Books; Search
Service, without Stock

Lana Pipes
1511 28th Street, NW
Washington, D.C. 20007
Short Name: **L Pipes**
Science Fiction; Detective
Fiction; Illustrated Books; First
Editions, Modern

James S Pipkin, Old & Rare
  Books
2324-A Rosewood Drive
Rock Hill, S.C. 29730
(803) 366-3839
Short Name: **J S Pipkin**
South Carolina; Ephemera;
Childrens' Books; Detective
Fiction; Comic Books

Phillip J Pirages Rare Books
315 North Prospect
Kalamazoo, Mich. 49007
(616) 345-7220
Short Name: **P J Pirages**
Rare Books; Press Books &
Fine Printing; Manuscripts;
Literature; Appraisals &
Appraisal Services

Pisces & Capricorn
514 Linden Avenue
Albion, Mich. 49224
(517) 629-3267
Short Name: **Pisces & Cap**
Hunting, Fishing & Angling;
Criminology; Law; Sporting

Judith Pitchforth
21 School Street, Box 155
Berwick, Maine 03901
(207) 698-1579
Short Name: **J Pitchforth**
Book Scouts; General

Plandome Book Auctions
113 Glen Head Road
Glen Head, N.Y. 11545
(516) 671-3209
Short Name: **Plandome**
Auctions & Auctioneers

The Plane Tree
2 Frederick Douglass Court, NE
Washington, D.C. 20002
Short Name: **Plane Tree**
*Fine & Rare Bindings;
Bookbinding & Restoration;
Horses; Middle East;
Orientalia; Typography & Type
Specimens*

Bud Plant, Inc
P O Box 1886
Grass Valley, Calif. 95945
(916) 273-9588
Short Name: **B Plant**
*Art; Cinema & Mass Media;
Comic Books; Illustrated
Books; Periodicals; Science
Fiction*

Pogonia Press
8 Sidney Place
Brooklyn, N.Y. 11201
Short Name: **Pogonia**
*19th Century Literature; 19th
Century Periodicals; Publishing
History*

John L Polley
3441 Walnut Avenue, SW
Seattle, Wash. 98116
Short Name: **J L Polley**
*Detective Fiction; Fiction; First
Editions; Literature; Women &
Feminism*

Jim Pollock
P O Box 11152
Palo Alto, Calif. 94306
Short Name: **J Pollock**
*Art; Photography; Voyages,
Travels, & Exploration; Erotica*

Pomander Book Shop
252 West 95th Street
New York, N.Y. 10025
Short Name: **Pomander**
*Art; Philosophy; Religion &
Theology; History; Biography;
Literature*

Pomona Book Exchange
Rockton, Ont. L0R 1X0
Short Name: **Pomona Exch**
*Botany; Farming, Ranching, &
Livestock; Gardening &
Horticulture; Natural History;
Out of Print, with Stock*

Poor Farm
P O Box 93
West Cornwall, Conn. 06796
(203) 672-6567
Short Name: **Poor Farm**
*Americana, Regional; Books
about Books; Childrens' Books;
Illustrated Books; Women &
Feminism; Press Books & Fine
Printing*

H J Popinski
4225 East
Berwyn, Ill. 60402
Short Name: **H J Popinski**
*Ephemera; Militaria; Out of
Print, with Stock; Paperbacks
(new); Rare Books; Search
Service, with Stock*

Bonita Porter-Books & Prints
2011 West Bethany Home Road
Phoenix, Ariz. 85015
(602) 242-9442
Short Name: **B Porter**
*Americana, Regional; First
Editions; Out of Print, with
Stock; Prints; Cowboy and
Western Art & Artists*

Nicholas Potter
203 East Palace Avenue
Santa Fe, N.Mex. 87501
Short Name: **N Potter**
*General; Southwestern America;
Photography; First Editions,
Modern; Music*

Evanell K Powell Books
P O Box 13623
Tampa, Fla. 33611
(813) 839-7350
Short Name: **E K Powell**
*Americana, Regional; Authors;
Florida*

Stephen Powell
P O Box 871
Torrington, Conn. 06790
Short Name: **S Powell**
Gambling

Eugene B Power
2929 Pymouth Road
Ann Arbor, Mich. 48105
Short Name: **E B Power**
*Voyages, Travels, &
Exploration*

Charles T Powner
P O Box 796
Chicago, Ill. 60690
Short Name: **C T Powner**
Freemasonry

Ken Prag
P O Box 531
Burlingame, Calif. 94010
(415) 343-0242
Short Name: **K Prag**
*Documents; Ephemera;
Railroads; Stock Market &
Wall Street*

Prairie Archives
641 West Monroe
Springfield, Ill. 62704
Short Name: **Prairie Archive**
*Lincoln & Lincoln
Assassination; Illinois; Civil
War & Confederacy; Ephemera;
Out of Print, with Stock; Search
Service, with Stock*

Daphne J Preece
530 Edgewood Road
Kensington, Conn. 06037
Short Name: **D J Preece**
*Out of Print, with Stock;
Women & Feminism*

Richard L Press
1228 N' Stret, #2 The Thayer
Sacramento, Calif. 95814
(916) 447-3413
Short Name: **R L Press**
*General; Fine Arts; Performing
Arts; Decorative Arts; Middle
East; Africa*

Princeton Antiques
2917-17 Atlantic
Atlantic City, N.J. 08401
Short Name: **Princeton Antiq**
*Antiques; Calligraphy; Out of
Print, with Stock; Outlaws &
Rangers; Scholarly Books;
Search Service, with Stock*

The Print Portfolio (Appt Only)
Glen Echo, Md. 20768
Short Name: **Print Portfolio**
Prints

Printer's Devil Bookshop
1660 Meriden Waterbery Road
Milldale, Conn. 06467
Short Name: **Print Dev-Mil**
*Paperbacks (new); Science
Fiction; Out of Print, without
Stock; Psychiatry, Psychology,
& Psychonanalysis; Philosophy*

The Printer's Devil
1 Claremont Court
Arlington, Mass. 02174
(617) 646-6762
Short Name: **Print Dev-Arl**
*Medicine & Science; Hunting,
Fishing & Angling; Ephemera;
Book Trade & Catalogues*

The Printery
46 Fieldstone Lane
Coventry, Conn. 06238
Short Name: **Printery**
*Graphic Arts; Catalogues
Raisonnes; Prints*

Donald F Proctor
1010 St Georges Road
Baltimore, Md. 21210
Short Name: **D F Proctor**
*American Indians; Detective
Fiction; Drawings; Illustrated
Books; Photography; Women &
Feminism*

Prospector
2529 West Main Street
Littleton, Colo. 80120
(303) 798-5552
Short Name: **Prospector**
*Americana, Regional; Hunting,
Fishing & Angling; Geology;
Naval & Marine; Railroads;
Natural History*

A & A Prosser, Booksellers
3118 North Keating Avenue
Chicago, Ill. 60641
(312) 685-7680
Short Name: **A & A Prosser**
*Author Collections; Religion &
Theology; Out of Print, with
Stock; First Editions, Modern;
Literature; Fiction*

Purple Bookcase
Woodmere Mall
Crossville, Tenn. 38555
(615) 484-2220
Short Name: **Purple Bkcase**
*Americana, Regional;
Geneaologies; General; History,
American*

Purple Mountain Press Limited
Main Street
Fleischmanns, N.Y. 12430
(914) 254-4062
Short Name: **Purple Mtn**
Hudson River Valley

Q

Quadrant Book Mart
20 North 3rd Street
Easton, Penna. 18042
(215) 252-1188
Short Name: **Quadrant**
*Biography; Fiction; Out of
Print, with Stock*

The Question Mark
420 Madison Avenue
Albany, N.Y. 12210
(518) 465-8135
Short Name: **Question Mark**
*Appraisals & Appraisal
Services; Americana; Cookery
& Gastronomy; Gardening &
Horticulture; Medicine &
Science; Rare Books*

Quill & Brush
7649 Old Georgetown Road
Bethesda, Md. 20014
Short Name: **Quill & Brush**
*First Editions, Modern; Rare
Books; Inscribed Books; Fiction;
Prints; Search Service, with
Stock*

Ingeborg Quitzau
P O Box 5160
Edmeston, N.Y. 13335
Short Name: **I Quitzau**
*Press Books & Fine Printing;
Search Service, with Stock;
Childrens' Books; General;
German Books & Literature;
Books about Books*

Quizzicum Bookstore
6860 Lee Highway
Arlington, Va. 22213
Short Name: **Quizzicum**
General

R

R And R Company
1309 Seventh Street
New Orleans, La. 70115
Short Name: **R & R**
Cookery & Gastronomy;
History; History, American;
Political, Social, & Cultural
History & Thought; Presidents;
Scholarly Books

Radio City Book Store
324 West 47th Street
New York, N.Y. 10036
(212) 245-5754
Short Name: **Radio City**
Cookery & Gastronomy; Hotels

Radiographics
P O Box 18492
Cleveland, Ohio 44118
Short Name: **Radiographics**
Technology; Computers;
Wireless Communication
History

Raintree Books
Eustis, Fla. 32726
(904) 357-7145
Short Name: **Raintree**
Americana; Cookery &
Gastronomy; Gardening &
Horticulture; Paperbacks (new);
Overland Narratives

Kathleen Rais
612 North Dunn
Bloomington, Ind. 47401
(812) 336-7687
Short Name: **K Rais**
Dogs; Fiction; First Editions;
Sporting; Authors

Ralston Popular Fiction
P O Box 4174
Fullerton, Calif. 92634
(714) 990-0432
Short Name: **Ralston**
Detective Fiction; Fiction;
Science Fiction; First Editions,
Modern; Childrens' Books;
Western Americana

Richard C Ramer
225 East 70th Street
New York, N.Y. 10021
(212) 737-0222
Short Name: **R C Ramer**
Brazil; Spain & The Spanish;
Central America; Latin
America; South America;
Voyages, Travels, &
Exploration

Rancho Books
P O Box 2040
Santa Monica, Calif. 90406
(213) 396-9567
Short Name: **Rancho**
Western Americana; History,
American; Voyages, Travels, &
Exploration; Overland
Narratives; Press Books & Fine
Printing; Printing & Printing
History

Randall House
185 Post Street
San Francisco, Calif. 94108
Short Name: **Randall Hse**
Americana; Collection
Development; Fiction; Press
Books & Fine Printing; Rare
Books; Voyages, Travels, &
Exploration

Kevin T Ransom, Bookseller
P O Box 2607
Amherst, N.Y. 14226
(716) 839-1510
Short Name: **K T Ransom**
First Editions, Modern;
Autographed Material &
Autographs; Literary Criticism;
Press Books & Fine Printing;
Detective Fiction; Childrens'
Books

Rare Book Company
P O Box 957
Freehold, N.J. 07728
(201) 780-1393
Short Name: **Rare Bk Co**
Autographed Material &
Autographs; First Editions;
Inscribed Books; Religion &
Theology; Christian Science

John C Rather
P O Box 273
Kensington, Md. 20795
Short Name: **J C Rather**
Chess, Checkers, & Draughts;
Photography; Mountaineering

G J Rausch
5853 County Trunk K P
Mazomanie, Wisc. 53560
Short Name: **G J Rausch**
Biography; Detective Fiction;
History; Out of Print, with
Stock

Raven Bookshop
40 West Broad Street
Pawcatuck, Conn. 06379
(203) 599-3535
Short Name: **Raven**
Out of Print, with Stock;
Americana; Civil War &
Confederacy; Poetry; Science
Fiction; Voyages, Travels, &
Exploration

Ravenstree Company
Rte #1, Box 28
Wellton, Ariz. 85356
Short Name: **Ravenstree**
Americana; Bibliography;
Classics; Rare Books; Religion
& Theology; STC & Wing
Books

Ravine Cottage Books
Durand Road
Randolph, N.H. 03570
(603) 466-5149
Short Name: **Ravine Cottage**
Ephemera; Manuscripts; Fine &
Rare Bindings; Woodcut Books

Jack Ray
12706 East Farnell
Baldwin Park, Calif. 91706
Short Name: **J Ray**
Automotive

Raymer's Old Book Store
920 Third Avenue
Seattle, Wash. 98104
Short Name: **Raymer's**
Metaphysics; History;
Biography; Fiction

Lewis L Razek
Rte #2, Box 213
Suttons Bay, Mich. 49682
Short Name: **L L Razek**
Hunting, Fishing & Angling;
Dogs; Sporting; Trade
Catalogues; Derrydale Press

Readables Books
P O Box 58
Wiarton, Ont. N0H 2T0
Short Name: **Readables**
Childrens' Books; Canada &
Canadiana

Readmore Books
843 Diversey Drive
Crestwood, Mo. 63126
Short Name: **Readmore**
Childrens' Books; Fiction; Out
of Print, with Stock;
Paperbacks (new); Search
Service, with Stock

Red Bank Book Store
6 Linden Place
Red Bank, N.J. 07701
Short Name: **Red Bank**
New Books; Search Service,
with Stock; Paperbacks (new)

Red Bridge Books
2523 Red Bridge Terrace
Kansas City, Mo. 64131
Short Name: **Red Bridge**
History, American; European
History; Psychiatry,
Psychology, & Psychonanalysis;
Series Books for Boys & Girls;
Economics & Business; General

Red River Books
P O Box 3606
Shreveport, La. 71103
Short Name: **Red River**
Petroleum; Texas; Louisiana;
Oklahoma (& Indian Territory);
Vegetarianism; Outlaws &
Rangers

Robert H Redding
391 West Spruce Street
Sequim, Wash. 98382
(206) 683-8202
Short Name: **R H Redding**
Americana; Arctica &
Antarctica; Literary Criticism;
Literature; Incunabula & Early
Printing; Rare Books

Redford Bookshop
22031 Grand River
Detroit, Mich. 48219
Short Name: **Redford**
Biography; Childrens' Books;
Illustrated Books; Out of Print,
with Stock; Religion &
Theology; Paperbacks (new)

Reedmor Magazine Company
 Inc
1229 Walnut Street
Philadelphia, Penna. 19107
(215) 922-6643
Short Name: **Reedmor**
Comic Books; Search Service,
without Stock; Science Fiction;
Magazines

William Reese Company
409 Temple Street
New Haven, Conn. 06511
(203) 769-8081
Short Name: **Wm Reese Co**
Americana; Voyages, Travels, &
Exploration; Farming,
Ranching, & Livestock; Natural
History; Overland Narratives;
American Indians

Reference Book Center
175 Fifth Avenue
New York, N.Y. 10010
(212) 677-2160
Short Name: **Reference**
Dictionaries; Reference

Regent House
108 North Roselake Avenue
Los Angeles, Calif. 90026
(213) 413-5027
Short Name: **Regent Hse**
English Literature; History,
American; American Literature;
Psychiatry, Psychology, &
Psychonanalysis

Regent Street Books
2747 Regent Street
Berkeley, Calif. 94705
Short Name: **Regent St**
Search Service, without Stock;
Scholarly Books; Psychiatry,
Psychology, & Psychonanalysis;
Medicine & Science;
Bibliography; Literary Criticism

Herbert Reichner
Shaker Hill Road
Enfield, N.H. 03748
Short Name: **H Reichner**
Archaeology; Art

Jo Ann Reisler
360 Glyndon Street, NE
Vienna, Va. 22180
(703) 938-2967
Short Name: **J A Reisler**
Childrens' Books; Illustrated
Books; Original Art of Book
Illustrations; Doll Books &
Paper Dolls

Reliable Books
P O Box 2033
Paterson, N.J. 07509
Short Name: **Reliable**
Out of Print, with Stock; Search
Service, with Stock

Remington's (Attn George
 Leinwall)
201 East Baltimore Street
Baltimore, Md. 21202
(301) 685-5007
Short Name: **Remington's**
Derrydale Press; Maryland;
Fore-Edge Painting; Maps,
Atlases, & Cartography

Renaissance Book Shop
834 North Plankinton
Milwaukee, Wisc. 53203
(414) 271-6850
Short Name: **Renaissance-Mil**
Out of Print, with Stock;
Fiction; General

The Renaissance
104 North Washington Road
Lake Forest, Ill. 60045
(312) 234-1173
Short Name: **Renaissance-Lak**
Childrens' Books; Biography;
Philosophy; Sporting;
Illustrated Books; Cookery &
Gastronomy

Renascence Bookshop
310 West Northwest Highway
Barrington, Ill. 60010
Short Name: **Renascence**
General

The Rendells, Inc
154 Wells Avenue
Newton, Mass. 02159
(617) 965-4670
Short Name: **Rendells**
Autographed Material &
Autographs; Manuscripts;
Manuscripts, Medieval &
Illuminated; Americana;
Appraisals & Appraisal
Services

Rendezvous Books
P O Box 2627
Taos, N.Mex. 87571
(800) 545-9170
Short Name: **Rendezvous**
American Indians; Voyages,
Travels, & Exploration;
History, American; Overland
Narratives; Out of Print, with
Stock; Americana

Stephen Resnick Paper
 Americana
36 Lincklaen Street
Cazenovia, N.Y. 13035
(315) 655-2810
Short Name: **S Resnick**
Autographed Material &
Autographs; Manuscripts; Rare
Books; Ephemera

Blossom Resnik
58 Midland Road
Roslyn Heights, N.Y. 11577
(516) 621-4898
Short Name: **B Resnik**
Illustrated Books; Periodicals;
Art; Posters; Prints; Childrens'
Books

Reston's Booknook
59 Rockton Street
Amsterdam, N.Y. 12010
(518) 843-1601
Short Name: **Reston's**
Americana; Ephemera; General;
Paintings; Prints; Science
Fiction

Resurrection Books
Rte #4, Box 131-B
Pittsboro, N.C. 27312
(919) 542-3403
Short Name: **Resurrection**
First Editions, Modern;
Authors; Author Collections;
Autographed Material &
Autographs; Inscribed Books;
Collection Development

Walter Reuben, Inc
667 Madison Avenue, #1006
New York, N.Y. 10021
Short Name: **W Reuben-NYC**
Americana, States; Latin
America; Manuscripts; Maps,
Atlases, & Cartography;
Voyages, Travels, &
Exploration

Walter Reuben, Inc
American Bank Tower, #910
Austin, Tex. 78701
(512) 478-3338
Short Name: **W Reuben-Aus**
Americana, States; Americana,
Regional; Latin America;
Manuscripts; Maps, Atlases, &
Cartography; Voyages, Travels,
& Exploration

John H Reuther
247 Lantern Lane
North Fort Myers, Fla. 33903
Short Name: **J H Reuther**
Biography; Mormons; Musical
Instruments

Revisionist Press
P O Box 200
Brooklyn, N.Y. 11202
Short Name: **Revisionist**
Cinema & Mass Media;
Caribbean; Central America;
Dictionaries; History;
Economics & Business

Frank E Reynolds
P O Box 805
Newburyport, Mass. 01950
Short Name: **F E Reynolds**
Civil War & Confederacy

J Bernard Reynolds
12 Main Street
Burnham, Maine 04922
Short Name: **J B Reynolds**
Fiction; Newspapers;
Paperbacks (new)

J E Reynolds
3801 Ridgewood Road
Willits, Calif. 95490
(707) 459-4321
Short Name: **J E Reynolds**
California; Western Americana;
Press Books & Fine Printing;
Outlaws & Rangers; Overland
Narratives; Pacific Region

Robert R Rhoads
3150 Backmeyer Road
Richmond, Ind. 47374
(317) 962-8056
Short Name: **R R Rhoads**
Color Plate Books; Natural
History

E P Rich
P O Box 666
Oak Park, Ill. 60303
(312) 386-7405
Short Name: **E P Rich**
Fine & Rare Bindings; First
Editions; Militaria; Rare
Books; Russia & Eastern
European Region; STC & Wing
Books

D Richards, Bookman
314 Belle Isle
Pittsburgh, Penna. 15226
(412) 531-0531
Short Name: **D Richards**
General

Paul C Richards, Autographs
High Acres
Templeton, Mass. 01468
(617) 939-8981
Short Name: **P C Richards**
Autographed Material &
Autographs; Documents;
Ephemera; Inscribed Books;
Manuscripts; Antique Stocks
and Bonds

Roger Richards
26 Horatio Street
New York, N.Y. 10014
(212) 924-2411
Short Name: **R Richards**
First Editions, Modern;
Autographed Material &
Autographs; Beat Literature

Herbert & Christine Richardson
209 Stratford Avenue
Westmont, N.J. 08108
(609) 854-3348
Short Name: **Richardsons**
Americana; Architecture;
Archaeology; Typography &
Type Specimens; Ephemera;
Voyages, Travels, &
Exploration

Robert H Richshafer
900-902 Vine Street
Cincinnati, Ohio 45202
Short Name: **R H Richshafer**
Americana; Documents;
Newspapers; Photography; Rare
Books; Voyages, Travels, &
Exploration

Ridge Books
P O Box 58
Stone Ridge, N.Y. 12484
Short Name: **Ridge**
First Editions, Modern; Little
Magazines & Literary Small
Presses; Poetry; Paperbacks
(new); Performing Arts

P R (Dick) Rieber, Inc
429 South Hansell Street
Thomasville, Ga. 31792
Short Name: **P R Rieber**
Juveniles; First Editions,
Modern; The South; Natural
History; Black Literature &
Black Studies

Branimir M Rieger
936 Sunset Drive
Greenwood, S.C. 29646
Short Name: **B M Rieger**
Americana; History; Literature;
Voyages, Travels, &
Exploration; Travel Guides;
Authors

Ray Riling Arms Books
   Company
6844 Gorsten Street
Philadelphia, Penna. 19119
(215) 438-2456
Short Name: **Riling Arms**
Firearms & Weapons; Hunting,
Fishing & Angling

Rinhart Galleries
Upper Grey
Colebrook, Conn. 06021
Short Name: **Rinhart Gall**
History, American; Presidents;
Photography; Graphic Arts

Rising Trout Sporting Books
P O Box 1719
Guelph, Ont. N1H 6Z9
Short Name: **Rising Trout**
Fishing & Angling; Sports;
Sporting; Sporting

Rittenhouse Book Store
1706 Rittenhouse Square
Philadelphia, Penna. 19103
Short Name: **Rittenhse**
Medical & Medicine; Health

Jack D Rittenhouse, Bookseller
P O Box 4422
Albuquerque, N.Mex. 87196
(505) 255-2479
Short Name: **J D Rittenhouse**
American Indians; Americana,
Regional; Outlaws & Rangers;
Overland Narratives; Rare
Books; Voyages, Travels, &
Exploration

Rivendell Bookshop
45 East 7th Street
New York, N.Y. 10003
Short Name: **Rivendell**
Folklore; Myths

Riverow Bookshop
204 Front Street
Owego, N.Y. 13827
Short Name: **Riverow**
Technology; Architecture;
Antiques; Crafts & Trades;
Ephemera

Riverrun
7 Washington
Hastings-On-Hudson, N.Y.
   10706
Short Name: **Riverrun**
20th Century Literature;
Literature in English
Translation; General

Riverside Mail Service
P O Box 713
Doylestown, Penna. 18901
(215) 345-7356
Short Name: **Riverside Mail**
Psychiatry, Psychology, &
Psychonanalysis; Women &
Feminism; Criminology; City &
Urban Planning

Richard Owen Roberts,
   Booksellers
205 East Kehoe Boulevard
Wheaton, Ill. 60187
Short Name: **R O Roberts**
Religion & Theology; Theology;
Bible & Bible Studies; Church
History; Biography; Christian
Books

Mary Beirne Robertson Books
4612 Larkin Drive
Covina, Calif. 91722
(213) 332-0968
Short Name: **M B Robertson**
Out of Print, with Stock; Asia;
Americana; Fiction; Pacific
Region

R Robertson
278 Birch Drive
Levittown, Penna. 19054
(215) 946-0643
Short Name: **R Robertson**
General; Americana; Geology;
Natural History; Voyages,
Travels, & Exploration

A G Robinson, Jr
670 East Mansfield
Pontiac, Mich. 48055
Short Name: **A G Robinson, Jr**
Americana, States; Comic
Books; Natural History; Science
Fiction; Collection
Development; Sporting

Carroll Minor Robinson
P O Box 501
Palm Beach, Fla. 33480
(305) 833-2028
Short Name: **C M Robinson**
Arctica & Antarctica;
Childrens' Books; Dogs;
Gardening & Horticulture;
Hunting, Fishing & Angling;
Paperbacks (new)

Cedric L Robinson, Bookseller
597 Palisado Avenue
Windsor, Conn. 06095
(203) 688-2582
Short Name: **C L Robinson-Wi**
Americana; Architecture;
Connecticut; American
Literature; Voyages, Travels, &
Exploration

Charles L Robinson Books
Pond Road, Box 57
Manchester, Maine 04351
(207) 622-1885
Short Name: **C L Robinson-Ma**
Appraisals & Appraisal
Services; Auctions &
Auctioneers; First Editions,
Modern; Illustrated Books;
Medicine & Science; Voyages,
Travels, & Exploration

Harry B Robinson
915 Texas Avenue
Columbia, Mo. 65201
(314) 449-1611
Short Name: **H B Robinson**
General; Biography; Natural
History; Search Service, with
Stock; History, American;
Americana

Ruth E Robinson
Rte #7, Box 162-A
Morgantown, W.Va. 26505
Short Name: **R E Robinson**
Americana, Regional;
Americana, States; Books about
Books; Bibliography

John Roby
3703 Nassau Drive
San Diego, Calif. 92115
(714) 583-4264
Short Name: **J Roby**
Aviation & Aeronautics;
Technology

Rockaway Books
P O Box 1435
Woodbridge, Va. 22193
Short Name: **Rockaway**
Paperbacks (new); Pulps; Comic
Books; Cinema & Mass Media;
Comic Books; Original Art of
Book Illustrations

Rockland Bookman
R D #1, Box 367
Reading, Penna. 19607
(215) 775-3833
Short Name: **Rockland**
Fine & Rare Bindings; Color
Plate Books; First Editions;
Natural History; Out of Print,
with Stock; Press Books & Fine
Printing

Rodden's Used Bookshop
350 East Broadway
Long Beach, Calif. 90802
(213) 432-5896
Short Name: **Rodden's**
General; Science Fiction;
Detective Fiction; Comic Books;
Paperbacks (new); Periodicals

Martin Roenick
26 Barton Hill
East Hampton, Conn. 06424
Short Name: **M Roenick**
Antiques; Architecture;
Gambling; Stock Market &
Wall Street; Mechanical
Musical Instruments; Trade
Catalogues

Rogers Park Bookstore
1422 West Morse
Chicago, Ill. 60626
(312) 262-3765
Short Name: **Rogers Park**
History; History, American;
General; Literature; Religion &
Theology; Humanities

Hans E Rohr (Trade Only)
P O Box 331
Byfield, Mass. 01922
Short Name: **H E Rohr**
Illustrated Books; Prints; Rare
Books

Ron-Dot Bookfinders
4700 Masillon Road
Greensburg, Ohio 44232
Short Name: **Ron-Dot**
Watchtower Books & Jehovah's
Witnesses; Americana;
Paperbacks (new); Search
Service, with Stock; First
Editions; Ohio

B & L Rootenberg
P O Box 5049
Sherman Oaks, Calif. 91403
(213) 788-7765
Short Name: **B & L Root'berg**
Medicine & Science; Rare
Books; Manuscripts;
Technology; Philosophy;
Continental Books

Pearl E Rose Bookseller
337 North Kilkea Drive
Los Angeles, Calif. 90048
Short Name: **P E Rose**
Civil War & Confederacy;
Americana; California

Mary S Rosenberg, Inc
17 West 60th Street
New York, N.Y. 10023
(212) 362-4873
Short Name: **M S Rosenberg**
German Books & Literature;
French Books & Literature;
Judaica & Hebraica; Out of
Print, with Stock

Rosengren's Books
312 Bonham Street
San Antonio, Tex. 78205
(512) 226-3473
Short Name: **Rosengren's**
Texas; Art; Childrens' Books;
New Books; Latin America;
Humanities

Bernard M Rosenthal, Inc
251 Post Street
San Francisco, Calif. 94108
(415) 982-2219
Short Name: **B M Rosenthal**
Bibliography; Manuscripts,
Medieval & Illuminated;
Middle Ages; Renaissance;
Scholarly Books

Rosetree Inn Books
P O Box 7
Tombstone, Ariz. 85638
(602) 457-3326
Short Name: **Rosetree Inn**
American Indians; Americana,
Regional; Outlaws & Rangers

Craig Ross
P O Box 148
Medina, N.Y. 14103
Short Name: **C Ross**
Americana; General; Rare
Books; Ephemera

Ross & Haines Old Books Co
639 East Lake
Wayzata, Minn. 55391
(612) 473-7551
Short Name: **Ross & Haines**
Americana; Militaria; History;
Biography

The Ross Valley Book Co, Inc
1407 Solano Avenue
Albany, Calif. 94706
Short Name: **Ross Valley**
Western Americana; Latin
America; South America

**Leona Rostenberg & Madeleine
Stern**
40 East 88th Street
New York, N.Y. 10028
(212) 831-6628
Short Name: **L Rostenberg**
Books about Books; Ephemera;
History; Political Science &
Theory; Rare Books;
Renaissance

Irving M Roth
89 Whittlesey Avenue
Norwalk, Ohio 44857
Short Name: **I M Roth**
Ohio; Local History; Postcards;
Posters; Trade Catalogues

Irene Rouse Bookseller
905 Duke Street
Alexandria, Va. 22314
Short Name: **I Rouse**
*Americana; Cookery &
Gastronomy; Mystery Fiction;
Folklore; Literature; Poetry*

Philip A Rousssel
19 Sheafe Street
Portsmouth, N.H. 03801
Short Name: **P A Rousssel**
Maps, Atlases, & Cartography

Erling Rovick
7104 Wooddale Avenue, South
Minneapolis, Minn. 55435
(507) 927-7518
Short Name: **E Rovick**
*Fishing & Angling; Hunting,
Fishing & Angling*

Royal Oak Bookshop
207 South Royal Avenue
Front Royal, Va. 22630
Short Name: **Royal Oak**
*Out of Print, with Stock; New
Books; Paperbacks (new);
Search Service, with Stock;
Prints*

Seth E Rubenstein
P O Box 370
Forest Hills, N.Y. 11375
Short Name: **S E Rubenstein**
Orientalia; Rockwell Kent

Robert H Rubin
P O Box 558
Stoughton, Mass. 02072
(617) 344-0740
Short Name: **R H Rubin**
*Economics & Business; Law;
Social Sciences; Political,
Social, & Cultural History &
Thought; Political Science &
Theory; Americana*

Joseph Rubinfine (Appt Only)
R F D #1
Pleasantville, N.J. 08232
(609) 641-3290
Short Name: **J Rubinfine**
*Autographed Material &
Autographs; Manuscripts*

Rue Morgue Bookshop
1200 Pearl
Boulder, Colo. 80302
Short Name: **Rue Morgue**
*Detective Fiction; Mystery
Fiction; Sherlock Holmes & A.
Conan Doyle*

Barbara J Rule-Books
P O Box 215
Rochester, Mich. 48063
Short Name: **B J Rule**
*Cookery & Gastronomy; Search
Service, with Stock; Out of
Print, with Stock; Biography;
Fiction; General*

Rupprecht's Book Persons
629 North Altadena
Royal Oak, Mich. 48067
(313) 542-2898
Short Name: **Rupprecht's**
*Technology; Farming,
Ranching, & Livestock;
Gardening & Horticulture*

Cecil Archer Rush
1410 Northgate Road
Baltimore, Md. 21218
(301) 323-7767
Short Name: **C A Rush**
*Orientalia; Erotica; Illustrated
Books; Search Service, with
Stock; Search Service, without
Stock; Specialized Publications*

John Rush-Books
396 Herkimer Street
Hamilton, Ont. L8P 2J3
Short Name: **J Rush**
Canada & Canadiana

Russica Book And Art Shop, Inc
799 Broadway
New York, N.Y. 10003
(212) 473-7480
Short Name: **Russica**
*Russia & Eastern European
Region; Rare Books; Art;
Reference; Literature; Search
Service, with Stock*

Terry Rutherford Bookseller
432 Homer Street
Vancouver, B.C.
Short Name: **T Rutherford**
Detective Fiction

Harriet V Ryan (Appt Only)
985 Fairfield Avenue
Bridgeport, Conn. 06605
Short Name: **H V Ryan**
*Childrens' Books; Art; Political
Science & Theory; Costumes;
Local History; Antiques*

L J Ryan, Scholarly Books
P O Box 243
Columbus, Ohio 43216
(614) 258-6558
Short Name: **L J Ryan**
*Americana; Foreign Affairs;
Political, Social, & Cultural
History & Thought; Religion &
Theology; Scholarly Books;
Social Sciences*

John Rybski, Bookseller
2319 West 47th Place
Chicago, Ill. 60609
(312) 847-5082
Short Name: **J Rybski**
*American Indians; Arctica &
Antarctica; History, American;
Civil War & Confederacy; Latin
America; Pacific Region*

S

S & S Books
80 North Wilder
St Paul, Minn. 55104
Short Name: **S & S**
*Detective Fiction; Out of Print,
with Stock; Out of Print,
without Stock; Science Fiction;
Search Service, with Stock;
Search Service, without Stock*

S-T Associates
1317 Cherokee Road
Louisville, Ken. 40204
Short Name: **S-T**
*First Editions; Literature; Rare
Books; Americana; First
Editions, Modern; Search
Service, with Stock*

**Rudolph W Sabbot, Ntrl History
Bks**
5239 Tendilla Avenue
Woodland Hills, Calif. 91364
Short Name: **R W Sabbot**
Natural History; New Books

Ben Sackheim
5425 East Fort Lowell
Tucson, Ariz. 85712
Short Name: **B Sackheim**
*First Editions, Modern;
Autographed Material &
Autographs; Illustrated Books;
Art; Prints*

M Douglas Sackman
P O Box 308
Deerfield, Mass. 01342
Short Name: **M D Sackman**
*Americana; Americana,
Regional*

Robert L Sadoff
326 Benjamin Fox Pavillion
Jenkintown, Penna. 19046
(215) 887-6144
Short Name: **R L Sadoff**
*Criminology; Law; Medicine &
Science; Psychiatry, Psychology,
& Psychoanalysis; Social
Sciences; Medical & Medicine*

Charlotte F Safir
1349 Lexington Avenue
New York, N.Y. 10028
Short Name: **C F Safir**
*Childrens' Books; Out of Print,
with Stock*

Sage Book Store
8 North 9th Street
Bozeman, Mont. 59715
(406) 587-5001
Short Name: **Sage**
*American Indians; Americana,
Regional; First Editions; Out of
Print, with Stock; Out of Print,
without Stock; Overland
Narratives*

Sager's Book Service
5461 Aldereley Road
Victoria, B.C. V8Y 1X9
Short Name: **Sager's**
Medicine & Science; Education

Albert Saifer
102 Longview Street
West Orange, N.J. 07052
Short Name: **A Saifer**
*Trade Catalogues; Technology;
Authors; Printing & Printing
History; Scholarly Books*

The Sail Loft (June-October)
Newcastle, Maine 04553
(207) 563-3209
Short Name: **Sail Loft-Summ**
*Childrens' Books; Illustrated
Books; Color Plate Books; Out
of Print, with Stock; Natural
History; Search Service, with
Stock*

The Sail Loft (November-May)
262 Cassidy Avenue
Lexington, Ken. 40502
(606) 266-6348
Short Name: **Sail Loft-Wint**
*Childrens' Books; Illustrated
Books; Color Plate Books; Out
of Print, with Stock; Natural
History; Search Service, with
Stock*

Lois St Clair
P O Box 247
Van Nuys, Calif. 91408
(213) 781-5376
Short Name: **L St Clair**
*Needlework; Art; Fiction;
General; Search Service,
without Stock*

St Nicholas Books
P O Box 863
Toronto, Ont. M4Y 2N7
(416) 922-9640
Short Name: **St Nicholas**
Childrens' Books

H & R Salerno
1 Given Court
Hauppauge, N.Y. 11787
Short Name: **H & R Salerno**
*Science Fiction; Photography;
Cinema & Mass Media; Out of
Print, with Stock; First Editions*

William Salloch (Appt Only)
Pines Bridge Road
Ossining, N.Y. 10562
(914) 941-8363
Short Name: **W Salloch**
*Rare Books; Renaissance;
Incunabula & Early Printing;
Emblem Books; Middle Ages;
Classics*

Alan Sample
38 Lynn Fells Parkway
Melrose, Mass. 02176
(617) 665-7307
Short Name: **A Sample**
*First Editions, Modern; Arctica
& Antarctica; Political, Social,
& Cultural History & Thought;
Stock Market & Wall Street*

Sample Bookshop
506 East Pine Street
Seattle, Wash. 98122
(206) 323-1146
Short Name: **Sample-Sea**
*Americana; Americana,
Regional; Folklore; Science
Fiction; Childrens' Books;
Detective Fiction*

P H Samuels
Star Route, Box 1281
Corrales, N.Mex. 87048
Short Name: **P H Samuels**
Art; Drawings; Paintings

San Fernando Books
P O Box 447
San Fernando, Calif. 91341
(213) 362-2173
Short Name: **San Fernando**
*Numismatics; Treasure
Hunting; Economics & Business*

San Francisciana
Cliff House, 1090 Pt Lobos
   Avenue
San Francisco, Calif. 94121
(415) 751-7222
Short Name: **San Franciscian**
*Photography; Posters; Prints;
Movie & Fan Magazines;
Ephemera; Postcards*

San Jose Bookstore
5121 San Jose Boulevard
Jacksonville, Fla. 32207
Short Name: **San Jose-Jack**
*Civil War & Confederacy; Color
Plate Books; Florida*

San Jose Book Shop
82 South Second Street
San Jose, Calif. 95113
(408) 295-5513
Short Name: **San Jose-San**
*General; Childrens' Books;
Remainders*

San Marco Books
1971 San Marco Boulevard
Jacksonville, Fla. 32207
Short Name: **San Marco**
*Color Plate Books; Florida;
Civil War & Confederacy; Art;
Periodicals; History*

**The San Francisco Mystery
   Bookstore**
746 Diamond Street
San Francisco, Calif. 94114
Short Name: **S F Mystery**
*Detective Fiction; Mystery
Fiction*

**Dino Moro Sanchez Book
   Dealer**
P O Box 8730
Universal City, Calif. 91608
Short Name: **D M Sanchez**
Mexico

Sand Dollar Books
1222 Solano Avenue
Albany, Calif. 94706
(415) 527-1931
Short Name: **Sand Dollar**
*Poetry; Out of Print, with
Stock; Little Magazines &
Literary Small Presses; Dance;
First Editions, Modern*

John R Sanderson, Ph.D.
West Main Street, Box 285
Stockbridge, Mass. 01262
(413) 274-6093
Short Name: **J R Sanderson**
*STC & Wing Books; Rare
Books; First Editions, Modern;
Inscribed Books; First Editions;
Humanities*

Sandpiper Books
P O Box 2933
San Rafael, Calif. 94912
Short Name: **Sandpiper**
*First Editions, Modern; Press
Books & Fine Printing; Ireland
& The Irish; Author
Collections; Collection
Development; Manuscripts*

Sangamon Book Shop
739 Marshall Avenue
St Louis, Mo. 63119
(314) 962-0522
Short Name: **Sangamon**
*Literature; Literary Criticism;
Philosophy; Poetry; Fiction;
Paperbacks (new)*

A D Santomasso-Books
P O Box 907
Jensen Beach, Fla. 33457
Short Name: **A D Santomasso**
*Medicine & Science;
Photography; Technology;
Wireless Communication
History; Science*

Harvey Satty
3155 Grand Concourse
Bronx, N.Y. 10468
Short Name: **H Satty**
*Science Fiction; Bibliography;
Fine & Rare Bindings;
Bookbinding & Restoration;
First Editions, Modern*

David Sauber
9901 Pine Avenue
Niagra Falls, N.Y. 14304
(716) 297-4965
Short Name: **D Sauber**
Rare Books; First Editions

Savoy Books
Chapel Road
Chapel, Mass. 01256
Short Name: **Savoy**
*Horticulture; Agriculture;
English Literature; American
Literature; Rare Books*

Savran's Books
301 Cedar Avenue
Minneapolis, Minn. 55454
Short Name: **Savran's**
*First Editions, Modern;
Detective Fiction; New Books;
Out of Print, without Stock;
Performing Arts; Search
Service, without Stock*

Stephen O Saxe Books
1100 Madison Avenue
New York, N.Y. 10028
Short Name: **S O Saxe**
*Printing & Printing History;
Typography & Type Specimens*

Saxifrage Books
13 Central Street
Salem, Mass. 01970
(617) 745-7170
Short Name: **Saxifrage**
*Art; Bookbinding &
Restoration; First Editions;
Natural History; Illustrated
Books*

Robert C Scace
P O Box 7156, Postal Station E
Calgary, Alb. T3C 3M1
(403) 253-3301
Short Name: **R C Scace**
*Canada & Canadiana;
Conservation; Geography*

Scarlet Letter Books (Sept-June)
Candlewood Mountain Road
New Milford, Conn. 06776
(203) 354-4181
Short Name: **Scarlet Letter**
*Illustrated Books; Childrens'
Books; Prints; Folklore;
Appraisals & Appraisal
Services; Periodicals*

Scattergood Books
P O Box 7043, Landscape Station
Berkeley, Calif. 94707
Short Name: **Scattergood**
Foreign Affairs; Political, Social, & Cultural History & Thought; Russia & Eastern European Region; Marxism-Leninism & Communism; Left Wing

William H Schab Gallery, Inc
37 West 57th Street
New York, N.Y. 10019
Short Name: **W H Schab**
Woodcut Books; Science; Medical & Medicine; Prints; Drawings

Mary A Schaefer
35-16 80th Street, #33-621
Jackson Heights, N.Y. 11372
Short Name: **M A Schaefer**
First Editions; Out of Print, without Stock; General

Scharf Art Travel
5040 Carolyn Drive
Pittsburgh, Penna. 15236
(412) 653-4402
Short Name: **Scharf Art**
Africa; Americana, States; Asia; Latin America; Orientalia; Voyages, Travels, & Exploration

Stephen Scharoun
33a State Street
Newburyport, Mass. 01950
Short Name: **S Scharoun**
Archaeology; Folklore; Literature

Karl Schick
180 East Hartsdale Avenue
Hartsdale, N.Y. 10530
(914) 725-0408
Short Name: **K Schick**
Medicine & Science; Philosophy; Psychiatry, Psychology, & Psychonanalysis; Rare Books

Howard Schickler
P O Box 745
Aptos, Calif. 95003
(408) 688-6361
Short Name: **H Schickler**
Photography

Wolfgang Schiefer
P O Box 474
New Haven, Conn. 06502
Short Name: **W Schiefer**
Brazil

Justin G Schiller, Ltd
36 East 61st Street
New York, N.Y. 10021
(212) 832-8231
Short Name: **J G Schiller**
Childrens' Books; Illustrated Books; Original Art of Book Illustrations; Education

Suzanne Schlossberg
529 Ward Street
Newton, Mass. 02159
(617) 964-0213
Short Name: **S Schlossberg**
Childrens' Books; Illustrated Books; Literature; General

Betty Schmid, Circusana (Mail Only)
485 Sleepy Hollow
Pittsburgh, Penna. 15228
(412) 341-4597
Short Name: **B Schmid**
Circus & Carnival

Annemarie Schnase
120 Brown Road, Box 119
Scarsdale, N.Y. 10583
(914) 725-1284
Short Name: **A Schnase**
Periodicals; Music; Reprints

Schneemann Books
5710 South Dorchester
Chicago, Ill. 60637
Short Name: **Schneemann**
Biography; Americana; Law; Philosophy; Religion & Theology; Search Service, with Stock

Larry Schnell's Papertiques
P O Box 252
Elberfeld, Ind. 47613
(812) 983-4009
Short Name: **L Schnell**
Out of Print, with Stock; Search Service, with Stock; Periodicals; General

Joseph E Schober
82-56 167th Street
Jamaica, N.Y. 11432
Short Name: **J E Schober**
Printing & Printing History; Calligraphy; Heraldry

The Scholar's Bookshelf
195 Nassau Street
Princeton, N.J. 08540
Short Name: **Scholar's**
Art; Philosophy; Religion & Theology; Science; Literature; History

Schooner Books
5378 Inglis Street
Halifax, N.S. B3H 1J5
(902) 423-8419
Short Name: **Schooner**
Canada & Canadiana

Schoyer's Books
1404 South Negley
Pittsburgh, Penna. 15217
(412) 521-8464
Short Name: **Schoyer's**
Americana; Art; Ephemera; General; Illustrated Books; Literature

Abner Schram
36 Park Street
Montclair, N.J. 07042
Short Name: **A Schram**
Art; Architecture; Calligraphy; Judaica & Hebraica

E K Schreiber
3140 Netherland
Riverdale, N.Y. 10463
(212) 884-9139
Short Name: **E K Schreiber**
Classics; Continental Books; IlluminatedManuscripts; Incunabula & Early Printing; Rare Books; Renaissance

Oscar Schreyer
230 East 79th Street
New York, N.Y. 10021
(212) 628-6227
Short Name: **O Schreyer**
Medicine & Science; Psychiatry, Psychology, & Psychonanalysis; Tobacco & Smoking; Rare Books; Judaica & Hebraica; Economics & Business

William E Schroeder
708 West Wisconsin Avenue
Milwaukee, Wisc. 53233
Short Name: **W E Schroeder**
Out of Print, with Stock; Paperbacks (new); Comic Books; Periodicals

Schroeder's Bookhaven
Rte #1, Box 531
Dickinson, Tex. 77539
Short Name: **Schroeder's**
Americana; Art; Cookery &
Gastronomy; Crafts & Trades;
History, American; Scholarly
Books

Len Schulman
P O Box 212
Downey, Calif. 90241
Short Name: **L Schulman**
American Indians; Americana;
Documents; Periodicals; STC &
Wing Books; Costumes

John F Schultz
Wood's Drive
Ancramdale, N.Y. 12503
Short Name: **J F Schultz**
General

Schuylkill Book & Curio Shop
873 Belmont Avenue
Philadelphia, Penna. 19104
(215) 473-4769
Short Name: **Schuylkill**
Rare Books; Scholarly Books;
Graphic Arts; Autographed
Material & Autographs;
Manuscripts; Appraisals &
Appraisal Services

Kurt L Schwarz
738 South Bristol Avenue
Los Angeles, Calif. 90049
Short Name: **K L Schwarz**
Archaeology; Architecture;
Orientalia; Illustrated Books;
Folklore; Printing & Printing
History

Science Fantasy Books
18 Eliot Street
Cambridge, Mass. 02138
Short Name: **Science Fantasy**
Science Fiction; Rare Books;
Paperbacks (new); Periodicals;
Out of Print, with Stock;
Cinema & Mass Media

Science Fiction Shop
56 Eighth Avenue
New York, N.Y. 10014
(212) 741-0270
Short Name: **Sci Fict**
Science Fiction; Out of Print,
with Stock; Rare Books

The Science Bookshelf
525 Fourth Street
Ann Arbor, Mich. 48103
Short Name: **Science Bkshlf**
Medicine & Science; Scholarly
Books; Natural History;
Gardening & Horticulture;
Technology; Search Service,
without Stock

Scientia
P O Box 14042
Minneapolis, Minn. 55414
(612) 379-7463
Short Name: **Scientia**
Medicine & Science; Natural
History; History of Medicine &
Science; Evolution;
Mathematics

John Scopazzi, Fine & Rare
Books
278 Post Street
San Francisco, Calif. 94108
Short Name: **J Scopazzi**
Press Books & Fine Printing;
Art; Illustrated Books; General;
Maps, Atlases, & Cartography;
Fine & Rare Bindings

Scotia Books
3980 Glanford Avenue
Victoria, B.C. V8Z 3Z4
Short Name: **Scotia**
American Indians; Arctica &
Antarctica; Canada &
Canadiana; Pacific Region;
Voyages, Travels, &
Exploration; Whaling

Barry Scott
15 Gramercy Park
New York, N.Y. 10003
Short Name: **B Scott**
First Editions, Modern;
Manuscripts; Press Books &
Fine Printing; Inscribed Books;
Illustrated Books; Art

The Scribbling Bookmonger
2324 Illinois Road
Northbrook, Ill. 60062
(312) 480-9840
Short Name: **Scribbling**
Reference; General; Literature;
Search Service, with Stock

The Scriptorium
427 North Canon Drive
Beverly Hills, Calif. 90210
Short Name: **Scriptorium**
Autographed Material &
Autographs; Manuscripts;
Movie & Fan Magazines;
Appraisals & Appraisal
Services

Seabook Search
Clinton Corners, N.Y. 12514
(914) 266-5800
Short Name: **Seabook**
Naval & Marine; Search
Service, with Stock; Voyages,
Travels, & Exploration;
Whaling

Seaport Autographs
10 Tipping Rock Road
Stonington, Conn. 06378
(203) 535-1224
Short Name: **Seaport**
Autographed Material &
Autographs

Search Service Specialists
443 South Lakeview Drive
Wauconda, Ill. 60084
Short Name: **Srch Srvce-Wau**
Out of Print, with Stock;
Collection Development

Seashell Treasures Books
P O Box 730
Oakhurst, Calif. 93644
Short Name: **Seashell Treas**
Marine Biology; Mollusks

Sebastopol Book Shop
133 North Main Street
Sebastopol, Calif. 95472
(707) 823-9788
Short Name: **Sebastopol**
Graphic Arts; Orientalia;
Medicine & Science; Asia; Self
Help

Second Debut Books
2827-1/2 De La Vina, Box
30268
Santa Barbara, Calif. 93105
(805) 687-2781
Short Name: **2nd Debut**
Religion & Theology;
Biography; Stock Market &
Wall Street; Performing Arts;
Search Service, with Stock;
Women & Feminism

Second Fiddle
1 Snell Street
Sturbridge, Mass. 01566
(617) 347-7564
Short Name: **2nd Fiddle**
*Americana; Art; Scholarly
Books; Sporting; Natural
History; General*

Second Floor Books
47 North Street
Pittsfield, Mass. 01201
(413) 528-1521
Short Name: **2nd Floor**
Americana, Regional

Second Life Books
Upper East Hoosac Street
Adams, Mass. 01220
Short Name: **2nd Life**
*Women & Feminism; Gardening
& Horticulture; First Editions,
Modern; First Editions;
Farming, Ranching, &
Livestock; Autographed
Material & Autographs*

Second Story Books
2724 Porter Street, Nw, #5
Washington, D.C. 20008
Short Name: **2nd Story**
*General; Rare Books; Out of
Print, with Stock; Search
Service, with Stock*

Second Time Around Bookshop
391 East Main Street
Ventura, Calif. 93003
(805) 643-3154
Short Name: **2nd Time Around**
*First Editions, Modern; Comic
Books; Americana; History;
Philosophy; Religion &
Theology*

**The Secret Sharer Book
    Company**
222 Park Avenue South, #11c
New York, N.Y. 10003
(212) 673-5993
Short Name: **Secret Sharer**
*Biography; Book Trade &
Catalogues; Books about Books;
Dictionaries; Literature;
Scholarly Books*

Lawrence Seeborg Books
8423 Greenbelt Road
Greenbelt, Md. 20770
(301) 552-2111
Short Name: **L Seeborg**
*Childrens' Books; Illustrated
Books; Original Art of Book
Illustrations; Arctica &
Antarctica*

Charles Seluzicki, Books
P O Box 12367
Salem, Ore. 97309
Short Name: **C Seluzicki**
*First Editions, Modern; Press
Books & Fine Printing;
Association Books; Inscribed
Books; Author Collections;
Manuscripts*

Seminary Book Service
3737 Seminary Road
Alexandria, Va. 22304
Short Name: **Seminary**
Religion & Theology

Serendipity Books, Inc
1790 Shattuck Avenue
Berkeley, Calif. 94709
(415) 841-7455
Short Name: **Serendipity**
*First Editions, Modern; Poetry;
Press Books & Fine Printing;
Black Literature & Black
Studies; Author Collections;
Appraisals & Appraisal
Services*

Sergio Old Prints
50 Maiden Lane
San Francisco, Calif. 94108
(415) 434-3312
Short Name: **Sergio**
*Prints; California; Hawaii;
Voyages, Travels, &
Exploration; Maps, Atlases, &
Cartography*

Serpent & Eagle Books
211 Main Street
Oneonta, N.Y. 13820
(607) 432-2990
Short Name: **Serpent & Eagle**
Folklore; Myths; Dance

Servant's Knowledge
2915-17-31 Atlantic
Atlantic City, N.J. 08401
Short Name: **Servant's Knowl**
*Antiques; Art; Gambling; Out of
Print, with Stock; Scholarly
Books; Search Service, with
Stock*

Charles Sessler, Inc
1308 Walnut Street
Philadelphia, Penna. 19107
Short Name: **C Sessler**
*Americana; Color Plate Books;
History, American; Maps,
Atlases, & Cartography; Naval
& Marine; Prints*

Seven Oaks Press
405 South 7th Street
St Charles, Ill. 60174
Short Name: **7 Oaks**
Fiction; Art; Literature

Seven Seas Book Service
Oak Street
Bewdley, Ont. K0L 1E0
Short Name: **7 Seas**
Animals; Fur Trade

Seville Books
660 East Government St, Box
    12144
Pensacula, Fla. 32590
Short Name: **Seville**
*Foreign Languages; Spain &
The Spanish; Literature;
Voyages, Travels, &
Exploration; Scholarly Books*

Sewards' Folly Books
139 Brook Street
Providence, R.I. 02906
Short Name: **Sewards' Folly**
*First Editions, Modern; Rare
Books; Rhode Island*

The Shadow Shop
Preston Street
Hillsboro, N.H. 03244
(603) 464-5413
Short Name: **Shadow**
General; Ephemera

Bennett Shaler
6 Tinder Lane
Lake Grove, N.Y. 11755
(516) 585-1931
Short Name: **B Shaler**
*Tobacco & Smoking;
Psychiatry, Psychology, &
Psychonanalysis; Religion &
Theology; Out of Print, with
Stock; Out of Print, without
Stock*

Shamus Books
1303 Willis Street
Richmond, Va. 23224
(804) 233-0864
Short Name: **Shamus**
*Detective Fiction; Paperbacks
(new); Periodicals; Search
Service, with Stock; Posters*

Oscar Shapiro
3726 Connecticut Avenue, NW
Washington, D.C. 20008
(202) 244-4446
Short Name: **O Shapiro**
*Chess, Checkers, & Draughts;
Music; Autographed Material
& Autographs; Violins; Musical
Instruments*

S R Shapiro
29 East 10th Street
New York, N.Y. 10003
(212) 673-0610
Short Name: **S R Shapiro**
*Art; Bibliography; Press Books
& Fine Printing; Folklore; Rare
Books; Typography & Type
Specimens*

Sharp's Bookstore
5041 Lankershim Boulevard
North Hollywood, Calif. 91601
Short Name: **Sharp's**
*Geneaologies; Religion &
Theology; History, American*

John B Shaw
1917 Fort Union Drive
Santa Fe, N.Mex. 87501
Short Name: **J B Shaw**
*Sherlock Holmes & A. Conan
Doyle*

Thomas W Shaw
11 Albright Avenue
Albany, N.Y. 12203
Short Name: **T W Shaw**
*Detective Fiction; Fiction; Out
of Print, with Stock; Search
Service, with Stock; General*

Shaw-Banfill Books
P O Box 14850
Columbus, Ohio 43214
Short Name: **Shaw-Banfill**
Science; Genetics; Evolution

C J Sheiner
275 Linden Boulevard
Brooklyn, N.Y. 11226
Short Name: **C J Sheiner**
Erotica; Curiosa; Sexology

**James & Vivian Shelton,
  Booksellers**
1019 Swann Avenue
Tampa, Fla. 33606
(813) 248-5902
Short Name: **J & V Shelton**
*General; Childrens' Books;
Literature; First Editions,
Modern; Search Service, with
Stock; New Books*

R L Shep
Box C-20
Lopez, Wash. 98261
Short Name: **R L Shep**
*Textiles; Costumes; Dance;
Performing Arts*

William P Shepard
2035 North Brower
Simi Valley, Calif. 93065
(805) 526-3285
Short Name: **W P Shepard**
*Pulps; Periodicals; Fiction;
Movie & Fan Magazines; First
Editions; Paperbacks (new)*

Anne Sherlock Books
1600-A Bloor Street, West
Toronto, Ont. M6P 1A7
(416) 533-3207
Short Name: **A Sherlock**
*Science Fiction; Fantasy;
Detective Fiction; Folklore;
Anthropology; Childrens' Books*

Sherlock Book Detective
P O Box 1174
Baltimore, Md. 21203
Short Name: **Sherlock**
Fiction; Juveniles

Emily Brown Shields
20 North Broadway
White Plains, N.Y. 10601
(914) 761-2288
Short Name: **E B Shields**
Calligraphy

Sarkis Shmavonian
1796 Shattuck, NE
Berkeley, Calif. 94709
(415) 843-5910
Short Name: **S Shmavonian**
*Asia; Fiction; Pacific Region;
Russia & Eastern European
Region; Voyages, Travels, &
Exploration*

Jerome Shochet ✓ Schochet
5773 Oakland Road
Sykesville, Md. 21784
(301) 744-0393
Short Name: **J Schochet**
Boxing

Harold J Shoebridge
Maple Hill
Lafayette, N.Y. 13084
(315) 677-3056
Short Name: **H J Shoebridge**
*Fine & Rare Bindings; Books
about Books; Press Books &
Fine Printing; Color Plate
Books; Fore-Edge Painting;
Inscribed Books*

Shorey Book Store
P O Box 21626
Seattle, Wash. 98111
(206) 624-0221
Short Name: **Shorey**
*Western Americana; Alaska;
Arctica & Antarctica; Ships &
The Sea; Natural History*

**Eugene Short, Geoscience
  Literature**
705 West 47th Avenue
Anchorage, Alas. 99503
(907) 277-8113
Short Name: **E Short**
*U.S. Government Publications;
Arctica & Antarctica; Whaling;
Mountaineering; Hunting,
Fishing & Angling; Alaska*

Jerry N Showalter
P O Box 84
Ivy, Va. 22945
(804) 295-6413
Short Name: **J N Showalter**
*Civil War & Confederacy;
Americana, Regional;
Americana; Americana, States*

Stephen Shuart
102 Pine Avenue
Kane, Penna. 16735
(814) 837-7786
Short Name: **S Shuart**
*Photography; Camera Manuals;
Trade Catalogues*

Shuey Book Search
8886 Sharkey Avenue
Elk Grove, Calif. 95624
(916) 685-3044
Short Name: **Shuey**
*Search Service, with Stock;
General*

Robert Shuhi
Rte #63, Box 268
Morris, Conn. 06763
Short Name: **R Shuhi**
*Americana; Hunting, Fishing &
Angling; Natural History;
Militaria; Literature; General*

Jacques V Sichel
1024 Sayre Road
Union, N.J. 07083
(201) 688-3757
Short Name: **J V Sichel**
*General; First Editions,
Modern; Press Books & Fine
Printing; Illustrated Books;
Animals; Sheet Music*

Sidney's Used Books
527 North Higgins Avenue
Missoula, Mont. 59801
Short Name: **Sidney's**
*Literature; Western Americana;
Religion & Theology;
Childrens' Books; Science
Fiction; Paperbacks (new)*

Sign Of The Unicorn
604 Kingstown Road, Box 297
Peacedale, R.I. 02883
(401) 789-8912
Short Name: **Sign Of Unicorn**
Out of Print, with Stock

Signed Limited Editions
P O Box 631
Port Washington, N.Y. 11050
Short Name: **Signed Limited**
*Signed, Limited Editions;
Inscribed Books; First Editions,
Modern; Woodcut Books*

Significant Books
P O Box 42461
Cincinnati, Ohio 45242
(513) 761-2694
Short Name: **Significant**
*General; Medicine & Science;
Natural History; Out of Print,
with Stock; Scholarly Books;
Technology*

Martin A Silver (Appt Only)
643 Willowglen Road
Santa Barbara, Calif. 93105
Short Name: **M A Silver**
Music

The Silver Door
P O Box 3208
Redondo Beach, Calif. 90277
Short Name: **Silver Door**
*Detective Fiction; First
Editions; First Editions,
Modern; Out of Print, with
Stock; Search Service, with
Stock*

Sindell Research Limited
529 Wiseman Avenue
Montreal, Que. H2V 3K1
(514) 277-8323
Short Name: **Sindell Res**
*Appraisals & Appraisal
Services; Bibliographical
Research Services;
Photography; American
Indians; Ephemera*

Singer Communications Inc
P O Box 6538
Buena Park, Calif. 90622
Short Name: **Singer Comm**
*Autographed Material &
Autographs*

Ralph B Sirrine
65 Glenwood Avenue
Stratford, Conn. 06497
Short Name: **R B Sirrine**
*Americana; First Editions;
General; Art; Illustrated Books*

Sisterhood Bookstore
1351 Westwood Boulevard
Los Angeles, Calif. 90024
(213) 477-7300
Short Name: **Sisterhood**
*Women & Feminism;
Homosexual & Gay Literature;
Posters; Jewelry*

Skeans And Clifford
P O Box 85
Deer Isle, Maine 04627
Short Name: **Skeans & Cliff**
*First Editions, Modern;
Americana, Regional*

John M Skutel Galleries
45 Unquowa Road
Fairfield, Conn. 06430
(203) 255-9098
Short Name: **J M Skutel**
*Appraisals & Appraisal
Services; Auctions &
Auctioneers; Civil War &
Confederacy; Crafts & Trades;
Ephemera; Voyages, Travels, &
Exploration*

Sky Books International Inc
48 East 50th Street
New York, N.Y. 10022
(212) 688-5086
Short Name: **Sky Bks Int**
*Aviation & Aeronautics;
Militaria; Naval & Marine*

W R Slater Books
1639 Humphrey Drive
Concord, Calif. 94519
(415) 825-2617
Short Name: **W R Slater**
Science Fiction; Fantasy

John P Slattery
352 Stanford Avenue
Palo Alto, Calif. 94306
(415) 323-9775
Short Name: **J P Slattery**
*Autographed Material &
Autographs; Ephemera;
Photography; Russia & Eastern
European Region; Travel
Guides*

Slavic Antiquities (Mail Only)
P O Box 38
Bloomingdale, Ill. 60108
Short Name: **Slavic Antiq**
*Folklore; Geneaologies; History;
Russia & Eastern European
Region*

Rosejeanne Slifer (Appt Only)
30 Park Avenue
New York, N.Y. 10016
(212) 685-2040
Short Name: **R Slifer**
*Autographed Material &
Autographs; Documents; Maps,
Atlases, & Cartography*

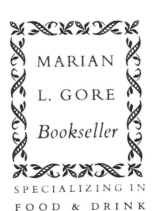

Larry Sloan
13507 Weld Country, #2-1/2
Brighton, Colo. 80601
(303) 659-1574
Short Name: **L Sloan**
Americana, Regional;
Astrology; Geology

Dorothy Sloan's Bookshelf
1651 North Grand Traverse
Flint, Mich. 48503
Short Name: **D Sloan's**
Americana; Art; Cookery &
Gastronomy; Out of Print, with
Stock; Religion & Theology;
Search Service, with Stock

P K Slocum
7733 Corey Street
Downey, Calif. 90242
Short Name: **P K Slocum**
Political Science & Theory;
Libertarianism; World Wars;
Authors

T Small-Books
P O Box 457
South Yarmouth, Mass. 02664
(617) 398-2652
Short Name: **T Small**
Childrens' Books; Illustrated
Books; Natural History;
Photography; Hunting, Fishing
& Angling; Press Books & Fine
Printing

Don Smith
3930 Rankin Street
Louisville, Ken. 40214
Short Name: **D Smith**
National Geographic Magazine

Fred W Smith
1010 Hook Avenue
Pleasant Hill, Calif. 94523
Short Name: **F W Smith**
Author Collections; First
Editions, Modern

John A Smith
83 Alpine Place
Franklin, Mass. 02038
Short Name: **J A Smith**
Americana; First Editions

John W Smith-Books
R R #1
Hensall, Ont. N0H 1X0
Short Name: **J W Smith**
Canada & Canadiana; Farming,
Ranching, & Livestock;
Gardening & Horticulture;
Arctica & Antarctica;
Collection Development;
Mennonites

Larry W Smith
50 Essex Street
Rochelle Park, N.J. 07662
(201) 843-0550
Short Name: **L W Smith**
Humanities; Hotels; Black
Literature & Black Studies;
Technology; Science; Computers

Linwood Smith, Books
P O Box 6970
Washington, D.C. 20032
Short Name: **L Smith**
Education; Fiction; Literature;
Africa; Paperbacks (new);
Political, Social, & Cultural
History & Thought

Nicholas T Smith, Bookseller
P O Box 66
Bronxville, N.Y. 10708
(914) 337-2794
Short Name: **N T Smith**
Bibliography; Fine & Rare
Bindings; Bookbinding &
Restoration; Books about
Books; Press Books & Fine
Printing; Papermaking &
Marbling

Patterson Smith
23 Prospect Terrace
Montclair, N.J. 07042
(201) 744-3291
Short Name: **P Smith**
Criminology; Gambling;
Technology; Social Sciences;
Law

Robert W Smith
6012 Southport Drive
Bethesda, Md. 20014
Short Name: **R W Smith**
First Editions, Modern; First
Editions; Literature; Sporting;
Rare Books; Biography

Sydney R Smith Sporting Books
Canaan, N.Y. 12029
(518) 794-8998
Short Name: **S R Smith**
Horses; Dogs; Hunting, Fishing
& Angling; Shooting &
Firearms

R W Smith-Bookseller
51 Trumbull Street
New Haven, Conn. 06510
(203) 776-5564
Short Name: **R W Smith-N Hav**
Antiques; Architecture; Art;
Photography

Smith's Book Service
Sunsmith House, Route #6a
Brewster, Mass. 02631
(617) 896-7024
Short Name: **Smith's-Brew**
Search Service, with Stock;
Natural History; Literature

Smoky Hill Booksellers
P O Box 2
Kansas City, Mo. 64141
Short Name: **Smoky Hill**
Kansas; Science; American
Diaries & Narratives;
Oklahoma (& Indian Territory);
Arkansas; American Indians

R M Smythe & Company, Inc
170 Broadway
New York, N.Y. 10038
Short Name: **R M Smythe**
Stock Market & Wall Street;
Railroads; Autographed
Material & Autographs

Snowbound Books (Mail Only)
R F D Box 510
Madison, Maine 04950
(207) 696-5081
Short Name: **Snowbound**
Maine Authors; Search Service,
with Stock; Militaria;
Childrens' Books; Fiction;
Biography

Gene Snyder
104-39 120th Street
Richmond Hill, N.Y. 11419
Short Name: **G Snyder**
Prints; Horse Drawn Vehicles

Soccer World Books
Fountain 9 Mall, Hway #35
Sea Girt, N.J. 08750
(201) 449-1333
Short Name: **Soccer World**
Soccer

Soldier Shop
1013 Madison Avenue
New York, N.Y. 10021
(212) 535-6788
Short Name: **Soldier**
*Civil War & Confederacy;
History; Militaria; Naval &
Marine; Shooting & Firearms*

Somerset Books
P O Box 6467
Concord, Calif. 94520
Short Name: **Somerset**
*Detective Fiction; Science
Fiction; First Editions*

Sons Of Liberty
735 Belmont Street
Manchester, N.H. 03104
(603) 622-5853
Short Name: **Sons Of Liberty**
*British Isles; Americana;
Shakespeare*

Anna Sosenko, Inc
76 West 82nd Street
New York, N.Y. 10024
(212) 247-4816
Short Name: **A Sosenko**
*Autographed Material &
Autographs; Manuscripts;
Performing Arts*

Sotheby Parke Bernet
980 Madison Avenue
New York, N.Y. 10021
Short Name: **SPB**
Auctions & Auctioneers

Source Book Store
232 West 3rd Street
Davenport, Iowa 52801
Short Name: **Source**
*Iowa; Local History; Inland
Waterways; General*

South Bay Books
1489 Plaza Boulevard
National City, Calif. 92050
Short Name: **South Bay**
*Appraisals & Appraisal
Services; First Editions; Press
Books & Fine Printing;
Childrens' Books; General;
Illustrated Books*

South By Southwest Books
P O Box 1561
Fayetteville, Ark. 72701
Short Name: **So By S'West**
*Americana, Regional;
Appraisals & Appraisal
Services; Civil War &
Confederacy; Outlaws &
Rangers*

South Side Books
8240 Pacific Avenue
Tacoma, Wash. 98408
Short Name: **South Side**
*General; Out of Print, with
Stock; Search Service, with
Stock*

Richard Spafford-Books
3036-13th Avenue
Regina, Sask. S4T 1N9
(306) 527-0844
Short Name: **R Spafford**
*Canada & Canadiana; Political,
Social, & Cultural History &
Thought*

Spector The Collector
34-10 94th Street
Jackson Heights, N.Y. 11374
Short Name: **Spector**
*Rockwell Kent; Art; Fore-Edge
Painting; Illustrated Books;
Fine & Rare Bindings; Whaling*

The Spectrum
Rte #2, Box 246
Phillips, Wisc. 54555
(715) 339-3663
Short Name: **Spectrum**
*Ephemera; Illustrated Books;
Paintings; Paperbacks (new);
Periodicals; Prints*

Richard W Spellman (Appt Only)
610 Monticello Drive
Brick Town, N.J. 08723
(201) 477-2413
Short Name: **R W Spellman**
*Maps, Atlases, & Cartography;
Newspapers; Prints*

Spencer Books
210 Post Street, #908
San Francisco, Calif. 94108
Short Name: **Spencer**
*Search Service, without Stock;
New Books*

Dorothy Spencer
P O Box 2010
Toluca Lake, Calif. 91602
(213) 761-3991
Short Name: **D Spencer**
*Kennedy Assasinations; Avant
Garde, Experimental, &
Modern Art; Art*

Robert Speray
515 East 8th Street
Bloomington, Ind. 47401
Short Name: **R Speray**
*Detective Fiction; Childrens'
Books; Paperbacks (new); Out
of Print, with Stock; Search
Service, with Stock; Book
Scouts*

Peter Sperling-Books
P O Box 300, Old Chelsea
  Station
New York, N.Y. 10113
Short Name: **P Sperling**
*Search Service, with Stock;
Fiction; Literature*

Shelly Spindel Books
1 Blackheath Road
Lido Beach, N.Y. 11561
Short Name: **S Spindel**
*Hunting, Fishing & Angling;
Sporting; Shooting & Firearms;
Dogs; Horses*

Spiratone, Inc
135-06 Northern Boulevard
Flushing, N.Y. 11354
Short Name: **Spiratone**
Photography

Sporting Bibliographic Press
145 East 49th Street
New York, N.Y. 10017
(212) 753-1783
Short Name: **Sporting Biblio**
*Sporting; Books about Books;
Hunting, Fishing & Angling;
Natural History*

Sporting Book Service
P O Box 177
Rancocas, N.J. 08073
Short Name: **Sporting**
*Hunting, Fishing & Angling;
Natural History; Shooting &
Firearms; Sporting*

Sportsman's Cabinet
P O Box 15
Manotick, Ont. K0A 2N0
Short Name: **Sportsman's**
*Sporting; Shooting & Firearms;
Hunting, Fishing & Angling;
Dogs; Mountaineering; Natural
History*

Roy A Squires
1745 Kenneth Road
Glendale, Calif. 91201
Short Name: **R A Squires**
Science Fiction; Fantasy

Lou Stamelman
48 Heron Road
Livingston, N.J. 07039
Short Name: **L Stamelman**
*Magazines; First Editions;
General*

Stan's Paperback Exchange
7 Montello Street
Brockton, Mass. 02401
(617) 583-6777
Short Name: **Stan's**
*Paperbacks (new); Western
Books; General; Science Fiction;
Comic Books*

Stanley Books
104 Maple Street
Hartford, Vt. 05147
(802) 295-9058
Short Name: **Stanley**
*General; Literary Criticism; Out
of Print, with Stock*

Jerrold G Stanoff
P O Box 1599
Aptos, Calif. 95003
(408) 724-4911
Short Name: **J G Stanoff**
*Japan; Chinese Civilization;
Art; Woodcut Books; Orientalia*

K Starosciak
190 Arguello Boulevard
San Francisco, Calif. 94118
Short Name: **K Starosciak**
*Architecture; Art; Books about
Books; First Editions, Modern;
Paintings; Photography*

Starr Book Company, Inc
37 Kingston Street
Boston, Mass. 02111
Short Name: **Starr-Bost**
*American Literature; English
Literature; Sets; Fiction;
History, American; General*

Starr Book Shop, Inc
29 Plympton Street
Cambridge, Mass. 02138
Short Name: **Starr-Camb**
*Sets; Encyclopedias; Classics;
Philosophy; American
Literature; General*

Dale W Starry, Sr
115 North Washington Street
Shippensburg, Penna. 17257
Short Name: **D W Starry, Sr**
*Pennsylvania; Illustrated Books;
Authors; Western Books;
Geneaologies*

Stationarius
P O Box 43
Vermillion, S.D. 57069
(605) 624-2759
Short Name: **Stationarius**
*Press Books & Fine Printing;
Printing & Printing History;
Typography & Type Specimens;
Ephemera*

Geoffrey Steele, Inc
Lumberville, Penna. 18933
Short Name: **G Steele**
Architecture; Art

Gary Steigerwald
1500 Maxwell Lane
Bloomington, Ind. 47401
Short Name: **G Steigerwald**
*Books about Books; Illustrated
Books; Incunabula & Early
Printing; Press Books & Fine
Printing; Printing & Printing
History; Rare Books*

Steinberg-Books
P O Box 342
New York, N.Y. 10156
Short Name: **Steinberg**
*Bibliography; Book Trade &
Catalogues; Books about Books;
Judaica & Hebraica; Printing &
Printing History; Papermaking
& Marbling*

Charles Steir
630 West 246th Street
Bronx, N.Y. 10471
(212) 543-2396
Short Name: **C Steir**
*Psychiatry, Psychology, &
Psychonanalysis*

Robert B Stephenson-Fine Books
Jaffrey Center, N.H. 03454
Short Name: **R B Stephenson**
*Voyages, Travels, &
Exploration; Arctica &
Antarctica; General*

Sterling Bookstore
Rte #12
Sterling, Mass. 01564
(617) 422-6897
Short Name: **Sterling**
*General; Out of Print, with
Stock; Paperbacks (new);
Childrens' Books; Comic Books;
Ephemera*

Sterling Valley Antiquities
P O Box 14
Syracuse, N.Y. 13215
Short Name: **Sterling Valley**
*American Indians; Americana;
Book Trade & Catalogues;
Color Plate Books; Social
Sciences; Search Service, with
Stock*

Harry L Stern
620 North Michigan Avenue
Chicago, Ill. 60611
Short Name: **H L Stern**
*Rare Books; Voyages, Travels,
& Exploration; History of
Medicine & Science; Classics*

Peter L Stern
P O Box 160
Sharon, Mass. 02067
(617) 784-7618
Short Name: **P L Stern**
*Detective Fiction; Sherlock
Holmes & A. Conan Doyle;
Literature; First Editions*

Paula Sterne
R F D #2, Huckleberry Road
West Redding, Conn. 06896
Short Name: **P Sterne**
*Dogs; Hunting, Fishing &
Angling; Shooting & Firearms*

Henry Stevens Son & Stiles
P O Box 1299
Williamsburg, Va. 23185
(804) 220-0925
Short Name: **H Stevens Son**
*Rare Books; Americana;
History, American; Maps,
Atlases, & Cartography;
Voyages, Travels, &
Exploration*

The Stevensons
90 West Thacker
Hoffman Estates, Ill. 60194
(312) 882-0421
Short Name: **Stevensons**
Boy Scouts

Steve Stewart
P O Box 118
Bayside, N.Y. 11361
Short Name: **S Stewart**
Ichthyology; Periodicals

Stinson House Books
Quincy Road
Rumney Village, N.H. 03266
(603) 786-3211
Short Name: **Stinson Hse**
*Natural History; Americana;
New Hampshire*

Peter Stockman
137 Fayette Street
Palmyra, N.Y. 14522
(315) 597-9696
Short Name: **P Stockman**
*General; Search Service, with
Stock; Little Magazines &
Literary Small Presses*

Stonehill's Books
114 North Walnut Street
Champaign, Ill. 61820
(217) 359-0287
Short Name: **Stonehill's**
*Fine & Rare Bindings;
Scholarly Books; Illinois;
General; Posters; Prints*

C A Stonehll, Inc
282 York Street
New Haven, Conn. 06511
(203) 865-5141
Short Name: **C A Stonehill**
*Incunabula & Early Printing;
Manuscripts; Appraisals &
Appraisal Services; English
Literature*

The Store
240 Main Street, Rte #11
Mount Crawford, Va. 22841
(703) 433-9388
Short Name: **Store**
*Ephemera; Prints; Maps,
Atlases, & Cartography;
Illustrated Books; Americana,
Regional; General*

Ivan Stormgart
24 Telegraph Street
Boston, Mass. 02127
(617) 268-3942
Short Name: **I Stormgart**
*Out of Print, with Stock; Rare
Books; Search Service, with
Stock; Women & Feminism;
Erotica; Sexology*

Strand Book Store-Rare Books
828 Broadway
New York, N.Y. 10003
(212) 473-1452
Short Name: **Strand-Rare**
*Art; Books about Books; First
Editions, Modern; General;
Rare Books; Scholarly Books*

Strand Book Store
828 Broadway
New York, N.Y. 10003
(212) 473-1452
Short Name: **Strand**
*Art; General; Remainders;
Fiction*

Strawberry Hill Press
2594 15th Avenue
San Francisco, Calif. 94127
(415) 664-8112
Short Name: **Strawberry Hill**
*Cookery & Gastronomy;
Political, Social, & Cultural
History & Thought; Religion &
Theology; Americana;
Biography; Fiction*

Strawbridge Books
631 Burns Avenue
Aptos, Calif. 95003
(408) 688-0520
Short Name: **Strawbridge**
*Art; Collection Development;
Out of Print, with Stock;
Reprints; Search Service, with
Stock; New Books*

Strictly Fiction
P O Box 10234
Alexandria, Va. 22310
Short Name: **Strictly**
*First Editions; First Editions,
Modern; Fiction; Rare Books;
Militaria; Railroads*

Paul A Stroock, Art Books
35 Middle Lane, Box 126
Jericho, N.Y. 11753
(516) 433-9018
Short Name: **P A Stroock**
*Architecture; Art; Graphic Arts;
IlluminatedManuscripts; Out of
Print, with Stock; Scholarly
Books*

Stroud Theological Booksellers
Star Route, Box 99-A
Williamsburg, W.Va. 24991
Short Name: **Stroud**
*Religion & Theology; Bible &
Bible Studies; Church History;
Methodism*

Stryker's Books Reg'd
5947 Park Avenue
Montreal Pq H2V 4H4
(514) 272-5240
Short Name: **Stryker's**
*Authors; Health; Natural
Healing*

Stuart's Second-Hand Books
2704 Ontario Road, NW
Washington, D.C. 20009
(202) 483-7740
Short Name: **Stuart's**
*Crafts & Trades; Natural
History; Out of Print, with
Stock; Technology*

Gustave H Suhm
81 Llewelyn Drive
Westfield, Mass. 01085
(413) 568-5627
Short Name: **G H Suhm**
*Animals; Biography; Birds &
Ornithology; Hunting, Fishing
& Angling; Natural History;
Shooting & Firearms*

George Sullivan
330 East 33rd Street
New York, N.Y. 10016
Short Name: **G Sullivan**
*Sporting; Childrens' Books;
Tobacco & Smoking*

John Sullivan
3748 North Damen
Chicago, Ill. 60618
Short Name: **J Sullivan**
Sporting

Rosemary Sullivan
52 South Wade
Washington, Penna. 15301
(412) 225-1964
Short Name: **T Sullivan**
*Americana; Pennsylvania; Civil
War & Confederacy; Ephemera;
Geneaologies; Out of Print, with
Stock*

E And S Summerhouse Books
P O Box 66
Dayton, Wyom. 82836
Short Name: **Summerhouse**
Western Americana; Wyoming

Sun Dance Books
1520 North Crescent Heights
Hollywood, Calif. 90046
(213) 654-2383
Short Name: **Sun Dance**
*Voyages, Travels, &
Exploration; Latin America;
American Indians; Pacific
Region; Overland Narratives;
Whaling*

Suncircle Books
P O Box 607
Fort Collins, Colo. 80522
Short Name: **Suncircle**
*First Editions; Literature;
Literary Criticism; Search
Service, with Stock; Paperbacks
(new); Sets*

Sunny Enterprises
2700 Neilson Way, #1521
Santa Monica, Calif. 90405
(213) 392-7955
Short Name: **Sunny**
*Holistic Health & Nutrition;
Vegetarianism*

Super Books
P O Box 688
Rye, N.Y. 10580
(914) 967-7994
Short Name: **Super**
Out of Print, without Stock

Surrencys Bookstore
1508 King Street
Jacksonville, Fla. 32204
Short Name: **Surrencys**
General

K W Sutcliffe
44 Arrowhead Lane
South Dartmouth, Mass. 02748
(617) 994-7129
Short Name: **K W Sutcliffe**
*Out of Print, with Stock;
Industry & Labor; Paperbacks
(new); Political Science &
Theory; Women & Feminism;
First Editions*

Swann Galleries, Inc
104 East 25th Street
New York, N.Y. 10010
Short Name: **Swann**
*Auctions & Auctioneers;
Appraisals & Appraisal
Services*

Swiss Village Books
912 North Street
Highland, Ill. 62249
(618) 654-2521
Short Name: **Swiss Village**
*Autographed Material &
Autographs; Childrens' Books;
Cookery & Gastronomy;
General; Women & Feminism;
Textiles*

Sykes & Flanders
P O Box 103, Route 77
North Weare Village, N.H.
03281
Short Name: **Sykes & Fla**
*Americana; Detective Fiction;
First Editions; Illustrated
Books; Natural History;
Voyages, Travels, &
Exploration*

Sylvester & Orphanos
2484 Cheremoya Avenue
Los Angeles, Calif. 90068
Short Name: **Sylvest & Orph**
*First Editions, Modern;
Literature; Press Books & Fine
Printing; Collection
Development; Poetry; Detective
Fiction*

R M Sylvester
4845 Vekasko Road
Syracuse, N.Y. 13215
(315) 469-1413
Short Name: **R M Sylvester**
*Americana, Regional;
Appraisals & Appraisal
Services; Ephemera; Rare
Books; Search Service, with
Stock*

Symposium Books
4458 Myrtle Avenue
Long Beach, Calif. 90807
Short Name: **Symposium**
Rare Books

**George P Szontagh,
Cartographica**
1514-1/2 Vermont Street
Houston, Tex. 77006
(713) 528-1848
Short Name: **G P Szontagh**
*Architecture; City & Urban
Planning; Maps, Atlases, &
Cartography; Prints; Reprints;
Voyages, Travels, &
Exploration*

T

Tainters
P O Box 36
Temple, N.H. 03084
Short Name: **Tainters**
*Search Service, with Stock; Out
of Print, with Stock*

Talbothay's Books
P O Box 287
Minetto, N.Y. 13115
(315) 343-0774
Short Name: **Talbothay's**
*Americana; First Editions;
Literary Criticism; Militaria;
Search Service, with Stock*

Talisman Press
P O Box 455
Georgetown, Calif. 95634
Short Name: **Talisman**
*California; Western Americana;
20th Century Literature;
Literature; Maps, Atlases, &
Cartography; Photography*

Victor Tamerlis
911 Stuart Avenue
Mamaroneck, N.Y. 10543
(914) 698-8950
Short Name: **V Tamerlis**
*Art; Prints; Printing & Printing
History; Illustrated Books;
Scholarly Books*

Tan Bark Books
P O Box 217
Williamsville, N.Y. 14221
Short Name: **Tan Bark**
*Cock Fighting; Dogs; Natural
History; Hunting, Fishing &
Angling; Local History;
Firearms & Weapons*

Melvin Tanditash
P O Box A-27
New York, N.Y. 10038
Short Name: **M Tanditash**
*H. G. Wells; Books about
Books; Economics & Business;
First Editions, Modern;
Literature; Poetry*

Hans Tanner
R D #2, 5990 Groveland Hill
Geneseo, N.Y. 14454
Short Name: **H Tanner**
*Americana, States; Broadsides;
Civil War & Confederacy;
Ephemera; Maps, Atlases, &
Cartography; Overland
Narratives*

Taos Book Shop
P O Box 827
Taos, N.Mex. 87571
(505) 758-3733
Short Name: **Taos**
*Western Americana; Authors;
Out of Print, with Stock; Search
Service, with Stock*

Tappin Book Mine
705 Atlantic Boulevard
Atlantic Beach, Fla. 32233
(904) 246-1388
Short Name: **Tappin**
*Americana, Regional; Civil War
& Confederacy; Comic Books;
Maps, Atlases, & Cartography;
Naval & Marine; Search
Service, with Stock*

E Tatro-Books
60 Goff Road
Wethersfield, Conn. 06109
Short Name: **E Tatro**
*Baseball; Boxing; Golf; Olympic
Games*

Tattered Cover
2823 East Second Avenue
Denver, Colo. 80206
Short Name: **Tattered Cover**
*Voyages, Travels, &
Exploration; Maps, Atlases, &
Cartography; Childrens' Books;
Classics; Poetry; Psychiatry,
Psychology, & Psychonanalysis*

Taurus Books
P O Box 830
Easthampton, Mass. 01027
Short Name: **Taurus**
*Books about Books; Collection
Development; Press Books &
Fine Printing; Printing &
Printing History; Scholarly
Books; Typography & Type
Specimens*

B Tauscher
P O Box 1064
Bristol, Va. 24201
(703) 669-2994
Short Name: **B Tauscher**
*Americana, Regional; Civil War
& Confederacy; Childrens'
Books; Detective Fiction; Out of
Print, with Stock; Search
Service, with Stock*

Joanna Taylor
2461 El Pavo
Rancho Cordova, Calif. 95670
Short Name: **J Taylor**
*Women & Feminism; Poetry;
History; Philosophy; Biography*

Robert B Taylor
218 57th Street
Sea Isle City, N.J. 08243
(609) 263-1435
Short Name: **R B Taylor**
*Search Service, without Stock;
Out of Print, without Stock;
General*

W Thomas Taylor
1310 West 42nd, Box 5343
Austin, Tex. 78763
Short Name: **W T Taylor**
*Press Books & Fine Printing;
Books about Books; Literature*

Leon Tebbetts Bookstore
164 Water Street
Hallowell, Maine 04347
Short Name: **L Tebbetts**
*Americana; Color Plate Books;
New Books; Out of Print, with
Stock; Rare Books; Cinema &
Mass Media*

Technical Info-Doc Ltd
4650 St Catherine Street, West
Westmount, Que. H3Z 1S5
(514) 937-0000
Short Name: **Tech Info-Doc**
*American Indians; Manuscripts;
Maps, Atlases, & Cartography;
History of Medicine & Science;
Incunabula & Early Printing;
Voyages, Travels, &
Exploration*

Temares Family Books
50 Heights Road
Plandome, N.Y. 11030
(516) 627-7822
Short Name: **Temares**
*Limited Editions Club; Series
Books for Boys & Girls;
Childrens' Books; Art;
Illustrated Books; Out of Print,
with Stock*

Temple Bar Bookshop
9 Boylston Street
Cambridge, Mass. 02138
(617) 876-6025
Short Name: **Temple Bar**
*Literature; First Editions; First
Editions, Modern; Architecture;
Voyages, Travels, &
Exploration; Illustrated Books*

Steven Temple
368 Queen Street, East
Toronto, Ont. M5A 1T1
(416) 368-5960
Short Name: **S Temple**
*Canadian Literature; First
Editions, Modern; Detective
Fiction; Literature; Poetry;
Literature in English
Translation*

Ten O'Clock Books ✓
2716 Manning Avenue
Los Angeles, Calif. 90064
Short Name: **10 O'Clock**
Search Service, without Stock

Ten Pound Island Books
227 East Main Street
Gloucester, Mass. 01930
(617) 283-5299
Short Name: **10 Pound**
*Americana, Regional; Naval &
Marine; Women & Feminism*

1023 Booksellers
1023 Q 'street
Lincoln, Neb. 68508
(402) 435-1669
Short Name: **1023**
*Biography; General; Literary
Criticism; Literature; Poetry;
Nebraska*

Terramedia Books
7 Homestead Road
Wellesley, Mass. 02181
(617) 235-8407
Short Name: **Terramedia**
*Africa; Asia; Hunting, Fishing
& Angling; Middle East;
Orientalia; Voyages, Travels, &
Exploration*

J Dale Terry
P O Box 22
Wichita Falls, Tex. 76307
Short Name: **J D Terry**
*Texas; Southwestern America;
Militaria; Outlaws & Rangers;
Americana*

Terry's Better Books
22702 123rd Avenue
Maple Ridge, B.C. V2X 4E4
(604) 467-3351
Short Name: **Terry's Better**
*Childrens' Books; Detective
Fiction; Illustrated Books;
Fiction; Paperbacks (new)*

Dennis Tessier
221 Springfield
Wilbraham, Mass. 01095
(413) 596-9522
Short Name: **D Tessier**
*Canada & Canadiana; Naval &
Marine*

D Testa Bookseller
P O Box 9064
North Newark, N.J. 07104
(201) 484-5291
Short Name: **D Testa**
*Antiques; Crafts & Trades; Out
of Print, without Stock;
Photography; Printing &
Printing History; U.S.
Government Publications*

Becky Thatcher Books
209-211 Hill Street
Hannibal, Mo. 63401
Short Name: **B Thatcher**
Mark Twain; Childrens' Books

Theatrebooks Inc
1576 Broadway, #312
New York, N.Y. 10036
(212) 757-2834
Short Name: **Theatrebooks**
*Performing Arts; Search
Service, with Stock; Inscribed
Books; Out of Print, with Stock;
Drama*

Thelema Publications
P O Box 1093
King Beach, Calif. 95719
(916) 546-2160
Short Name: **Thelema**
*First Editions; Collection
Development; Religion &
Theology; Rare Books; Author
Collections*

Theological Book Center
518 Central Street
Winchendon, Mass. 01475
(617) 297-1006
Short Name: **Theological**
Religion & Theology; Theology

Theoria Scholarly Books
P O Box 369
Forest Hills, N.Y. 11375
Short Name: **Theoria**
*Philosophy; Reference; Religion
& Theology; Scholarly Books;
Search Service, with Stock;
Social Sciences*

Theta Books
P O Box 600
Clearwater, Fla. 33517
(813) 446-3556
Short Name: **Theta**
*Authors; Dictionaries; Religion
& Theology; Science Fiction;
Periodicals*

**Thirteen Colonies Books &
 Prints**
P O Box 2122
Reston, Va. 22090
Short Name: **13 Colonies**
*Book Scouts; Out of Print,
without Stock; Search Service,
without Stock; Prints*

This Old House Bookshop
5399 West Holt
Montclair, Calif. 91763
(714) 624-5144
Short Name: **This Old Hse**
*Cookery & Gastronomy; Crafts
& Trades; Fiction; Religion &
Theology; Scholarly Books;
Search Service, with Stock*

Eleanor C Thomas
R R #1
Farmersville, Ill. 62533
(217) 227-4173
Short Name: **E C Thomas**
*Out of Print, with Stock; Rare
Books; First Editions; History;
Civil War & Confederacy;
Russia & Eastern European
Region*

Frank J Thomas
2271 Cheremoya Avenue
Los Angeles, Calif. 90068
(213) 467-3800
Short Name: **F J Thomas**
*Art; Ephemera; Graphic Arts;
Illustrated Books; Photography;
Press Books & Fine Printing*

William Thomas
210 West Marble Street
Mechanicsburg, Penna. 17055
Short Name: **W Thomas**
Americana; Pennsylvania

Mrs John L Thomason
Old Hickory Boulevard, Box 35
White Creek, Tenn. 37189
Short Name: **Mrs Thomason**
*Childrens' Books; Doll Books &
Paper Dolls; Miniature Books;
Tennessee*

Thomolsen Books
P O Box 180
Bayside, N.Y. 11361
Short Name: **Thomolsen**
*Detective Fiction; Criminology;
Gardening & Horticulture*

Leroy Thompson
3471 Highway A
Festus, Mo. 63028
(314) 937-0184
Short Name: **L Thompson**
*Aviation & Aeronautics; Civil
War & Confederacy; Militaria;
Naval & Marine; Shooting &
Firearms*

Thoreau Lyceum Bookshop
156 Belknap Street
Concord, Mass. 01742
(617) 369-5912
Short Name: **Thoreau Lyceum**
*Transcendentalism &
Transcendentalists; Local
History; Natural History*

Three Arts
3 Collegeview Avenue
Poughkeepsie, N.Y. 12603
Short Name: **3 Arts**
Americana, Regional; Prints

Three Geese
54g Tinker Street
Woodstock, N.Y. 12498
(914) 679-8787
Short Name: **3 Geese**
*Myths; Folklore; Childrens'
Books*

Thrifty Reader
9 West Burdick Street
Oxford, Mich. 48051
(313) 628-6817
Short Name: **Thrifty Reader**
*General; Paperbacks (new); Out
of Print, with Stock; Search
Service, with Stock*

Thunderbird Books
P O Box 2129
Sidney, B.C. V8L 3S6
Short Name: **Thunderbird**
*Aviation & Aeronautics; Naval
& Marine; Militaria; Hunting,
Fishing & Angling; Arctica &
Antarctica*

Tim W Tingle
3012 Headly Drive
Austin, Tex. 78745
Short Name: **T W Tingle**
*First Editions, Modern;
Literature; Literary Criticism;
Author Collections; Search
Service, with Stock; Collection
Development*

Titcomb's Bookshop
432 Rte #6a, Box 45
East Sandwich, Mass. 02537
Short Name: **Titcomb's**
*Americana; Fishing & Angling;
Naval & Marine; Local History*

Titles, Inc
1931 Sheridan Road
Highland Park, Ill. 60035
(312) 432-3690
Short Name: **Titles**
*Rare Books; Illustrated Books;
Photography; Press Books &
Fine Printing; Childrens' Books;
Chicago*

Toad Hall
P O Box 902
Berkeley, Calif. 94701
Short Name: **Toad Hall**
*Gardening & Horticulture;
Childrens' Books*

Russ Todd
4301 East Sahauro Drive
Phoenix, Ariz. 85028
(602) 996-7277
Short Name: **R Todd**
*Americana, Regional; First
Editions, Modern; Detective
Fiction; Outlaws & Rangers;
Science Fiction*

Tolliver's Books
1634 South Stearns Drive
Los Angeles, Calif. 90035
Short Name: **Tolliver's**
*Birds & Ornithology;
Herpetology; Ichthyology;
Mammalogy; Mexico*

Totteridge Book Shop
247a North Road, R D #1
Amenia, N.Y. 12501
Short Name: **Totteridge**
*First Editions; Illustrated
Books*

Gordon Totty
576 Massachusetts Avenue
Lunenburg, Mass. 01462
Short Name: **G Totty**
*Americana; Civil War &
Confederacy; General; History,
American; Newspapers;
Voyages, Travels, &
Exploration*

Tower House
80 East Elm Street
Greenwich, Conn. 06830
(203) 869-8295
Short Name: **Tower Hse**
*Collection Development; First
Editions; General; Out of Print,
with Stock; Search Service, with
Stock*

The Townsends
5721 Antietam Drive
Sarasota, Fla. 33581
(813) 924-9170
Short Name: **Townsends**
*Geneaologies; Local History;
Church Records*

Towson Books-Gary Cheek
141 Brighton 10th Street
Brooklyn, N.Y. 11235
Short Name: **Towson**
*Inscribed Books; First Editions;
Rare Books*

The Toxophilite Collector
P O Box 363
Simsbury, Conn. 06070
(203) 653-3319
Short Name: **Toxophilite**
Archery

Timothy Trace
144 Red Mill Road
Peekskill, N.Y. 10566
Short Name: **T Trace**
*Architecture; Decorative Arts;
Antiques; Crafts & Trades*

The Tracery
P O Box 29733
Dallas, Tex. 75229
(214) 361-5269
Short Name: **Tracery**
Search Service, with Stock

Trackside Books
8819 Mobud Drive
Houston, Tex. 77036
(713) 772-8107
Short Name: **Trackside**
*Railroads; Texas; Search
Service, with Stock; Americana;
Outlaws & Rangers; Out of
Print, with Stock*

Trade & Sell Shop
1545 Scott Boulevard
Covington, Ken. 41012
Short Name: **Trade & Sell**
*Americana; Americana,
Regional; Biography*

**The Trail To Yesterday Book
 Niche**
5652-I Little Ben Circle
Columbus, Ohio 43229
(614) 890-5170
Short Name: **Trail To Y'day**
*Arizona; Western Americana;
Outlaws & Rangers; Out of
Print, with Stock*

George Tramp
709 2nd Street
Jackson, Mich. 49203
Short Name: **G Tramp**
*Western Americana; Civil War
& Confederacy; Asia; Australia
& Oceania; Biography; 18th
Century Literature*

Trans Allegheny Book Service
Rte #1, Box 148
Walker, W.Va. 26180
Short Name: **Trans Allegheny**
*West Virginia; Americana,
Regional; Ohio; Western
Pennsylvania; Authors*

Transition Books
445 Stockton Street
San Francisco, Calif. 94108
Short Name: **Transition**
*First Editions, Modern; English
Literature; American Literature;
French Books & Literature;
Illustrated Books; Press Books
& Fine Printing*

Travellers' Books And Maps
483 Bloor Street, West
Toronto, Ont. M5S 1Y2
Short Name: **Travellers'**
*Archaeology; Maps, Atlases, &
Cartography; Voyages, Travels,
& Exploration*

Clifford K Travis
5 Harvard Lane
Hastings-On-Hudson, N.Y.
 10706
Short Name: **C K Travis**
Photography; Camera Manuals

Treasures In Books
P O Box 53
Andes, N.Y. 13731
(914) 676-4613
Short Name: **Treasures**
*American Indians; Americana;
Americana, Regional; History,
American; Out of Print, with
Stock; Search Service, without
Stock*

Trebizond Rare Books
667 Madison Avenue
New York, N.Y. 10021
(212) 371-1980
Short Name: **Trebizond**
*Voyages, Travels, &
Exploration; Continental Books;
Books about Books; Rare
Books; STC & Wing Books;
Poetry*

The Tree House
76 Plaza West Shopping Center
St Cloud, Minn. 56301
Short Name: **Tree Hse**
*Childrens' Books; Parenting;
Games & Pasttimes;
Phonograph Records*

Treehorn Books
105 3rd Street
Santa Rosa, Calif. 95401
(707) 525-1782
Short Name: **Treehorn**
*Childrens' Books; Illustrated
Books; Industry & Labor;
Political, Social, & Cultural
History & Thought; Search
Service, with Stock*

Treetops
2119 Hampshire
Quincy, Ill. 62301
(217) 223-1535
Short Name: **Treetops**
*Literature; Biography; Art;
First Editions, Modern*

Tri-Town Book Mart
95 Main Street
Livermore Falls, Maine 04254
(207) 897-2111
Short Name: **Tri-Town**
*Paperbacks (new); General;
Fiction; First Editions; First
Editions, Modern; Detective
Fiction*

Trotting Book Shop
P O Box 63
Hinsdale, Ill. 60521
Short Name: **Trotting**
*Farming, Ranching, &
Livestock; Horses; Sporting*

H N Trueb
1826 East Cloud Court
Simi Valley, Calif. 93065
(805) 526-3108
Short Name: **H T Trueb**
Greek & Latin Classics;
Metaphysics; Philosophy;
Transcendentalism &
Transcendentalists; Search
Service, with Stock

The Truth Seeker Company
P O Box 2832
San Diego, Calif. 92112
(714) 291-2297
Short Name: **Truth Seeker**
Religion & Theology

**Tryon County Bookshop-R
    Montgomery**
R D #1, Box 207, Rte #2
Johnstown, N.Y. 12095
Short Name: **Tryon Cnty**
General

The Tuckers
2236 Murray Avenue
Pittsburgh, Penna. 15217
(412) 521-0249
Short Name: **Tuckers**
Out of Print, with Stock; Search
Service, with Stock; Appraisals
& Appraisal Services; Scholarly
Books; Humanities; Western
Pennsylvania

Tucson Books-Paul Gaudette
714 Euclid Street
Tucson, Ariz. 85719
(602) 622-2326
Short Name: **Tucson**
Aviation & Aeronautics;
Militaria; Naval & Marine

Peter Tumarkin
1370 Lexington Avenue
New York, N.Y. 10028
Short Name: **P Tumarkin**
German Books & Literature;
Rare Books; First Editions

David Tunick, Inc
12 East 81st Street
New York, N.Y. 10028
(212) 570-0090
Short Name: **D Tunick**
Prints; Drawings

Turkey Hill Books
46 South Turkey Hill
Westport, Conn. 06880
Short Name: **Turkey Hill**
Childrens' Books; First
Editions; Fiction; Poetry; Art

Tusitala Bookshop
116b Heklili Street
Kailua, Haw. 96734
(808) 262-6343
Short Name: **tusitala**
Pacific Region

O W Tuthill
500 King Muir Road
Lake Forest, Ill. 60045
Short Name: **O W Tuthill**
Press Books & Fine Printing;
Authors

Tuttle Antiquarian
P O Box 541
Rutland, Vt. 05701
(802) 773-8930
Short Name: **Tuttle Antiq**
General; Geneaologies; Maps,
Atlases, & Cartography; Local
History; Americana, States;
Americana, Regional

George H Tweney
16660 Marine View Drive, SW
Seattle, Wash. 98166
(206) 243-8243
Short Name: **G H Tweney**
Americana; Appraisals &
Appraisal Services; Books
about Books; Out of Print, with
Stock; Overland Narratives;
Voyages, Travels, &
Exploration

Twice Sold Tales
P O Box 351
Jamestown, N.Y. 14701
Short Name: **Twice Sold**
Women & Feminism; Childrens'
Books; Illustrated Books;
Scholarly Books; Folklore

221 Books
4420 Regents Court
Westlake Village, Calif. 91361
Short Name: **221**
First Editions; Sherlock
Holmes & A. Conan Doyle;
Authors; H. G. Wells; Search
Service, with Stock

Mary Twyce Antiques & Books
601 East 5th Street
Winona, Minn. 55987
(507) 454-4412
Short Name: **M Twyce**
Americana, States; Americana,
Regional; Childrens' Books;
Search Service, with Stock;
Americana

The Typographeum Bookshop
The Stone Cottage, Bennington
    Road
Francestown, N.H. 03043
Short Name: **Typographeum**
Literature; First Editions; Rare
Books; Books about Books

Margaret L Tyrrell
117 North 40th Street
Allentown, Penna. 18104
Short Name: **M L Tyrrell**
Antiques; Childrens' Books;
Ephemera; General; Search
Service, without Stock

Tyson Books
334 Westminster Mall
Providence, R.I. 02903
(401) 421-3939
Short Name: **Tyson**
Americana; Rhode Island; First
Editions; History, American;
Search Service, with Stock;
General

U

Ukiyo-E Trading Company
69-53 Park Drive East
Kew Gardens Hills, N.Y. 11367
Short Name: **Ukiyo-E**
Japan; Woodcut Books

Under Cover Books
53 The Arcade
Cleveland, Ohio 44114
(216) 574-9500
Short Name: **Under Cover-Cle**
*Archaeology; Architecture;
Judaica & Hebraica; Press
Books & Fine Printing; Search
Service, without Stock;
Typography & Type Specimens*

Under Cover Books
20201 Van Aken Boulevard
Shaker Heights, Ohio 44122
(216) 991-3600
Short Name: **Under Cover-Sha**
*Archaeology; Architecture;
Judaica & Hebraica; Press
Books & Fine Printing; Search
Service, without Stock;
Typography & Type Specimens*

Robert E Underhill
85 Underhill Road
Poughkeepsie, N.Y. 12603
(914) 452-5986
Short Name: **R E Underhill**
*Farming, Ranching, &
Livestock; Gardening &
Horticulture; Natural History;
New Books; Out of Print,
without Stock; Search Service,
without Stock*

Unicorn Bookshop
24 North Washington Street
Easton, Md. 21601
Short Name: **Unicorn-Eas**
*Maryland; Art; Hunting,
Fishing & Angling; Civil War &
Confederacy; Yachts, Yachting,
& Sailing; H. L. Mencken*

Unicorn Book Store
4104 Archer Avenue
Chicago, Ill. 60632
Short Name: **Unicorn-Chi**
*American Indians;
Parapsychology*

The Unique Antique
P O Box 485
Putney, Vt. 05346
(802) 387-4488
Short Name: **Unique Antiq**
*Antiques; Art; Drawings;
Paintings; Prints; General*

Unique Book Stall
912 South Virginia Street
Reno, Nev. 89502
Short Name: **Unique Stall**
Nevada

U S Games Systems
38 East 32nd Street
New York, N.Y. 10016
Short Name: **U S Games**
Playing Cards; Renaissance

Univelt Inc
P O Box 28130
San Diego, Calif. 92128
(714) 746-4005
Short Name: **Univelt**
Technology; Reference; History

University Book Store
623 North Manhattan Avenue
Manhattan, Kan. 66502
Short Name: **Univ Bk St-Man**
*New Books; General;
Paperbacks (new)*

University Place Bookshop
821 Broadway
New York, N.Y. 10003
(212) 254-5998
Short Name: **University Pl**
*Africa; Black Literature &
Black Studies; Caribbean;
Chess, Checkers, & Draughts;
Incunabula & Early Printing*

Urban Books
295 Grizzly Peak Boulevard
Berkeley, Calif. 94708
Short Name: **Urban**
*Political Science & Theory;
Economics & Business;
California; City & Urban
Planning; Labor History*

Ursus Books, Ltd
667 Madison Avenue
New York, N.Y. 10021
Short Name: **Ursus**
*Illustrated Books; Scholarly
Books; Art; Prints* 772-8787

Used Book Place
P O Box 206
Dyer, Ind. 46311
(219) 322-4247
Short Name: **Used-Dye**
*Out of Print, with Stock; Search
Service, with Stock; Self-
Sufficiency; Libertarianism*

The Used Book Place
3627 South Dixie Highway
West Palm Beach, Fla. 33405
(305) 833-8826
Short Name: **Used-West**
*Americana; Biography; Books
about Books; History; History,
American; Out of Print, with
Stock*

Ute-Or-Ida Books
P O Box 279
West Jordan, Utah 84084
Short Name: **Ute-Or-Ida**
*Idaho; Utah; Mormons; Western
Americana; Rare Books;
Northwest*

V

Vagabond Books
2076 Westwood Boulevard
Los Angeles, Calif. 90025
(213) 475-2700
Short Name: **Vagabond**
*First Editions; Literature;
Cinema & Mass Media;
Detective Fiction; Performing
Arts; First Editions, Modern*

**R Valdez, Bookseller &
Bookbinder**
P O Box 5762
Calexico, Calif. 92231
(714) 357-2043
Short Name: **R Valdez**
*Bookbinding & Restoration;
Books about Books; Authors;
Mexico; Immigration*

Valley Book City
5249 Lankershim Boulevard
North Hollywood, Calif. 91601
Short Name: **Valley Bk City**
*Art; Science Fiction; Cinema &
Mass Media; Metaphysics;
Photography; Biography*

Valley Books
111 South Elmer Avenue
Sayre, Penna. 18840
(717) 888-9785
Short Name: **Valley-Say**
*Art; Ephemera; Prints; General;
Paintings; Drawings*

Valley Book Shop
5 East Pleasant Street
Amherst, Mass. 01002
(413) 549-6052
Short Name: **Valley-Amh**
*Literary Criticism; Literature;
Paperbacks (new); Fiction*

Valley Book Shop
P O Box 37
Galena, Ill. 61036
Short Name: **Valley-Gal**
*American Indians; Americana;
Civil War & Confederacy;
Outlaws & Rangers; Overland
Narratives; Railroads*

Valley Forge Books
P O Box 344
Phoenixville, Penna. 19460
Short Name: **Valley Forge**
Militaria

Willis Van Devanter
P O Box 32426
Washington, D.C. 20007
Short Name: **W Van Devanter**
*Cookery & Gastronomy; Black
Literature & Black Studies;
Voyages, Travels, &
Exploration*

Van Norman Book Company
422-4 Bank Of Galesburg
  Building
Galesburg, Ill. 61401
Short Name: **Van Norman**
*Middle West; Western
Americana; American Diaries &
Narratives; English Literature*

Anne Vanasse
P O Box 93
Carversville, Penna. 18913
Short Name: **A Vanasse**
Sporting; Horses; Sports

Graeme Vanderstoel
P O Box 599
El Cerrito, Calif. 94530
(415) 527-2882
Short Name: **G Vanderstoel**
*Africa; Asia; Orientalia;
Australia & Oceania*

Robert L Veatch
P O Box 985
Smithtown, N.Y. 11787
Short Name: **R L Veatch**
*Book Trade & Catalogues;
Books about Books; Press
Books & Fine Printing; Printing
& Printing History; Typography
& Type Specimens*

Carlos Juan Vega
140 West End Avenue, #27k
New York, N.Y. 10023
(212) 799-6573
Short Name: **C J Vega**
*Art; Latin America; Voyages,
Travels, & Exploration; First
Editions, Modern*

Vegetarian Society, Inc
P O Box 5688
Santa Monica, Calif. 90405
(213) 396-8998
Short Name: **Vegetarian Soc**
Vegetarianism; Health

Robert Verhines, Bookseller
631 Best Avenue
Dekalb, Ill. 60115
Short Name: **R Verhines**
Trade Catalogues

Vi & Si's Antiques
8970 Main Street
Clarence, N.Y. 14031
Short Name: **Vi & Si's**
*Childrens' Books; Musical
Instruments; Music;
Phonograph Records*

Henry J Vickey
9 Brook Street
Stoughton, Mass. 02072
Short Name: **H J Vickey**
Out of Print, with Stock

Victoria Book Shop
303 Fifth Avenue
New York, N.Y. 10016
(212) 683-7849
Short Name: **Victoria-NYC**
*Childrens' Books; Illustrated
Books; Miniature Books; Rare
Books; Original Art of Book
Illustrations*

Village Bookshelf
1531 Amherst Road, Ne, Box
  708
Massillon, Ohio 44648
Short Name: **Village-Mass**
Science Fiction; Pulps; Horror

Village Book Store
102 Main Street
Littleton, N.H. 03561
Short Name: **Village-Lit**
New Hampshire; History,
American

The Village Booksmith
223 Main Street
Hudson Falls, N.Y. 12839
Short Name: **Village-Hud**
General; Presidents; Hunting,
Fishing & Angling; Cookery &
Gastronomy; Show Business;
Performing Arts

Vintage Book Company
P O Box 16182, Elway Station
St Paul, Minn. 55116
(612) 690-2363
Short Name: **Vintage-St P**
Astronomy; Mathematics

Vintage Books
P O Box 285
Boston, Mass. 02135
Short Name: **Vintage-Bost**
American Literature; English
Literature; Avant Garde,
Experimental, & Modern Art

Virginia Book Company
114 South Church Street, Box
 431
Berryville, Va. 22213
(703) 955-1428
Short Name: **Va Bk Co**
Americana, States; Americana,
Regional; Civil War &
Confederacy; Geneaologies;
History, American; Manuscripts

Scott Vogel
464 Quan Avenue
St Louis, Mo. 63122
Short Name: **S Vogel-St L**
Architecture; Art; First
Editions, Modern; Beverages;
Fiction; Hunting, Fishing &
Angling

Shelly Vogel
629 Lower State Street
Santa Barbara, Calif. 93101
(805) 966-3852
Short Name: **S Vogel-San**
Literature; Art; Photography;
Paintings; Prints; Illustrated
Books

H Volker
14834 Elmwood Avenue
Pierrefonds, Que. H9H 1S9
(514) 626-5981
Short Name: **H Volker**
Militaria; Naval & Marine;
Shooting & Firearms; Voyages,
Travels, & Exploration;
Aviation & Aeronautics

Volkoff & Von Hohenlohe
1514 La Coronilla
Santa Barbara, Calif. 93109
(805) 966-2100
Short Name: **Volkhoff & Von**
Rare Books; Manuscripts;
Medicine & Science; Political
Science & Theory; Philosophy;
European History

Volume One Used Books
1405 Second Street
Napa, Calif. 94558
(707) 252-1466
Short Name: **Vol One Used**
General; Fiction; Paperbacks
(new)

Von Blons Books
1111 Colcord
Waco, Tex. 76707
Short Name: **Von Blons**
Texas; Oklahoma (& Indian
Territory); Civil War &
Confederacy; Railroads; Search
Service, with Stock; General

W

John Wade
P O Box 991041
Cincinnati, Ohio 45201
Short Name: **J Wade**
Americana; Childrens' Books;
Ephemera; First Editions; Rare
Books; Prints

Wahrenbrock's Books
649 Broadway
San Deigo, Calif. 92101
Short Name: **Wahrenbrock's**
California; Autographed
Material & Autographs; Latin
America; Rare Books; Sets;
Voyages, Travels, &
Exploration

Paul G Waite
402 Clemons Avenue
Madison, Wisc. 53704
(608) 249-3006
Short Name: **P G Waite**
Rare Books; Art; Drawings;
Illustrated Books

Waiting For Godot (Mail Only)
~~12 Goodwin Place~~
~~Brookline, Mass. 02146~~ 137 Magazine
(617) 734-8291 Cambridge
Short Name: **Wait Godot** mass
First Editions, Modern; Fiction; 02139
Literature; Poetry

Wake-Brook House
P O Box 153
Hyannis, Mass. 02601
Short Name: **Wake-Brook-Hyan**
Out of Print, with Stock;
Miniature Books; Fore-Edge
Painting; Bookbinding &
Restoration; Fine & Rare
Bindings

Wake-Brook House
960 NW 53rd Street
Fort Lauderdale, Fla. 33309
Short Name: **Wake-Brook-Ft L**
Joseph C. Lincoln; Gene
Stratton-Porter; Cape Cod &
Martha's Vineyard; Miniature
Books; National Geographic
Magazine

Morris Waldstein Books
586 Ramapo Road
Teaneck, N.J. 07666
Short Name: **M Waldstein**
Astronomy; Physics; Rare
Books; Fine & Rare Bindings

Francis G Walett
369 High Street
Abington, Mass. 02351
Short Name: **F G Walett**
Americana; Americana,
Regional; Civil War &
Confederacy; Bibliography;
Rare Books

L A Wallrich
280 Queen Street, West
Toronto, Ont. M5V 2A1
Short Name: **L A Wallrich**
Appraisals & Appraisal
Services; Books about Books;
First Editions, Modern;
General; Literature

Walt Whitman Books
1412 Sutter Street
San Francisco, Calif. 94109
Short Name: **Walt Whitman**
Homosexual & Gay Literature

Ray S Walton-Rare Books
1708 Cromwell Hill
Austin, Tex. 78703
Short Name: **R S Walton**
Western Americana; Texas;
Voyages, Travels, &
Exploration; General

Wangner's Bookshop
9 Midland Avenue
Montclair, N.J. 07042
(201) 744-4211
Short Name: **Wangner's**
Book Scouts; General

Wantagh Rare Book Co
18 East Sunrise Highway
Freeport, N.Y. 11520
(516) 868-1511
Short Name: **Wantagh**
Americana; American Indians;
Civil War & Confederacy;
Railroads; Rare Books;
Voyages, Travels, &
Exploration

David Ward
2140 Regent Street
Madison, Wisc. 53705
(608) 231-1247
Short Name: **D Ward**
Americana, Regional; History,
American; American Indians;
First Editions; Fine & Rare
Bindings; Antiques

Samuel Ward
La Plata, Md. 20646
(301) 934-8298
Short Name: **S Ward**
U.S. Government Publications

Wards Corner Book Shop, Inc
7524 Granby Street
Norfolk, Va. 23505
(804) 587-3303
Short Name: **Wards Corner**
Civil War & Confederacy;
General; Out of Print, with
Stock; Paperbacks (new); Rare
Books; Science Fiction

Oliver E Warrick
4308 Pacific
Omaha, Neb. 68105
Short Name: **O E Warrick**
Western Americana; Nebraska

Warwick Bookstore
11 Main Street
Warwick, N.Y. 10990
(914) 986-2522
Short Name: **Warwick**
Rare Books; First Editions;
Collection Development;
Literature; Art; Medicine &
Science

Waverly Books O P
P O Box 222
Waverly, Penna. 18471
(717) 945-7801
Short Name: **Waverly**
Auctions & Auctioneers; First
Editions, Modern; Illustrated
Books; Photography;
Americana; Autographed
Material & Autographs

Waves Press & Bookshop
4040 MacArthur Avenue
Richmond, Va. 23227
(804) 264-9819
Short Name: **Waves**
Books about Books; Detective
Fiction; First Editions, Modern;
Graphic Arts; Literature; Out of
Print, with Stock

G Wayner
Rte #3, Box 18
Fort Payne, Ala. 35967
(205) 845-5866
Short Name: **G Wayner**
Botany; Gardening &
Horticulture; Natural History;
Scholarly Books; Sporting;
Rare Books

The Wayside Bookshop
Langworthy Road, Box 501
Westerley, R.I. 02891
Short Name: **Wayside**
First Editions; Inscribed Books;
Naval & Marine; Science
Fiction; Mystery Fiction; Press
Books & Fine Printing

Wayward Books
2748 Stephenson Lane, NW
Washington, D.C. 20015
Short Name: **Wayward**
First Editions, Modern; Press
Books & Fine Printing; General;
Out of Print, with Stock; Search
Service, with Stock; Women &
Feminism

R M Weatherford-Books
10902 Woods Creek Rd
Monroe, Wash. 98272
(206) 794-4318
Short Name: **R M Weatherford**
American Indians; Americana;
Appraisals & Appraisal
Services; Outlaws & Rangers;
Overland Narratives; Voyages,
Travels, & Exploration

George E Webb, Jr
P O Box 686
Paris, Tenn. 38242
(901) 642-8436
Short Name: **G E Webb, Jr**
*Americana; Tennessee; Fine &
Rare Bindings; Manuscripts;
Music; Psychopharmacology*

R F Webb-Autobooks
P O Box 891
Fresno, Calif. 93714
(209) 268-5965
Short Name: **R F Webb**
Automotive

Dale Weber Books
5740 Livernois
Rochester, Mich. 48063
Short Name: **D Weber**
*Authors; Roycrofters & Elbert
Hubbard*

L Weidler
P O Box 133
Hillsboro, Ill. 62049
Short Name: **L Weidler**
*General; Out of Print, with
Stock; Search Service, with
Stock*

Jeffery H Weinberg
P O Box 2122
Lowell, Mass. 01851
(617) 891-6583
Short Name: **J H Weinberg**
*Beat Literature; Fiction; First
Editions, Modern; Literature;
Little Magazines & Literary
Small Presses; Search Service,
without Stock*

A G Weindling
69 Ball Pond Road
Danbury, Conn. 06810
Short Name: **A G Weindling**
*Cookery & Gastronomy;
Childrens' Books; Fiction*

Samuel Weiser, Inc
740 Broadway
New York, N.Y. 10003
Short Name: **S Weiser**
*Astrology; Orientalia; Religion
& Theology; Philosophy;
Archaeology*

Dale Weiss
1411 Lorain Avenue
Bethlehem, Penna. 18018
Short Name: **D Weiss**
*Pennsylvania; Manuscripts;
Autographed Material &
Autographs; Hunting, Fishing
& Angling; First Editions;
Americana*

Joy Weiss
123 Oxford Street
Guelph, Ont. N1H 2M8
(519) 822-1792
Short Name: **J Weiss**
*Religion & Theology; Canada
& Canadiana; History;
Biography; Philosophy; Fiction*

Bernice Weiss-Rare Books
36 Tuckahoe Avenue
Eastchester, N.Y. 10707
Short Name: **B Weiss**
*First Editions; Poetry; Press
Books & Fine Printing;
Illustrated Books; Childrens'
Books*

Leo Weitz & Herbert E Weitz
1377 Lexington Avenue
New York, N.Y. 10028
(212) 831-2213
Short Name: **L & H Weitz**
*Appraisals & Appraisal
Services; Fine & Rare Bindings;
Bookbinding & Restoration;
Fore-Edge Painting; Illustrated
Books; Sets*

Weller Victoria Books
1250 South Marengo Avenue
Pasadena, Calif. 91106
(213) 441-1690
Short Name: **Weller Victoria**
*First Editions, Modern;
Literary Criticism; Detective
Fiction; Author Collections;
Literature in English
Translation; Black Literature &
Black Studies*

Wessex Books
1083 El Camino
Menlo Park, Calif. 94025
(415) 321-1333
Short Name: **Wessex**
*Fiction; First Editions, Modern;
Humanities; Literature; Out of
Print, with Stock; Scholarly
Books*

West Los Angeles Book Center
Los Angeles, Calif. 90025
(213) 473-4442
Short Name: **West L A Center**
*Art; First Editions; General;
Literature; Poetry; Science
Fiction*

West Side Book Shop
113 West Liberty
Ann Arbor, Mich. 48103
(313) 995-1891
Short Name: **West Side**
*Arctica & Antarctica; First
Editions, Modern; Illustrated
Books; Naval & Marine;
Photography; Voyages, Travels,
& Exploration*

West's Booking Agency
P O Box 406
Elm Grove, Wisc. 53122
(414) 786-7084
Short Name: **West's Agency**
*Detective Fiction; Americana;
First Editions; Science Fiction;
Illustrated Books; Childrens'
Books*

Western Book Company
1618 Franklin Street
Oakland, Calif. 94612
Short Name: **Western**
Christian Books

Western Hemisphere
1613 Central Street
Stoughton, Mass. 02072
Short Name: **Western Hemi**
*U.S. Government Publications;
Periodicals; Americana;
Economics & Business*

Westfall Spring Books
3533 La Entrada Road
Santa Barbara, Calif. 93105
Short Name: **Westfall Spring**
*Guns; Hunting, Fishing &
Angling; Sporting*

Westmount Parnassus
320 Victoria Avenue,
   Westmount
Montreal, Que.
Short Name: **Westmount**
*First Editions, Modern; Canada
& Canadiana; Literature*

**Sonya Wetstone-Books &
  Cheese**
529 Farmington Avenue
Hartford, Conn. 06105
Short Name: **S Wetstone**
*New Books; Childrens' Books;
Women & Feminism;
Homosexual & Gay Literature;
Mystery Fiction*

Weyhe Art Books
794 Lexington Avenue
New York, N.Y. 10021
(212) 838-5466
Short Name: **Weyhe**
Art; Architecture

Whaling Research
P O Box 5034
Berkeley, Calif. 94715
Short Name: **Whaling**
*Whaling; Naval & Marine;
Search Service, with Stock;
Voyages, Travels, &
Exploration; Arctica &
Antarctica*

Bern Wheel, Books
834 Wenonah
Oak Park, Ill. 60304
Short Name: **B Wheel**
Foreign Languages

Dr Joe L Wheeler
Drawer A
Keene, Tex. 76059
Short Name: **J L Wheeler**
*Zane Grey; Harold Bell Wight;
Paperbacks (early &
collectible); Literature;
Illustrated Books; Popular
Culture*

D E Whelan
P O Box 729
Newberry, Fla. 32669
Short Name: **D E Whelan**
*Astrology; Church Records;
Herbology·& Herbs; UFOs;
Myths*

Whistler's Books
5316 West 95th Street
Prairie Village, Kan. 66207
(913) 341-2060
Short Name: **Whistler's**
*New Books; Literature; Out of
Print, without Stock; Judaica &
Hebraica; Search Service,
without Stock*

White House Books
P O Box 16
Boyertown, Penna. 19512
Short Name: **White Hse**
*Political Science & Theory;
Presidents*

**The White Rabbit Children's
  Books**
7777 Girard Avenue
La Jolla, Calif. 92037
(714) 454-3518
Short Name: **White Rabbit**
Childrens' Books

White's Galleries
607 Lake Avenue
Asbury Park, N.J. 07712
(201) 774-9300
Short Name: **White's**
*Biography; First Editions;
Naval & Marine; Gardening &
Horticulture; Psychiatry,
Psychology, & Psychonanalysis*

Whitlock Farm Booksellers
20 Sperry Road
Bethany, Conn. 06525
Short Name: **Whitlock Farm**
*Farming, Ranching, &
Livestock; Natural History;
Americana, Regional; Sporting;
General*

Whitlock's, Inc
15 Broadway
New Haven, Conn. 06511
Short Name: **Whitlock's**
*Americana; Fine & Rare
Bindings; Color Plate Books;
Out of Print, with Stock; First
Editions; Out of Print, with
Stock*

R G Wilborn
P O Box 70
Moke Hill, Calif. 95245
Short Name: **R G Wilborn**
*Nicola Tesla;
Astrology; Herbology & Herbs;
Self Help; Freemasonry*

Ann Wilder
299 Tappan Street, #6
Brookline, Mass. 02146
Short Name: **A Wilder**
Childrens' Books

Wildwood Enterprises
P O Box 560
Old Forge, N.Y. 13420
(315) 369-3397
Short Name: **Wildwood**
*Americana, Regional; Hunting,
Fishing & Angling; Natural
History; Photography; Prints;
Adirondacks*

F J Wilhelm Publications
Chicago, Ill. 60660
(312) 338-1951
Short Name: **F J Wilhelm**
*Autographed Material &
Autographs; Comic Books;
Foreign Languages;
Newspapers; Periodicals;
Science Fiction*

Robin Wilkerson Books
55 Reservoir Street
Cambridge, Mass. 02138
(617) 491-1971
Short Name: **R Wilkerson**
*Gardening & Horticulture;
Literature; Antiques; Women &
Feminism; First Editions,
Modern; Childrens' Books*

William-Roberts Co, Inc
P O Box 543
Mineola, N.Y. 11501
(516) 741-0781
Short Name: **William-Roberts**
*Maps, Atlases, & Cartography;
Antiques; Horology*

Williams Bookstore
20 Spring Street
Williamstown, Mass. 01267
(413) 458-5717
Short Name: **Williams**
*New Books; Search Service,
without Stock; Poetry;
Photography; Out of Print,
without Stock; Art*

E C Williams (Mail Only)
Damariscotta River Road
Boothbay, Maine 04537
Short Name: **E C Williams**
*First Editions; History,
American; Manuscripts,
Medieval & Illuminated; Naval
& Marine; Out of Print, with
Stock; Search Service, with
Stock*

Philip Williams
329 Columbus Avenue
New York, N.Y. 10023
Short Name: **P Williams**
Art; Graphic Arts; Prints;
Posters

Tom Williams
P O Box 4126, Station C
Calgary, Alb. T2T 5M9
Short Name: **T Williams**
Arctica & Antarctica; Canada
& Canadiana; Mountaineering;
Out of Print, with Stock; Search
Service, with Stock; Voyages,
Travels, & Exploration

Willmann-Bell Inc
126 East Main Street
Dundee, Mich. 48131
(313) 529-5277
Short Name: **Willmann-Bell**
Transgenderism; Optics;
Astronautics & Rocketry

Wilsey Square Bookstore
30 Wilsey Square
Ridgewood, N.J. 07450
(201) 652-2999
Short Name: **Wilsey Square**
Books about Books; Press
Books & Fine Printing; Graphic
Arts; Illustrated Books;
Typography & Type Specimens;
Papermaking & Marbling

Fred Wilson
80 East 11th Street, #334
New York, N.Y. 10003
(212) 533-6381
Short Name: **F Wilson**
Chess, Checkers, & Draughts

Gail Wilson, Bookseller
198 Queen Street, West
Toronto, Ont. M5V 1Z2
(416) 598-2024
Short Name: **G Wilson**
Books about Books; Cookery &
Gastronomy; Farming,
Ranching, & Livestock;
Folklore; Political, Social, &
Cultural History & Thought;
Technology

M C Wilson
1735 Sherbourne
Los Angeles, Calif. 90035
Short Name: **M C Wilson**
Detective Fiction; Science
Fiction; World Wars

The Wilson Bookshop
3118 Routh Street
Dallas, Tex. 75201
(214) 747-5804
Short Name: **Wilson**
Texas; Southwestern America;
Fine & Rare Bindings; Books
about Books; First Editions;
Press Books & Fine Printing

C B Wimsey
P O Box 1001
Hillsborough, N.C. 27278
Short Name: **C B Wimsey**
Religion & Theology; Detective
Fiction; English Literature;
Typography & Type Specimens

Windage Farm Books
P O Box 287, Rte #1
Glen Gardner, N.J. 08826
(201) 832-2104
Short Name: **Windage Farm**
Dance; Ephemera

Windhover Books
8491 Cartier Stret
Vancouver, B.C. V6P 4T7
(604) 266-2929
Short Name: **Windhover**
First Editions; First Editions,
Modern; Rare Books

Wine & Food Library
1207 West Madison Street
Ann Arbor, Mich. 48103
(313) 663-4894
Short Name: **Wine & Food**
Beverages; Cookery &
Gastronomy; Gardening &
Horticulture; Hotels; Out of
Print, with Stock; Wines

Wings Of The Eagle
811 Hopkins Road, Haddon
Township
Haddonfield, N.J. 08033
(609) 428-2244
Short Name: **Wings Of Eagle**
Americana; Biography;
Literature; Out of Print, with
Stock; Religion & Theology;
History

Winsted Shop
140 South Winsted Street
Spring Green, Wisc. 53588
Short Name: **Winsted**
Wisconsin; Cookery &
Gastronomy; Childrens' Books;
Americana

Winter Farm Books
RFD 2, Box 42-A
Pittsfield, Maine 04967
(207) 938-4141
Short Name: **Winter Farm**
Maine; Geneaologies; History,
American; Maps, Atlases, &
Cartography

J M Winters-Books
680 Summit Avenue
Hackensack, N.J. 07601
Short Name: **J M Winters**
First Editions; Science Fiction;
Nostalgic Fiction; Magazines

Wise Owl Books
P O Box 377
Lake Delton, Wisc. 53941
Short Name: **Wise Owl**
Childrens' Books; Americana,
States; Series Books for Boys &
Girls; Wisconsin

Thomas J Wise Memorial Books
P O Box 259
Baldwin Place, N.Y. 10505
(914) 628-9308
Short Name: **Thomas J Wise**
First Editions, Modern;
General; Literature; Paperbacks
(new); Sets

With Pipe & Book
117 Main Street
Lake Placid, N.Y. 12946
(518) 523-9096
Short Name: **With Pipe**
Adirondacks; New York;
Skating; Tobacco & Smoking;
Out of Print, with Stock

Witherspoon Art & Book Store
12 Nassau Street
Princeton, N.J. 08540
(609) 924-3582
Short Name: **Witherspoon**
Authors; Middle East;
Scholarly Books; Out of Print,
with Stock; Rare Books; Sets

Witkin Gallery
41 East 57th Street
New York, N.Y. 10022
Short Name: **Witkin**
Photography

Laurence Witten
181 Old Post Road, Box 490
Southport, Conn. 06490
Short Name: **L Witten**
*Incunabula & Early Printing;
Manuscripts, Medieval &
Illuminated; Illustrated Books;
Fine & Rare Bindings;
Autographed Material &
Autographs; Appraisals &
Appraisal Services*

Andrew Wittenborn
152 Mountain Road
Pleasantville, N.Y. 10570
Short Name: **A Wittenborn**
Automotive

Wittenborn Art Books
1018 Madison Avenue
New York, N.Y. 10021
Short Name: **Wittenborn**
*Archaeology; Architecture; Art;
Graphic Arts; Illustrated Books;
Antiques*

**Jon Wobber-Vicarious
   Experience**
60 West Sierra
Cotati, Calif. 94928
Short Name: **J Wobber**
*First Editions, Modern;
Literature; Poetry; Music*

D E Wojack
18700 Codding
Detroit, Mich. 48219
Short Name: **D E Wojack**
*Cinema & Mass Media;
History; History, American;
Militaria*

Wolf's Head Books
198 Foundry Street, Box 1048
Morgantown, W.Va. 26505
(304) 296-0706
Short Name: **Wolf's Head**
*Americana; Civil War &
Confederacy; Out of Print, with
Stock; Illustrated Books;
Search Service, with Stock;
West Virginia*

William P Wolfe
P O Box 1190
Pointe Claire, Que. H9S 5K7
(514) 697-1630
Short Name: **W P Wolfe**
*Canada & Canadiana;
Americana; Voyages, Travels, &
Exploration; Rare Books;
Periodicals; Judaica &
Hebraica*

Women's Words Books
12 Main Street
Contoocook, N.H. 03229
(603) 746-4483
Short Name: **Women's Words**
Women & Feminism; Suffrage

Womrath's Bookshop
229 Fulton Avenue
Hempstead, N.Y. 11550
Short Name: **Womrath's**
*General; Paperbacks (new);
Militaria; Naval & Marine;
Astrology; New Books*

Charles B Wood Iii
The Green
South Woodstock, Conn. 06267
Short Name: **C B Wood Iii**
*Architecture; Photography;
Illustrated Books*

F P Wood
254a Main Street
Springvale, Maine 04083
Short Name: **F P Wood**
*Americana; Shakers; Maine;
New England*

Elisabeth Woodburn
Booknoll Farm
Hopewell, N.J. 08525
(609) 466-0522
Short Name: **E Woodburn**
*Gardening & Horticulture;
Beverages; Farming, Ranching,
& Livestock*

Wooden Spoon Books
200 North 4th Avenue
Ann Arbor, Mich. 48104
(313) 769-4775
Short Name: **Wooden Spoon**
*Science Fiction; Cookery &
Gastronomy; Gardening &
Horticulture; Literary
Criticism; Americana, Regional;
History, American*

Jay Woods Consultant
1 Bohoskey Drive
Yakima, Wash. 98901
Short Name: **J Woods-Yak**
*Geology; Manuscripts, Medieval
& Illuminated; Middle Ages;
Natural History; Scholarly
Books; Science Fiction*

John Woods
Main Street
Coventry, Conn. 06238
(203) 742-7457
Short Name: **J Woods-Cov**
Connecticut

Woodspurge Books
P O Box 1367
Staunton, Va. 24401
(703) 886-6403
Short Name: **Woodspurge**
*Authors; English Literature;
Illustrated Books; Autographed
Material & Autographs; Prints*

Grant Woolmer
1436 McGill Collage
Montreal, Que. H3A 1Z6
Short Name: **G Woolmer**
*Arctica & Antarctica; Canada
& Canadiana; Fur Trade*

J Howard Woolmer-Rare Books
Marienstein Road
Revere, Penna. 18953
(215) 847-5074
Short Name: **J H Woolmer**
*Appraisals & Appraisal
Services; Author Collections;
First Editions, Modern;
Inscribed Books; Literature;
Manuscripts*

Word Bookstore
469 Milton Street
Montreal, Que.
Short Name: **Word**
*Classics; Humanities;
Literature; Paperbacks (new);
Poetry*

Words Worth
30 Brattle Street
Cambridge, Mass. 02138
(617) 354-5201
Short Name: **Words Worth**
*Performing Arts; Science
Fiction; Childrens' Books;
Women & Feminism;
Architecture; Cookery &
Gastronomy*

World Wide Book Service
251 Third Avenue
New York, N.Y. 10010
(212) 673-6160
Short Name: **World Wide-NYC**
First Editions; Orientalia;
Paperbacks (new); Gambling;
Geneaologies; Americana

Worldwide Antiquarian
P O Box 326
Arlington, Mass. 02174
(617) 491-1734
Short Name: **Worldwide-Arl**
Middle East; Orientalia; Africa;
Joseph C. Lincoln; Color Plate
Books

William P Wreden
200 Hamilton Avenue
Palo Alto, Calif. 94302
(415) 325-6851
Short Name: **W P Wreden**
Americana; General; Rare
Books; Literature; Manuscripts;
Press Books & Fine Printing

Clark Wright-Book Dealer
Waxahachie, Tex. 75165
Short Name: **C Wright**
Americana, Regional; Farming,
Ranching, & Livestock; Latin
America; Out of Print, with
Stock; Outlaws & Rangers;
Search Service, with Stock

Wurlitzer-Bruck Music
60 Riverside Drive
New York, N.Y. 10024
(212) 787-6431
Short Name: **Wurlitzer-Bruck**
Autographed Material &
Autographs; Out of Print,
without Stock; Performing Arts;
Photography; Prints; Rare
Books

X

Xanadu Books
P O Box 91
Braintree, Mass. 02184
(617) 848-8584
Short Name: **Xanadu**
Americana; Americana,
Regional; Antiques; Art; First
Editions; Out of Print, with
Stock

Ximenes Rare Books
120 East 85th Street
New York, N.Y. 10028
Short Name: **Ximenes**
First Editions; Literature;
Americana; STC & Wing
Books; Economics & Business;
Medicine & Science

Y

Yankee Peddler Bookshop
94 Mill Street
Pultneyville, N.Y. 14538
Short Name: **Yankee Peddler**
New York; Photography; Civil
War & Confederacy;
Americana; Aviation &
Aeronautics; Illustrated Books

Ye Olde Fantastique Book
  Shoppe
1218 West Beauregard
San Angelo, Tex. 76901
Short Name: **Ye Olde Fan**
History, American; Texas;
Religion & Theology;
Metaphysics; General

Herb Yellin, Books
19073 Los Alimos Street
Northridge, Calif. 91324
(213) 363-6621
Short Name: **H Yellin**
First Editions, Modern; First
Editions; Science Fiction;
Poetry

Yellow Press
P O Box 14141
San Francisco, Calif. 94114
Short Name: **Yellow Press**
*Newspapers; Periodicals; Games
& Pasttimes; Antiques;
Gambling; Comic Books*

Yellowstone Books
P O Box 332
Brookfield, Ill. 60513
(312) 485-4643
Short Name: **Yellowstone**
*Science Fiction; Mystery
Fiction; Western Books*

Yesterday's Books
Baptist Corner Road
Ashfield, Mass. 01330
(413) 628-3249
Short Name: **Yesterday's-Ash**
*Out of Print, with Stock;
Classics; Literature*

Yesterday's Books
4702 Wisconsin Avenue
Washington, D.C. 20016
(201) 363-0581
Short Name: **Yesterday's-Was**
Rare Books; General

Yesterday's Books
P O Box 32
Parchmont, Mich. 49004
Short Name: **Yesterday's-Par**
*General; Out of Print, with
Stock*

Yesterday's Books, Etc
258 Whittington Avenue, Box
 1728
Hot Springs, Ark. 71901
(501) 624-2216
Short Name: **Yesterday's-Hot**
*General; Out of Print, with
Stock; Search Service, with
Stock; Biography; Poetry;
Americana*

Yesterday's Gallery
P O Box 142
West Granby, Conn. 06090
(203) 653-2158
Short Name: **Yesterday's-Wes**
*Color Plate Books; Illustrated
Books; Maps, Atlases, &
Cartography; Natural History;
Prints; Voyages, Travels, &
Exploration*

Yesteryear
420 Lincoln Avenue
Lincoln, Ill. 62656
(217) 732-6474
Short Name: **Yesteryear-Lin**
*General; Americana;
Americana, States*

Yesteryear Book Shop
256 East Paces Ferry Road, NE
Atlanta, Ga. 30305
(404) 237-0163
Short Name: **Yesteryear-Atl**
*Appraisals & Appraisal
Services; Civil War &
Confederacy; First Editions;
Illustrated Books; Militaria;
Rare Books*

Yesteryear Shoppe
12251 First Street, South
Nampa, Idaho 83651
Short Name: **Yesteryear-Nam**
*Idaho; Western Americana;
Postcards; Trade Cards; Science
Fiction; Comic Books*

Ben Yolleck
P O Box 14, Postal Station Z
Toronto, Ont. M5N 1A0
Short Name: **B Yolleck**
*Western Americana; Canada &
Canadiana; Jack London;
History of Medicine & Science;
Judaica & Hebraica*

Rollin Yorty, Books
Rte #2, Box 267
Roscommon, Mich. 48653
(517) 821-9242
Short Name: **R Yorty**
*Childrens' Books; Comic Books;
First Editions; Out of Print,
with Stock; Prints; Rare Books*

Morris N Young
170 Broadway
New York, N.Y. 10038
(212) 685-2250
Short Name: **M N Young**
Memory & Mnemonics

The Young Antiquarian
270 Babcock Street, #21j
Boston, Mass. 02215
Short Name: **Young Antiquar**
*Russia & Eastern European
Region; Fiction; First Editions,
Modern*

Samuel Yudkin & Associates
1125 King Street
Alexandria, Va. 22314
(703) 549-9330
Short Name: **S Yudkin**
*Auctions & Auctioneers;
Childrens' Books; General;
Prints; Science Fiction; Search
Service, with Stock*

M J Yuill
P O Box 42
Whippany, N.J. 07981
(201) 386-9176
Short Name: **M J Yuill**
Civil War & Confederacy

American Book Collector has computerized all the names, addresses, and book specialties for the 3,000 dealers found in this directory and for a growing list of dealers who will appear in subsequent editions. We can provide mailing labels for these dealers, selected by specialty if you wish, at reasonable cost. Write for our price schedule. *ABC,* 274 Madison Avenue, New York, N.Y. 10016.

Z

Maria D Zambelli (Catalogues Only)
156 Fifth Avenue
New York, N.Y. 10010
(212) 734-2141
Short Name: **M D Zambelli**
Middle Ages; Renaissance; Philosophy; Bibliography

B Zaremba
3 Livermore Place
Cambridge, Mass. 02141
(617) 491-3246
Short Name: **B Zaremba**
Natural History; Search Service, with Stock

W L Zeigler
10 Lincolnway West
New Oxford, Penna. 17350
(717) 624-2347
Short Name: **W L Zeigler**
Farming, Ranching, & Livestock

Zeitlin & Ver Brugge
815 North La Cienega Boulevard
Los Angeles, Calif. 90069
(213) 655-7581
Short Name: **Zeitlin & Ver B**
Author Collections; Natural History; Overland Narratives; Press Books & Fine Printing; Technology

Zeitlin Periodicals Company, Inc
817 South La Brea Avenue
Los Angeles, Calif. 90036
(213) 933-7175
Short Name: **Zeitlin Period**
Periodicals; Reprints

Zellner's Book Service
2839 Norton Avenue
Easton, Penna. 18042
Short Name: **Zellner's**
Series Books for Boys & Girls; Western Books; Civil War & Confederacy; Pennsylvania

Margaret Zervas
P O Box 562
Manhasset, N.Y. 11030
Short Name: **M Zervas**
Americana; Autographed Material & Autographs; Childrens' Books; Medicine & Science; Rare Books; Voyages, Travels, & Exploration

Anthony G Ziagos Bookseller
P O Box 28
Lowell, Mass. 01853
Short Name: **A G Ziagos**
Freemasonry; Local History; Rare Books; Appraisals & Appraisal Services; Book Scouts; Search Service, without Stock

Ziesing Brothers' Book Emporium
768 Main Street
Willimantic, Conn. 06226
Short Name: **Ziesing Bros**
Poetry; Science Fiction; Literature; Literary Criticism; Scholarly Books; Search Service, with Stock

Zita Books
760 West End Avenue
New York, N.Y. 10025
(212) 866-4715
Short Name: **Zita**
Original Art of Book Illustrations; Japan; Art; Asia; Music

Zollinger's Book Service
1528 North Ashland Avenue
Chicago, Ill. 60622
Short Name: **Zollingers**
Search Service, without Stock

John T Zubal Inc
2969 West 25th Street
Cleveland, Ohio 44113
(216) 241-7640
Short Name: **J T Zubal**
Periodicals; Literary Criticism; Literature; Russia & Eastern European Region; First Editions; Collection Development

Irving Zucker Art Books
256 Fifth Avenue
New York, N.Y. 10001
Short Name: **I Zucker**
Illustrated Books; Color Plate Books; Natural History; Voyages, Travels, & Exploration; Rare Books

Adirondacks

Adirondack	Corner Stone	Northwoods	Wildwood
Bk St-Nap	Jenison's	R A Paulson	With Pipe

Adventure

Bk Addict-Por   Examino

Africa

R H Adelson	E Enzler	Norumbega	Scharf Art
Asian-Cam	Ethnograph Arts	Oceanic Primitive	L Smith
Bayview	Hacker Art	S Ottenberg	Terramedia
Bk Lady	Int Univ Bkslrs	Paragon Gall	University Pl
Burkwood	H Johnson	G Pettinger	G Vanderstoel
L Collins	McBlain	R L Press	Worldwide-Arl
Dee Cee			

Agriculture

Hurley   D A Lawyer   Pennyroyal   Savoy

Aircraft & Aerospace History

Hampton   P & D Kenyon   D W McLennan

Alabama

Bk Shelf-Cle   J P Cather

Alaska

Bkst-Fai   Family   B Nelson   Shorey
D J   Jack London   Old Harbor   E Short

Horatio Alger

B & K Stamps   Canterbury-Geo   P F Miller   Old Bk Sh-Ken

Alternative Energy

Armchair Sailor   Bk Stacks-Burl

American Diaries & Narratives

J M W Borg   R F Lucas   Smoky Hill   Van Norman

American Discovery

Arkway   G Javitch

American Illustrative Art

Amer Bk & Gal	J Goffman	C G Martignette	Paper Person
D Bissett			

American Indians

Aardvark-Tuc	L Collins	E Jaksto	A Philpott
Acoma	Conrad's	G Javitch	D F Proctor
Amer So'West	Country Craft	G Javitch	Wm Reese Co
Ancient Cty Pr	D J	P Jenkins	Rendezvous
Ancient Cty Bk	E Davis	H Johnson	J D Rittenhouse
H R Andrews	Davison	Los Artesanos	Rosetree Inn
Antiq Bkvestors	J Dowd	M S Lambeth	J Rybski
W G Arader III	Dragoman	Las Lenguas	Sage
K G Arthurton	D N Dupley	Libros Latinos	L Schulman
Authors Of West	El Cascajero	L N Lien	Scotia
Barjon's	B Ellis	Little Read	Sindell Res
D Blomberg	Ethnograph Arts	K Lopez	Smoky Hill
Bk Gall-Gai	B Fein	S C Lunsford	Sterling Valley
Bk Keeper-Mit	Grady's	T N Luther	Sun Dance
Bk Nook	Guthman	Mason's-Wab	Tech Info-Doc
Bkst-Vern	R Hansen	Oceanic Primitive	Treasures
Bkworm-Cor	Heinoldt	Ohio Bkhntr	Unicorn-Chi
W M Boulton	Hist Real	Old Bkshelf	Valley-Gal
Chamblin	Hungry Eye	Once Read	Wantagh
D M Chase	Indian Head	T C Packard	D Ward
Chiricahua	Iroqrafts	D Perier	R M Weatherford
A H Clark	A Jacobs		

American Literature

Addison	W T Clermont	Int'l Bkfndrs	Savoy
Austin	Dauber & Pine	Joseph Provider	Starr-Bost
J M W Borg	Dwyer's	J & M Laurie	Starr-Camb
Brick Row	C L Feick	J O'Gara	Transition
Brownstone	B J Hecht	Regent Hse	Vintage-Bost
R F Casavant	In Our Time	C L Robinson-Wi	

American Mercury Magazine

W B Fye   Morrell's

Americana

ABC Theological
Abraham Lincoln
Abraxas
Academic
Adams
R H Adelson
Adobe
B Agranoff
Alpha Omega
Alta Calif
K Altau
Amer Bks
Amer Mail Auct
Americanist
Anderson's
Andover Square
Antiq Bksllrs
Antiq Michiana
Antiquus
Appleland
W G Arader III
Argonaut
Argosy
Arkway
K Armens
G Armitage
K G Arthurton
Artifacts
Athenaeum
Attic-Hodg
Attic-Wins
Authors Of West
L Balish
Bargain-Par
Barnette's
C Baron
J N Bartfield
M B Beal
D B Belcher
F A Berk
L Berliawsky

Bick & Barc
W Blake
Blitz
Bloch & Co
Bob's-App
Bohling
Bk Attic
Bk Caravan
Bk Case-Hou
Bk Den-San
Bk Haven-Law
Bk Hse-Arl
Bk Mart-San
Bk Mart Anx-San
Bk Ranger
Bk Srch-Pit
Bk Shelf-Cle
Bk Sh-Salt
Bk Stall-Roc
Bk Trader-Fai
Bk Warehouse
Bk World
Bkfinders-Fair
W J Bkhunter
Bkleggers
Bkpress
Bks For Every
Bksource
Bkst-Vern
Bkst-Jenk
Bk Traders
Bkworm-Cor
Borderland
J M W Borg
L Bowling
V A Bradley
Branford
Broadfoot's
M A Bromsen
G D Brown
Brownstone

W J B Burger
H M Burstein
R Butterfield
Cabinet Of
Cape Cod-San
Caravan-Sti
A Carduner
B C Carltiz
Carnegie
Carry Back
R F Casavant
J P Cather
Centauri
Cherokee
Childs Gall
Chimney Smoke
Chiricahua
G J Cielec
A H Clark
Colebrook
Colls' Cntr-Den
Coll's Old
Conrad's
Constant Reader
Conversation
Coosa Valley
Country Lane
Court Place
Curiosity-St J
Current
L W Currey
Q M Dabney
Dakota
Danville
Darian
J C Daub
Dauber & Pine
E Davis
B Dawson
J A Desch
R B Desmarais

R Diamond
J Distefano
Don's
M C Dooling
Mrs K R Dorn
Drew's
E F Dunlap
M Dunn
D N Dupley
C Dvorak
R Dworcyk
Edison Hall
I Ehrlich
R M Eisenberg
A M Ellis
D J Ernst
Evergreen
E C Fales
Family Album
Far Corners-Mob
Farley's
D Fay
J J Felcone
Find A Bk
S Finer
C G Fisher
P T Fisher
Footnote
Fortune Finders
Fox & Suther
Fox-Mad
Fox Hill
Fransen's
Froghollow
Fron Amer
Fuller's
A & R Gardiner
W C Gates
W T Gavin
Genessee
M Gibbs

R Gilbo
M Ginsberg
Glenn
Golden Hill
Goodsp'd's-Beac
Goodsp'd's-Milk
Graedon
W A Graf
Gryphon's Lair
A Gud
Guthman
G Hall, Jr
W D Hall
W E Hallberg
Hamill & Barker
M Hammer
R Hansen
Happy Source
J Harder
T Harper
J D Hawkins
R G Hayman
Heinoldt
S Heller
H C Hensel
Heritage-Son
Heritage-Bow
G S Herron
Hirschtritt's
Hist Real
History House
Hock-Hocking
Hoffman Resch
H'wood Bk Shop
Holmes-Oak
Holmes-S F
Hoosier School
G Houseman
D B Howes
M Hudson
T Hughes
P C Hull
Hunted
In Our Time
Info
Int'l Bkfndrs
Irene's
D Ishii
Jack's Used
A Jacobs
B A James
G Javitch
Jenkins
P Jenkins
T J Joyce
H R Kahn
E J Kearin

J B Keeler
C Kellinger
J K King
G Klemm
Knight's
E F Kramer
H P Kraus
R Lasley
J Lazarus
K Leach
Leaves Of Grass
J Levine
Librarium
W Lillywhite
Little Hundred
London-Alb
Long's-Lin
Lorenz Books
J Lorson
R F Lucas
S C Lunsford
T MacAluso
A B W MacEwen
M A MacIntosh
R A MacKsey
G S MacManus
W Madden
Madonna Hse
G H Mahfuz
T D Mahoney
J Majer
J Makarewich
J & L Mallis
Marg & Moss
Maverick
B E McCaslin
J O McMeans
Memory Aisle
R L Merriam
Military
C E Miller
E Miller
T T Moebs
W Monie
Monroe
E Moore
L A Moore, Sr
E Morrill
Mostly-Oma
H S Mott
Much Loved
S & C Najarian
Nationwide
K Nebenzahl
D R Nelson
New Engl-Benn
N Y Bound

R G Newman
F M O'Brien
D L O'Neal
S T Oakley, Jr
Ohio Bkhntr
Old Bkshed
Old Edtns
Old Lou Books
Old Mystic
Old Bk Rm-Gow
Old Bk St-Akr
Old Print Gall
E Orth
J Owen
K C Owings Jr
Owl Creek
Owl Pen
T C Packard
Page One
Pageant
E Panos
Parker's
M R Parks
Past History
N M Pawlett
Pendragon
R F Perotti
Perry's Antiq
E Phalen
Question Mark
Raintree
Randall Hse
Raven
Ravenstree
R H Redding
Wm Reese Co
Rendells
Rendezvous
Reston's
Richardsons
R H Richshafer
B M Rieger
M B Robertson
R Robertson
C L Robinson-Wi
H B Robinson
Ron-Dot
P E Rose
C Ross
Ross & Haines
I Rouse
R H Rubin
L J Ryan
S-T
M D Sackman
Sample-Sea

Schneemann
Schoyer's
Schroeder's
L Schulman
2nd Fiddle
2nd Time Around
C Sessler
J N Showalter
R Shuhi
R B Sirrine
D Sloan's
J A Smith
Sons Of Liberty
Sterling Valley
H Stevens Son
Stinson Hse
Strawberry Hill
T Sullivan
Sykes & Fla
Talbothay's
L Tebbetts
J D Terry
W Thomas
Titcomb's
G Totty
Trackside
Trade & Sell
Treasures
G H Tweney
M Twyce
Tyson
Used-West
Valley-Gal
J Wade
F G Walett
Wantagh
Waverly
R M Weatherford
G E Webb, Jr
D Weiss
West's Agency
Western Hemi
Whitlock's
Wings Of Eagle
Winsted
Wolf's Head
W P Wolfe
F P Wood
World Wide-NYC
W P Wreden
Xanadu
Ximenes
Yankee Peddler
Yesterday's-Hot
Yesteryear-Lin
M Zervas

Americana, States

Aceto
Anglican Bib
Appleland
Back Tracts
C V Barnes
M E Bennett
C J Boardman
Bohling
Bk Haven-Law
Bk Mart Anx-San
Bk Shelf-Cle
Bk Sh-Salt
Bk Trader-Fai
W M Boulton
V Burgman

Chantiicleer
Colls' Cntr-Den
Coll's Old
Colo Bkman
M L Cook
Coosa Valley
H O Dendurent
C Derowitsch
Evergreen
J J Felcone
C G Fisher
Franklin
N W Getman
Global
R Hansen

Haslam's-St P
J D Hawkins
R G Hayman
Heinoldt
P Henderson
Hermitage
G S Herron
A Hills
A C Hunter
R King
Y Kishi
Lamp
Mitch's
Mooers
Old Monterey

G R Osgood, Jr
Ozark
W Reuben-NYC
W Reuben-Aus
A G Robinson, Jr
R E Robinson
Scharf Art
J N Showalter
H Tanner
Tuttle Antiq
M Twyce
Va Bk Co
Wise Owl
Yesteryear-Lin

Americana, Regional

Aah!
Amer Eagle
Amer Wrlds
Ancient Cty Pr
Antiq Sh-Ste
Antiq Bkvestors
Antiquariat
Appleland
Argus
F Armstrong
Asian Amer
Athenaeum
Attic-Wins
Back Tracts
Banyan
C V Barnes
Beaver
Bk Bin-Dal
Bk Center-Ath
Bk Habit
Bk Sh-Boise
Bk Stop-Tuc
Bk Case-Fres
Bk Cellar-Tem
Bk Mart-San
Bk Shelf-Cle
Bk Sh-Salt

Bks By Mail
Bks Unltd-Ind
Bkstack-Elk
Bkst-Jenk
W M Boulton
Boysag
Brassers
Brennan
Browsery
Bunkhse
Burke's
J Burtniak
Cabin In Pines
Carolina
Carry Back
Chafey's
Chamblin
Chantiicleer
Chiricahua
A H Clark
Clark's
E Clement
Coll's Old
Colleen's
Conrad's
Coosa Valley
Country Craft

Court Place
Croton
Curious-Bost
J C Daub
Don's
Donegan
Mrs K R Dorn
E F Dunlap
A A Dunn
El Piasano
Estate
O O Evans
Evergreen
J J Felcone
Forest Park
Fox-Mad
Fron Amer
Galvez
N W Getman
L Ginsberg
W D Hall
R Hansen
Haslam's-St P
J D Hawkins
R G Hayman
P Henderson
Heritage-Son

G S Herron
W W Hildreth
Homestead
Homesteader
Hoosier Bksh
Hope Farm
Hungry Eye
A C Hunter
Info
J Appleseed
L S Kaiser
P Krapp
L La Berge
Leekley Srch
J G Leishman
Liberty Rock
Lift Bridge-Bro
Long's-Lin
P M Lumb
G S MacManus
Magnalia
Manuscript
Mason's-Wab
F Mavis
B E McCaslin
Mitchell's-San
Mostly-Oma

Mt Falcon
D S Mull
Nemaha
Nimue
Ozark
P'back Exch
D Perier
A Philpott
Poor Farm
B Porter
E K Powell
Prospector

Purple Bkcase
W Reuben-Aus
J D Rittenhouse
R E Robinson
Rosetree Inn
M D Sackman
Sage
Sample-Sea
2nd Floor
J N Showalter
Skeans & Cliff

L Sloan
So By S'West
Store
R M Sylvester
Tappin
B Tauscher
10 Pound
3 Arts
R Todd
Trade & Sell
Trans Allegheny

Treasures
Tuttle Antiq
M Twyce
Va Bk Co
F G Walett
D Ward
Whitlock Farm
Wildwood
Wooden Spoon
C Wright
Xanadu

America's Cup

Anchor & Dol

Bk Den East

Liberty Lore

Ancient Civilizations

W E Beaver

Cartesian

Hyman & Son-L A

Animals

7 Seas

J V Sichel

G H Suhm

Anthropology

Bay Side
Bloomsbury

Bk Land-Tor
T N Haviland

E Klein

A Sherlock

Antique Stocks and Bonds

Abbot   P C Richards

Antiques

J P Adzima	De Ville	Keramos	Servant's Knowl
Alicat	Forsyth Travel	L La Berge	R W Smith-N Hav
Antiq Bkvestors	From Another	R L Merriam	D Testa
Barbara's	L Galinsky	Northeast	T Trace
Bargain-Par	Gem Antiq	K C Owings Jr	M L Tyrrell
Barra	Ginger	P'back Exch	Unique Antiq
Bethlehem	G F Glaeve	Papermill	D Ward
Bk Shelf-Way	Golden Hill	Parnassus Svce	R Wilkerson
Bk Warehouse	Hacker Art	Princeton Antiq	William-Roberts
Bkst-Jenk	L Honan	Riverow	Wittenborn
Colo Bkman	Horchow	M Roenick	Xanadu
Dance Mart	G Houle	H V Ryan	Yellow Press

Apiculture

Bk Exch-Corn   Mrs L M Brew   A Christiansen   Marple

Appalachia

Appalachia   Bkworm & Silver   Hound Dog

Appraisals & Appraisal Services

Abraham Lincoln   Acoma   Adams   R H Adelson

aGatherin'
T Alford
Ampersand
Ancient Cty Pr
Antiq Sh-Ste
Appelfeld
Arcane
Ark
Astronomy
B Babcock
Back Tracts
M B Beal
Bkworm & Silver
Brennan
M A Bromsen
Buckabest
R H Cady
Cartographics
Christian-Mil
Clipper Ship
Coll's Old
Copper Fox
J S Edgren

Bkman-Gran
R O Estes, Sr
E C Fales
Family Album
Firstborn
Fletcher's
J Gach
Garciagarst
M Gibbs
Grolier
D Grossblatt
Gutenberg's
D Halloran
J F Hendsey
Cj Hinke
Hobbit
Hoosier Bksh
Isaiah Thomas
B A James
Jenkins
H Johnson
T J Joyce

Lake Law
Leaves Of Grass
S B Lebo
J G Leishman
W B Liebmann
J Lowe
T D Mahoney
Manuscript
B McKittrick
W F Mobley
E Moore
Murray
R G Newman
Nugent & Assoc
Old Mill
Old Bk Rm-Gow
Old Print Gall
Performing Arts
Peri Lithon
Pharos
P J Pirages
Question Mark

Rendells
C L Robinson-Ma
Scarlet Letter
Schuylkill
Scriptorium
Serendipity
Sindell Res
J M Skutel
South Bay
So By S'West
C A Stonehill
Swann
R M Sylvester
Tuckers
G H Tweney
L A Wallrich
R M Weatherford
L & H Weitz
L Witten
J H Woolmer
Yesteryear-Atl
A G Ziagos

Archaeology

Abatis
Abelard
Acoma
C S Berkowitz
F A Bernett
G A Bernstein
Bloomsbury
Blue Rider
G D Brown
Cartesian

D M Chase
Conrad's
Dragoman
El Cascajero
B Fein
T T Foley
Hacker Art
W F Hale
H'wood Bk Shop
L Honan

Hyman & Son-L A
P Jenkins
H Johnson
H Karno
B Koenig's
F L Kovacs
Lee & Lee
Libros Latinos
W Madden
J Normile

Period Ludw
H Reichner
Richardsons
S Scharoun
K L Schwarz
Travellers'
Under Cover-Cle
Under Cover-Sha
S Weiser
Wittenborn

Archery

P J Drabeck

Hoffman Lane

Landau

Toxophilite

Architecture

Anchor & Dol	De Ville	L Loewenthal	M Roenick
Ars Libri	R Dean	T MacAluso	A Schram
Artcraft	M C Dooling	Mandrake	K L Schwarz
Arts & Lett	El Cascajero	McDuffies	R W Smith-N Hav
Athenaeum	Ex Libris-NYC	L McGilvery	K Starosciak
Bargain-San	Fir Tree	P Miller	G Steele
Barra	L Goldschmidt	A H Minters	P A Stroock
C S Berkowitz	M Goldsholl	J B Muns	G P Szontagh
F A Bernett	Hacker Art	Museum Gall	Temple Bar
Blue Rider	Henn & Ing	Nimue	T Trace
Bk Gall-Whit	L Honan	Orange Cat	Under Cover-Cle
Bk Mark-Phil	Hortolus	S Orr	Under Cover-Sha
Bkfndrs-Mia	E Howe	E Orth	S Vogel-St L
Bkpress	Keith & Martin	N M Pawlett	Weyhe
H W Brewer	D Ladner	Richardsons	Wittenborn
K Buck	Lee & Lee	Riverow	C B Wood III
Caravan-Sti	Liberty Rock	C L Robinson-Wi	Words Worth
L Collins	E Llewellyn		

Arctica & Antarctica

Aah!	I Ehrlich	J Kidston	W & L Pinkney
Academic	F & I	E J Lefkowicz	R H Redding
Ainslie	Family	S C Lunsford	C M Robinson
Angel's	C L Feick	Magnalia	J Rybski
H Anson-Cart	B Finch	Maps & Bks	A Sample
Arctician	Frontier P'neer	R W Mattila	Scotia
Bayview	Graedon	F Mavis	L Seeborg
Bk Addict-Albu	Grt No'West	J P McGahern	Shorey
Bkst-Vern	J H Hale	Mtn Travel	E Short
E R Bowes	J Harder	Nautica	J W Smith
British Stamp	D N Harding	B Nelson	R B Stephenson
Bryant's	C Hinchliffe	Observatory	Thunderbird
J Burnett	D Hood	Okanagan	West Side
Caravan-Marit	J C Huckans	Old Bk Sh-Morr	Whaling
A G Clegg	H R Kahn	Old Harbor	T Williams
Country Lane	J J Keleher	A W Paine	G Woolmer

Arizona

Alcazar

Bisbee

Trail To Y'day

Arkansas

Dickson St

C Payton

Smoky Hill

Armed Forces Editions

A Lauberts

Morrell's

Art

Aardvark-S F
Abreyde
Academy-NYC
Academy-Hon
Acorn
R H Adams
J P Adzima
Albion Graphics
Alicat
Alpha Omega
Alron
E Andrews
Antiq Bksllrs
P P Appel
G Armitage
Ars Libri
Art Catalogues
Artcraft
Artistic End
Arts & Lett
Asian-NYC
Athenaeum

AVH Bkshop
J Bambach
Barbara's
Bargain-San
Barra
J W Beattie
C S Berkowitz
L Berliawsky
Biermaier's
Blue Rider
Bk & Tackle
Bk Bin-Kin
Bk Caravan
Bk Gall-Whit
Bk Shelf-Way
Bk Sh-Sou
Bk Studio
Bk Cellar-Ful
Bk Hse-Arl
Bk Mark-Phil
Bk Ranger
Bk St-San

Bk St-Engl
Bk Warehouse
Bkfndrs-Mia
Bks & Thngs-Boc
Bks-Gre
Bksh-War
Bkstock
V A Bradley
H W Brewer
British Stamp
Broude Bros
G D Brown
Camelot
Chimney Smoke
Choreogr
Christopher's
G J Cielec
T Coffman
Cole's-La J
Coll's List
Columbia
Cornwall Hse

M R Cutler
Cyrano's
W & V Dailey
H C Daitz
~~Dauber & Pine~~
Davis & Schorr
De Victor's
De Ville
R Dean
R Diamond
Don's
R E Donovan
M C Dooling
D Doonan
P Dumas
El Cascajero
B Ellis
R & D Emerson
Estate
Ethnograph Arts
Fain's First
B Fein

A L Feldman
Fields
T T Foley
Folger
K G Gaisser
L Galinsky
Genessee
J Giller
J Goffman
E Gordon
M Gordon
Graedon
Grt So'West
Greenwich
Grub St
H W K
Hacker Art
W F Hale
J W Harmand
Harris Srch
Henn & Ing
J N Herlin
Hermeticus
Hobbit
Hock-Hocking
H'wood Bk City
L Honan
Horchow
Horse In Attic
G Houle
L Hunegs
W M Hutter
I Am I
D Isaacson
Isaiah Thomas
H Johnson
Jolly Roger

R T Jordan
Junction
K Karith
K Karmiole
H Karno
C Kellinger
R J Kempe
Keramos
J Klein
L'estampe
N L Laird
Landau
Landmark
Lee & Lee
Librarium
Libros Latinos
Lion Ent
Littwin & Fel
L Loewenthal
T MacAluso
W Madden
Maelstrom
Magazine Center
T D Mahoney
J Makarewich
Mandrake
Mansfield
Martin's
L McGilvery
J Michaels
Midnight-Mar
E Miller
A H Minters
Moe's
T T Moebs
J B Muns
Neikrug

New Canaan
Noyes
O'Neills
Old Block
Old Delavan
Old Glory
S Ottenberg
Out-Of-Prnt-NYC
P M
Pansy Patch
Papermill
B Parrington
S Penner
People's
Perception Plus
Period Ludw
B Plant
J Pollock
Pomander
H Reichner
B Resnik
Rosengren's
Russica
H V Ryan
B Sackheim
L St Clair
P H Samuels
San Marco
Saxifrage
Scholar's
Schoyer's
A Schram
Schroeder's
J Scopazzi
B Scott
2nd Fiddle
Servant's Knowl

7 Oaks
S R Shapiro
R B Sirrine
D Sloan's
R W Smith-N Hav
Spector
D Spencer
J G Stanoff
K Starosciak
G Steele
Strand-Rare
Strand
Strawbridge
P A Stroock
V Tamerlis
Temares
F J Thomas
Treetops
Turkey Hill
Unicorn-Eas
Unique Antiq
Ursus
Valley Bk City
Valley-Say
C J Vega
S Vogel-St L
S Vogel-San
P G Waite
Warwick
West L A Center
Weyhe
Williams
P Williams
Wittenborn
Xanadu
Zita

Art Catalogues, Periodicals, & Books

| Art Catalogues | R Dean | L McGilvery | Oceanic Primitive |

Asia

| Academy-Hon | Asian-Cam | Bennett & Marsh | Dee Cee |
| Asian Amer | Asian-NYC | Cheng & Tsui | East & West |

J S Edgren
E Enzler
F & I
J D S
Keramos

Y Kishi
Mtn Travel
Old Mill
Paragon Gall

M B Robertson
Scharf Art
Sebastopol
S Shmavonian

Terramedia
G Tramp
G Vanderstoel
Zita

Association Books

S Alsberg
B Babcock
J M W Borg

B Cassidy
D Harris
Hse Of Bks Ltd

Joseph Provider
S Koschal

G S MacManus
C Seluzicki

Astrology

Bk Exch-Corn
City Bk & Coin
Gateway
E V Glaser

Holistic Health
Mason's
Mayflower
Metaphsic-L A

Ollies
Philos Bk Ser
L Sloan
S Weiser

D E Whelan
R G Wilborn
Womrath's

Astronautics & Rocketry

Arc Bks

A Cheslock

Willmann-Bell

Astronomy

Abatis
Celestial

Corn Mill
H A Luft

G B Manasek
Vintage-St P

M Waldstein

Atlases

D N Harding   Manning's

Auctions & Auctioneers

CBAG-Hol   Harris Auct   Oinonen Auct   J M Skutel
CBAG-S F   J F Hendsey   Petrilla/Kane   SPB
Canada Bk Auct   Longo Auct   Phillips   Swann
Christie's   Lust Auct   Plandome   Waverly
G F Glaeve   K W Nims   C L Robinson-Ma   S Yudkin
Hanzel Gall   No'West Auct

Australia & Oceania

Chapman & Berry   F & I   G Tramp   G Vanderstoel

Author Collections

C Appelbaum   C Farkas   S Orr   F W Smith
B Babcock   J Hansen   A & A Prosser   Thelema
Burton's   Cj Hinke   Resurrection   T W Tingle
J R Butterworth   Johnson & O'D   Sandpiper   Weller Victoria
Clipper Ship   Library-Dal   C Seluzicki   J H Woolmer
J A Dermont   R A MacKsey   Serendipity   Zeitlin & Ver B

Authors

J G Amadeo   Antic Hay   Bailey Srch   Boardwalk
Anchor & Dol   Associates   Berry Hill   N Bond

Bk Barn-Sio
Bk Mart-Ash
Bk Shelf-Cle
H Bridges
A Brutico Jr
Burton's
Choctaw Traders
Coll-Pad
R L Collins
Country Bkshlf
D & D
J E De Turck
W De Freitas
Deeds
Diablo

Dickson St
L Evans
Fleuron
Fox-Mad
R Gardner
C Garvin
Goodwin & Zein
E S Hickok
Cj Hinke
Hobby Helpers
Howe
P & D Kenyon
R King
Koths

J Landry
Lift Bridge-Fai
D M H Lowe
C Lowenberg
Michael's
S Noto
Old Monterey
V Owens
Owl Creek
P & H
Pacific Writers
Pan
E K Powell
K Rais

Resurrection
B M Rieger
A Saifer
P K Slocum
D W Starry, Sr
Stryker's
Taos
Theta
Trans Allegheny
O W Tuthill
R Valdez
D Weber
Witherspoon
Woodspurge

Auto Racing

Autobks E   J Finney

Autographed Material & Autographs

Abraham Lincoln
aGatherin'
J Aldrich
T Alford
Alron
Amer Mail Auct
Antic Hay
C Appelbaum
Archives Hist
Artistic End
atticus
Autos & Autos
B & B
B Babcock
R Batchelder
M B Beal
Benjamin Autogr
S C Bernard
Bk Barn-Sio
Bk Case-Fres
Bk City Coll
Bk Look-War
J M W Borg
V A Bradley

M Breslauer
M A Bromsen
W J B Burger
J H Burke
Burkwood
A Buschke
J R Butterworth
R H Cady
Carnegie
B Cassidy
G J Cielec
Clipper Ship
A P Collins
Confederate
E J Craig
Dan's
Dance Mart
H M Darvick
C Derowitsch
R B Desmarais
E Driscoll
Bkman-Gran
H R Emler
Fricelli

W B Fye
R Gardner
A Goodman
Goodsp'd's-Beac
Goodsp'd's-Milk
J Granat
Green Thought
Greenwich
A Gud
C Hamilton
D Harris
W S Hay
H E Heinrich
J S Helms
Hist Real
Hofmann & Free
Hoosier School
G Houle
Hse Of Bks Ltd
D B Howes
D M Jacobs
Jenny Lind
Johnson & O'D
S Koschal

M Kronovet
Lambda Rising
J Landau
J Lazarus
J Lehr
W B Liebmann
Lion Heart
J Lowe
C Lowenberg
J & J Lubrano
Marshall Field
T L McCook
Memor Amer
Mil-Air
Million Year
G R Minkoff
Mitch's
E Moore
H S Mott
M F Neville
H Noble Jr
North Shore
Nouveau
Nugent & Assoc

K C Owings Jr
P'back Exch
O Patterson
Pendragon
K T Ransom
Rare Bk Co
Rendells
S Resnick

Resurrection
P C Richards
R Richards
J Rubinfine
B Sackheim
Schuylkill
Scriptorium
Seaport

2nd Life
O Shapiro
Singer Comm
J P Slattery
R Slifer
R M Smythe
A Sosenko
Swiss Village

Wahrenbrock's
Waverly
D Weiss
F J Wilhelm
L Witten
Woodspurge
Wurlitzer-Bruck
M Zervas

Automobiles, Classic

D C Allen

Amer Eagle

J & W Bursten

T C Packard

Automotive

A C H
Again
Bk Fair
Bkland-Hay

Broken Kettle
Cypress-Park
Fortune Finders
Hungry Eye

P Kufus
E A Lehwald
Milestone Auto
B Parrington

J Ray
R F Webb
A Wittenborn

Avant Garde, Experimental, & Modern Art

Backworks
R Dean
Ex Libris-NYC

L Fox
E Gordon

Icart Vendor
D Miranda

D Spencer
Vintage-Bost

Aviation & Aeronautics

Aeroprint
Again
Air Age
Ajay Ent

J Aldrich
Amer Bk & Gal
Antheil
Auslender

Autos & Autos
Aviation
Bkseller-Akr
Caravan-L A

Comstock's
B Denver
R Dworcyk
Fortune Finders

B Gould
N Houle
Hungry Eye
Mil-Air

E Moran
Pendleton Publ
J Roby

Sky Bks Int
L Thompson
Thunderbird

Tucson
H Volker
Yankee Peddler

Baseball

Baseball   Hall's Nostalg   E Tatro

Basketry

Antiques-Hil   P Howard   Old Bks-Brun

L. Frank Baum & Oziana

Bk Treasury   A T Ford   Oz & Ends   B A Pinchot

Beat Literature

atticus   R Richards   J H Weinberg

Bells

Abatis   B Koenig's

Beverages

Bkwood	C F Hamsa	M M E Maxwell	Wine & Food
L Ginsberg	Hsehold Words	S Vogel-St L	E Woodburn
M L Gore	T Mawson		

Bible & Bible Studies

M G Alfs	Bk Fair	Hyman & Son-Tor	R O Roberts
Allenson-Breck	R O Estes, Sr	Koths	Stroud
Baptist Bourse			

Bibliographical Research Services

J Jurist	Sindell Res

Bibliography

Allenson-Breck	Colophon	Int'l Bkfndrs	W T O'Malley
Arcane	Core Coll	Ivycrest	Oak Knoll
Athenaeum	Dakota	W S Johnson	E Offenbacher
Barnstable	De Simon	Jokal	Old Galen's
Bear	De Simon	Junius	R F Perotti
Biblio	D C Dickinson	E M Katt	Ravenstree
Bibliophile-Pas	M W Dowhan	H A Levinson	Regent St
Bk Case-Hou	M Dunn	Library-Dal	R E Robinson
T G Boss	W B Fye	J Lorson	B M Rosenthal
Brick Row	R Gardner	D M H Lowe	H Satty
Brownstone	E Gordon	R L Merriam	S R Shapiro
H M Burstein	F M Hill	Midnight-West	N T Smith
Cath Bk Coll	J A Hill	Morrell's	Steinberg
Christiania	D Hood	B Morrow	F G Walett
Colls' Cntr-Den	Hsehold Words	Much Loved	M D Zambelli

Fine & Rare Bindings

Appelfeld
Ayrshire
J N Bartfield
M E Battersby
Bibliopolis-Cle
Bk Block-Gree
Bk Sail
T G Boss
Brentano's-NYC
M Breslauer
Burkwood
R H Cady
Caravan-L A
Chafey's

Cherokee
Curiosity-St J
Dauber & Pine
Detering
Et Cetera
A Fair
Fir Tree
Fletcher's
D Frohnsdorff
Glenn
Gryphon's Lair
Harcourt Bind
L C Harper
Heritage-L A

Hinds
R J Hoffman
J Appleseed
Johnson & O'D
London-Chi
D M H Lowe
Marshall Field
Pendragon
Peninsula Antiq
R Perata
Plane Tree
Ravine Cottage
E P Rich
Rockland

H Satty
J Scopazzi
H J Shoebridge
N T Smith
Spector
Stonehill's
Wake-Brook-Hyan
M Waldstein
D Ward
G E Webb, Jr
L & H Weitz
Whitlock's
Wilson
L Witten

Biography

A To Z
Action Bks
Al's
Alpine
Anglican Bib
At The Sign
Back Row
L J Bain
J Bambach
Baptist Bourse
P E Baracca
Barn Sale
R Bever
Big John's
Bird's Nest
E G Blankman
Bk Addict-Por
Bk End-Mon
Bk Cellar-Fre
Bk Srch-Pit
Bk Stall-Roc
Bk Swap
Bkman Arcady
Bks Then & Now
Bksource
O H Brady
Bread, Wine
Browsery

Burkwood
G F Bush
Cabin In Pines
Canterbury-Chi
E Clement
W T Clermont
T Coffman
Colonial
Common Reader
Curiosity-Eau
J A Desch
Diff Drum-Wes
E & M Ediger
Elgen
Fain's First
Franklin
J L Fraser
I Galis
George Sand
R Glassman
Graedon
Greenblatt
Griffin
H W K
T N Haviland
D Henson
Hobson's Ch

J & C
Jennies
Kalonbooks
J J Keleher
J J Lefebvre
Lennies
Libra
London-Chi
P M Lumb
B Lysecki
Main St
Memorable
Merlin's
C Morelle
N R S
W D Nelson
New Engl-Benn
S T Oakley, Jr
Okman's
J Owen
Owl Creek
P M
Palma
M R Parks
N M Pawlett
Perry's Antiq
Pomander

Quadrant
G J Rausch
Raymer's
Redford
Renaissance-Lak
J H Reuther
R O Roberts
H B Robinson
Ross & Haines
B J Rule
Schneemann
2nd Debut
Secret Sharer
R W Smith
Snowbound
Strawberry Hill
G H Suhm
J Taylor
Trade & Sell
G Tramp
Treetops
Used-West
Valley Bk City
J Weiss
White's
Wings Of Eagle
Yesterday's-Hot

Birds & Ornithology

Antiq Bkvestors	Callahan & Co	Janus-Hun	Parnassus Svce
Bird & Bk	B E Cassie	P Ledlie	G H Suhm
Blue Jay	Chickadee	J E Norris	Tolliver's
Buteo			

Black Literature & Black Studies

Al's	Carolina	R Gilbo	P R Rieber
Amer Lib Srvce	H C Daitz	International	Serendipity
Athenaeum	D C Dickinson	Maiden Voy	L W Smith
Bloch & Co	A M Ellis	McBlain	University Pl
Bk Sh-Sou	H R Emler	Memor Amer	W Van Devanter
Bkworm & Silver	C L Feick	Morningside-Oak	Weller Victoria
Bryn Mawr-N Hav			

Book Scouts

Baseball	R Chalfin	J Jurist	R Speray
Bazemore's	Forest	M S Lambeth	13 Colonies
Blue Eye	I Galis	Literary Seal	Wangner's
Bk Look-War	N W Getman	J Pitchforth	A G Ziagos

Book Swapping

Annie's-Act	Annie's-Nat	Annie's-Wes

Book Trade & Catalogues

Bargain-Par	Ivycrest	G R Osgood, Jr	Steinberg
Bk Case-Hou	W S Johnson	Print Dev-Arl	Sterling Valley
Colebrook	W S Johnson	Secret Sharer	R L Veatch
Eagle	I Keats		

Bookbinders Services

Binders Press	D Gouey	Harcourt Bind	Markey & Asp

Bookbinding & Restoration

M E Battersby	David's	Jenkins	H Satty
Bayview	De Simon	D M H Lowe	Saxifrage
M E Bennett	Enterprise	Maxwell's	N T Smith
H J Besnia	Eu Be Co	Memorable	R Valdez
Bkseller-Akr	L M Gottlieb	Million Year	Wake-Brook-Hyan
Broadfoot's	Harcourt Bind	Oak Knoll	L & H Weitz
Buckabest	Hobbit	Plane Tree	

Bookplates & Ex Libris

A Lauberts	Midnight-West

Books about Books

E L Anderson	Arts & Lett	Bargain-Par	D Benson
The Antiquarium	Assoc Bk Svc	G E C Barnes	P C Beyer
Appelfeld	Atlanta	Barnstable	Biblio

Bibliopolis-Cle
R Bleiweiss
Bk Case-Hou
Bk Cellar-Ful
Bk Mark-Phil
Bked Up
Bkpress
M Braiterman
Brownstone
R H Cady
Canterbury-Chi
Cape Cod-San
J Cashman
B Chaney Jr
Chimney Smoke
Coll's Crnr
Colls' Cntr-Den
S F Cullins'
Colophon
Confederate
Mrs D Cook
Cornwall Hse
K Cutler
Dawson's
De Simon
R B Desmarais

Dolphin-NYC
R P Dunaway
P C Duschnes
Dwyer's
Elmcress
Enterprise
Estes Service
Fransen's
G J M
R Gardner
Ginger
J Goldman
E Gordon
L M Gottlieb
W A Graf
J Granat
R D Greenlee
Gutenberg's
Harcourt Bind
Hartfield
W S Hay
Heartwood
High Ridge
F M Hill
Hobson's Ch
Hurley

W M Hutter
Indolent Antiq
Ivycrest
Jean's
C Kellinger
G Lange
J & M Laurie
Leaves Of Grass
J Levine
Limestone Hills
Lion's Head
E Llewellyn
J Makarewich
J W Martin
R L Merriam
Methodist
Midnight-West
B Morrow
Much Loved
H Noble Jr
W T O'Malley
Oak Knoll
Out Of Prnt-Whi
Pendragon
J Petty
Poor Farm

I Quitzau
R E Robinson
L Rostenberg
Secret Sharer
H J Shoebridge
N T Smith
Sporting Biblio
K Starosciak
G Steigerwald
Steinberg
Strand-Rare
M Tanditash
Taurus
W T Taylor
Trebizond
G H Tweney
Typographeum
Used-West
R Valdez
R L Veatch
L A Wallrich
Waves
Wilsey Square
G Wilson
Wilson

Botany

Antiq Scientist
Banyan
Bk Chest
Bk Home
W F Broderick
J Buck

R M Eisenberg
Elgen
Eubiotics
E V Glaser
K Gregory
Hortolus

I Jackson
J Johnson
D A Lawyer
Lubrecht & Cram
B L Means
J J Nadolny

Old Galen's
Orange Cat
Peterson Bk Co
Pomona Exch
G Wayner

Boxing

J Schochet   E Tatro

Boy Scouts

Adventure	C J Bedore	R L George	Stevensons
D Bearce	T Catledge		

Brazil

R C Ramer	W Schiefer

British Isles

Bkphil	Dwyer's	J M Hays	In Our Time
L Diehl	I Galis	Hse Of Bks-Ana	Sons Of Liberty

Broadsides

Bkman Arcady	W F Mobley	Paper Person	H Tanner
W Loewy			

Edgar Rice Burroughs

Adventure	Canterbury-Geo	G T McWhorter	Perry's Antiq
Bailey Srch			

California

Alta Calif	Carlos	D Henson	Old Bk Sh-S F
H R Andrews	Danville	P Howard	J E Reynolds
Argus	R Dean	Hungry Eye	P E Rose
Assoc Bk Svc	Diablo	R W Jimerson	Sergio
F A Berk	Douglas	Manning's	Talisman
Bkmark-Sto	Et Cetera	Mitchell's-San	Urban
Campbell-Camp	A S Fischler	S Noto	Wahrenbrock's
Caravan-L A	Grady's		

Calligraphy

Chiswick	M Goldsholl	Memory Box	J E Schober
J E Conner	E Howe	Other	A Schram
Ginger	J Mashman	Princeton Antiq	E B Shields
J Goldman			

Camera Manuals

S Shuart	C K Travis

Canada & Canadiana

Academic	Biblio	Frontier P'neer	G Javitch
Acadia	H Black's	J Gagnon	Johnson & Small
Amer Bks	Blue River	M Ginsberg	H R Kahn
Anglican Bib	Bk Bazaar	A Goodman	J J Keleher
H Anson-Cart	E R Bowes	Grt No'West	J Kidston
Arctician	Bullock's	J H Hale	D & E Lake
Mrs A L Ashton	De Haviland	Hannelore	Dr L M Lande
Attic	Diamond-Mon	Haunted Bksh	J J Lefebvre
Beaver	P Dumas	Heritage-Cal	Lib Quebecoise
J R Becker	M Dunn	Highway	Looking Glass
J A Benoit	I Ehrlich	W Hoffer	S C Lunsford
K Benson	B Ellis	D Hood	B Lysecki

R & A MacKay
Madonna Hse
Mansfield
Maps & Bks
D Mason
F A L Mathewson
J P McGahern
Montgomery

Nostalgia
Odd Bk
Okanagan
Old Favorites
Old Mystic
O Oughtred
Pansy Patch
W & L Pinkney

Readables
J Rush
R C Scace
Schooner
Scotia
J W Smith
R Spafford

D Tessier
J Weiss
Westmount
T Williams
W P Wolfe
G Woolmer
B Yolleck

Canadian Literature

Alphabet

Grt No'West

W Nelson

S Temple

Cape Cod & Martha's Vineyard

Bryant's

Hingham

Parnassus Svce

Wake-Brook-Ft L

Caribbean

Amer Lib Srvce
E J Craig
D N Harding

Jeltrups'
H Karno
Libros Latinos

Lighthse
H S Mott
A W Paine

Parnassus Svce
Revisionist
University Pl

Cartoons & Caricature

Bk Roundup

R Graham

W H Helfand

J S Iavarone

Catalogues Raisonnes

M Gordon   Printery

Catholica

Celtic Cross   Madonna Hse

Cats

Cat Center   Eubiotics

Cattle & Range Industry

S L Heritage   B E Pingenot
Los Artesanos

Central America

Acoma   H Karno   R C Ramer   Revisionist
Ethnograph Arts   Libros Latinos

Chess, Checkers, & Draughts

D Benson
A Buschke
Caissa

Checker
Landau
R W Mattila

Old Edtns
J C Rather
O Shapiro

University Pl
F Wilson

Chicago

Goodwin & Zein

E F Keenan

L Laws

Titles

Childrens' Books

A To Z
Abraxas
Acres-Tre
Action Bks
J Addams
R H Adelson
Adventure Kids
Again
Aleph-Bet
Allen
Amer Frag
Antiq Bks
Antiquus
Arkadyan
Armchair Sailor
As You Like It
Mrs A L Ashton
Avocet
L J Bain
Bargain-Par
Barn Sale
Barn Loft
G E C Barnes
Barrow
Bear
D B Belcher
J & J Berger
Bibliophile-Pas
Bicentennial

D Blomberg
C Blomgren
A Bloom's
Bk Gall-Tac
Bk Barn-Bea
Bk Center-Ath
Bk Dales
Bk End-Mon
Bk Peddlers
Bk Shelf-Way
Bk Sh-Ket
Bk St-Oly
Bk Case-Fres
Bk Cellar-Brat
Bk Cottage
Bk Ends-Arl
Bk Haven-Law
Bk Nook
Bk Stall-Oak
Bk Stop-Day
Bk Stop III
Bk St-Engl
Bkcell
Bkfnder-Pen
Bkfndrs-Bol
Bkhaven-Spr
Bkleggers
Bkmark-Sto
Bkmark-Pro

Bks Etc-Hast
Bks-Gre
Bks Unltd-Nat
Bks Unltd-Ind
Bks & Thngs-Ter
Bkseller-Cher
Bkshelf-El D
Bkshelf-Cla
Bkstock
Bkst-Jenk
Bkst-Fai
Bound Pleas
M Braiterman
Bryn Mawr-N Hav
Bryn Mawr-Alb
Bullock's
Bunker
H M Burstein
J & W Bursten
Canterbury-Geo
Caravan-Sti
Carrocell
M Castelli
Chafey's
S F Chapin
Chappaqua
Cherokee
Chimney Sweep
Clark's

Cogitator
Cole's-La J
Colls' Cntr-Den
S F Cullins'
Columbia
Computer Locate
Conversation
Mrs D Cook
Corner-Cas
Country Lane
J Criscione
Curiosity-St J
Curious-Bost
Dana's Doorway
D Davis
Davison
B Dawson
De Victor's
Debra
H & E Deines
Dennis
Dennis
J A Desch
Dictionary
J Distefano
Diva
C Docheff
Dr Nostlgia
Donaldsons

Donegan
Drusilla's
A Dumler
H H Eastman
Echo
Edison Hall
H R Emler
Escargot
L E Evans
Farley's
B Farnsworth
D Fay
First Impress
Floating Mtn
T T Foley
A T Ford
Forest Park
Fortune Finders
Fox-Mad
Froghollow
D Frohnsdorff
Frontier P'neer
H Galewitz
L Galinsky
Garciagarst
F R Gardner
R Gardner
R L George
D & P Gilbert
K Glackin
Grady's
Greenblatt
P Greene
K Gregory
Griffin
Gryphon's Lair
Guerin Editeur
Gutenberg's
J Hall
Hampton
Harris Srch
Haslam's-St P
Haunted Bksh
F Hawkins
H E Heinrich
Cj Hinke
D Hirsch

Hirschtritt's
Hobby Helpers
Homestead
Homesteader
Horse In Attic
M Hunley
Huntley
Illustrated Ant
Inn
J & C
Janus-Hun
L S Kaiser
J B Keeler
Kent's Crossing
J Klein
G Klemm
V Kraft
G Krueger
P Kufus
Lange's
R Lasley
Librarium
Little Prof
E Llewellyn
Lyrical Ballad
M & M
Maestro
Magic Mtn
Marvelous
S Marx
R McCarthy
H McKee
J S McKenna
McLean
Memory Box
Merlin's Closet
Metacomet
R A Mezoff
F Michelli-Nwk
Midway
E Miller
Miller's
D Miranda
Mithras
E Moody
C Morelle
Morrell's

H S Mott
Murray's
D R Nelson
W P Northrop
Old Block
Old Bks & Coll
Old Bk Sh-Ken
Old Glory
Old Mill
Old Bk Rm-Gow
Orange Cat
M E Owen
Owl Creek
Owl Pen
E Panos
Pansy Patch
M R Parks
Paul's
F Paws
Peacock
Pendleton Publ
Peninsula Antiq
Perry's Antiq
E Phalen
Pharos
W Pierce
B A Pinchot
Pinocchio's
J S Pipkin
Poor Farm
I Quitzau
Ralston
K T Ransom
Readables
Readmore
Redford
J A Reisler
Renaissance-Lak
B Resnik
C M Robinson
Rosengren's
H V Ryan
C F Safir
Sail Loft-Summ
Sail Loft-Wint
St Nicholas
Sample-Sea

San Jose-San
Scarlet Letter
J G Schiller
S Schlossberg
L Seeborg
J & V Shelton
A Sherlock
Sidney's
T Small
Snowbound
South Bay
R Speray
Sterling
G Sullivan
Swiss Village
Tattered Cover
B Tauscher
Temares
Terry's Better
B Thatcher
Mrs Thomason
3 Geese
Titles
Toad Hall
Tree Hse
Treehorn
Turkey Hill
Twice Sold
M Twyce
M L Tyrrell
Vi & Si's
Victoria-NYC
J Wade
A G Weindling
B Weiss
West's Agency
S Wetstone
White Rabbit
A Wilder
R Wilkerson
Winsted
Wise Owl
Words Worth
R Yorty
S Yudkin
M Zervas

Chinese Civilization

East & West   J G Stanoff

Christian Books

R O Roberts   Western

Christian Science

Mostly-L A   Rare Bk Co

Church History

Allenson-Breck   Cartesian   R O Roberts   Stroud
R Bever   Obsolescence

Church Records

Bk Gall-Gai   Librarius   Townsends   D E Whelan

Sir Winston Churchill

Churchilliana   D W McLennan

Cinema-Sea
Coll's List
Coll's Bkcase
Constant Reader
Corner-NYC
J Craig
Crofter's
Curious-Los G
Drama
A M Ellis
George Sand

M Goldsholl
Gotham
Hampton
J N Herlin
L Herndon
H'wood Bk City
P Hunt
P Jenkins
R T Jordan
E M Katt
Kay's

P Krapp
J Kuwalsky
Kwasniewski
La Scala
L Laws
L Loewenthal
Longhorn
G H Mahfuz
M M E Maxwell
Okman's
Perception Plus

Performing Arts
Pett & Lieber
B Plant
Revisionist
Rockaway
H & R Salerno
Science Fantasy
L Tebbetts
Vagabond
Valley Bk City
D E Wojack

Circus & Carnival

B & G
E M Katt

L Kohrs

Meyerbks

B Schmid

City & Urban Planning

Fir Tree
F Metcalf

Riverside Mail

G P Szontagh

Urban

Civil War & Confederacy

Abraham Lincoln
J P Adzima
K Altau
Amer Mail Auct
Antiq Bks
Appalachia
Appleland
Balaclava
Benjamin Autogr
Bishop Of Bks
Bloch & Co
Bk Hse-Arl
Bk Swap
Bk Trader-Fai
Bks & Thngs-Ter
Bkworm-Cor

Bkworm & Silver
Borderland
W M Boulton
British Stamp
Broadfoot's
Burke's
J Burnett
Carolina
J P Cather
Choctaw Traders
Coll's Old
Confederate
Corner Shelf-Cul
Crabtree
Danville
E Davis

De La Pena
G Deeds
C Derowitsch
Don's
Douglas
E F Dunlap
C Elder
L Evans
O O Evans
Fox-Mad
Franklin
Fron Amer
Fuller's
L Ginsberg
D Grossblatt
Guidon

M T Hall
Haslam's-St P
J D Hawkins
J L Heflin, Jr
H C Hensel
J A Hess
Historic News
Hist Real
Hoosier Bksh
Hope Farm
T Hughes
W M Hutter
Inland River
J F F
J K King
C E Law

Lennies
L N Lien
MacDonald's Mil
Memor Amer
Mil-Air
Military
T T Moebs
Mooers
L A Moore, Sr
Morningside-Oak
Morningside-Pob
Mt Falcon
D S Mull
Neikrug

Nemaha
R G Newman
H Noble Jr
Obsolescence
Old Bkshelf
Old Lou Books
Old Quenzel
Ostby's
Page One
J L Parker
Pendragon
Prairie Archive
Raven
F E Reynolds

P E Rose
J Rybski
San Jose-Jack
San Marco
J N Showalter
J M Skutel
Soldier
So By S'West
T Sullivan
H Tanner
Tappin
B Tauscher
E C Thomas
L Thompson

G Totty
G Tramp
Unicorn-Eas
Valley-Gal
Va Bk Co
Von Blons
F G Walett
Wantagh
Wards Corner
Wolf's Head
Yankee Peddler
Yesteryear-Atl
M J Yuill
Zellner's

Classics

Abelard
Abreyde
Albion
W H Allen
Amer Bks
At The Sign
Atticus-Tor
P Berry
Bloomsbury
Bk End-Free

Bk Cottage
Bk Stop III
Bksource
T W Burrows
Cartesian
Clark's
Coventry
Encyclopedias
C Farkas
Hinds

Huntley
Inn
Kregel's
Krown & S'man
D Ladner
M Mahoney
D Mason
D Moore
Old Corner
G R Osgood, Jr

R A Palket
Ravenstree
W Salloch
E K Schreiber
Starr-Camb
H L Stern
Tattered Cover
Word
Yesterday's-Ash

Cock Fighting

J E Norris

Tan Bark

Collecting & Collectibles

J P Adzima
Coll's Bkcase

H'wood Bk City

Nickelodeon

Papermill

Collection Development

C Ackerman	Cheng & Tsui	G Klemm	Sandpiper
C Appelbaum	L Collins	Latin Amer	Srch Srvce-Wau
Argosy	H C Daitz	Leekley Srch	J W Smith
Attic-Hodg	Davis & Schorr	W McDonnell	Strawbridge
S Ballinger	J S Edgren	L McGilvery	Sylvest & Orph
Baseball	Educo	Noahs Ark	Taurus
M B Beal	Elliot's	Perryman	Thelema
Bibliopolis-Cle	J Gach	A J Phiebig	T W Tingle
Bk Look-War	H'wood Bk Shop	Randall Hse	Tower Hse
Bunter	Int Univ Bkslrs	Resurrection	Warwick
D Carbonneau	Jolie's	A G Robinson, Jr	J T Zubal

Colonial America & Revolutionary War Era

Fuller's	Indian Head

Color Plate Books

R H Adams	E Davis	P Jenkins	N & N Pavlov
Amer Frag	G Deeds	J Johnson	Peninsula Antiq
Antiq Bksllrs	C Derowitsch	I Keats	R R Rhoads
Appelfeld	C Docheff	V Kraft	Rockland
W G Arader III	R Dworcyk	L'estampe	Sail Loft-Summ
L Balish	E Enzler	M & S	Sail Loft-Wint
Bargain-Par	L E Evans	I MacKenzie	San Jose-Jack
J N Bartfield	L Fox	J Majer	San Marco
Bk Block-Gree	W T Gavin	Marvelous	C Sessler
V A Bradley	K Gregory	Mithras	H J Shoebridge
H W Brewer	A Gutkin	Moe's	Sterling Valley
W F Broderick	H W K	T T Moebs	L Tebbetts
J Buck	D N Harding	Nimue	Whitlock's
M Castelli	Cj Hinke	Olympia	Worldwide-Arl
T Clark	M S Hollander	Out Of Prnt-Whi	Yesterday's-Wes
Country Lane	Illustrated Ant	Parker's	I Zucker
J Cummins			

Colorado

Cache   A M Griffiths   Old Corner

Comic Books

Appalachia	City Bk & Coin	J S Iavarone	J S Pipkin
AVH Bkshop	Coll's Bkcase	Imagine That	B Plant
L J Bain	Comic Art	Jolie's	Reedmor
Barjon's	Corner Stone	E M Katt	A G Robinson, Jr
Bee Gee's	Curious-East	P Kufus	Rockaway
H C Blackerby	Dennis	Longhorn	Rockaway
C Blomgren	Dr Nostlgia	McDuffies	Rodden's
Bk Sail	Dragon's Lair	Midway	W E Schroeder
Bk Broker	Escargot	Million Year	2nd Time Around
Bk Exch-Mis	G N Gabbard	K Mitchell	Stan's
Bk Gall-Gai	Golden Age	Mostly-Farm	Sterling
Bk Mart	Grand	N'Woods Funnies	Tappin
Bkie	D Gratz	O'Leary's	F J Wilhelm
Bks Unltd-Ind	Hall's Nostalg	Old Bk St-Akr	Yellow Press
Bkstack-Elk	Haslam's-St P	Omega	Yesteryear-Nam
Bk Traders	C Held	Paperback Jack	R Yorty
Chamblin	L Herndon	Passaic	

Commodities Trading

R Bever   Info

Computers

Arc Bks	Dictionary	Merlin's	L W Smith
A Cheslock	Jay's	Radiographics	

Connecticut

W E Hallberg   C L Robinson-Wi   J Woods-Cov

Conservation

Blue River   Callahan & Co   Old Print Gall   G Pettinger
Buckabest   Oblong   Peterson Bk Co   R C Scace

Construction, Building Materials, & Materials Science

Chamisa   Cypress-Park   W D Nelson

Continental Books

Articles Of War   Hofmann & Free   B McKittrick   B & L Root'berg
E V Glaser   Hse Of Fict   E Offenbacher   E K Schreiber
D E Guice   J Mancevice   A J Phiebig   Trebizond

Cookery & Gastronomy

A C H   Avocet   Bk Sh-Sou   Bkmark-Sto
Abraxas   M E Bennett   Bk Cellar-Ful   Bkmark-Pro
Acorn   A Bloom's   Bk Cellar-Brat   Bkpost-Dal
Al's   Bk & Tackle   Bk Den East   Bks Etc-Hast
Antiques-Hil   Bk Attic   Bk Harbor   Bks-Gre
Argus   Bk Peddlers   Bk Srch-Pit   Bks Unltd-Nat
As You Like It   Bk Shelf-Way   Bk Stall-Oak   Bkseller-Cher

Bkshelf-Cla
Bkst-Jenk
L Bowling
Mrs L M Brew
British Stamp
Bryn Mawr-N Hav
Bunker
Cape Cod-San
Caravan-L A
Carrocell
K Caughren
Chamisa
Chappaqua
Cookery Bkery
Corner-NYC
Cosmopolitan
Dish Hollow
Eagle's-Vero

Eagle's-Chel
E C Fales
T T Foley
Footnote
Frontier P'neer
M L Gore
H Halbach
R Hittel
N W Hoffman
Homestead
Horchow
Hsehold Words
Inn
J & C
Janus-Hun
J Klein
P Kufus
Lantern

Little Prof
C Lowenberg
T Mawson
M M E Maxwell
Montrose
Mother Tongue
New Canaan
O'Leary's
E Olcott
Old Bk Rm-Cro
Orange Cat
Other
R A Palket
E Panos
D Perier
Question Mark
R & R
Radio City

Raintree
Renaissance-Lak
I Rouse
B J Rule
Schroeder's
D Sloan's
Strawberry Hill
Swiss Village
This Old Hse
W Van Devanter
Village-Hud
A G Weindling
G Wilson
Wine & Food
Winsted
Wooden Spoon
Words Worth

Costumes

P Howard   H V Ryan   L Schulman   R L Shep

Counterfeit Stamps & Coins

L H Finn   H Herst, Jr

Cowboy and Western Art & Artists

Guidon   B Porter

Crafts & Trades

A C H   R E Abel   B Agranoff   Artcraft

Bk Cellar-Brat
Bk Exch-Corn
Bk Fair
Bks Etc-Hast
Bks In Trans
Bkst-Fai
Bryant's
Christiania

M R Cutler
Ginger
Global
N W Hoffman
Horchow
Jokal
Kneedeep
Kwasniewski

W McDonnell
Montgomery
H Nestler
Old Bk Rm-Gow
Other
E Panos
B Parrington

Riverow
Schroeder's
J M Skutel
Stuart's
D Testa
This Old Hse
T Trace

Criminology

K G Arthurton
Chappaqua
Cosmopolitan
Curious-Los G
J Fisher

Folkways
Hoffman Resch
Keith & Martin
J O'Shea

Okman's
Old Bk Rm-Gow
Old Verities
Pisces & Cap

Riverside Mail
R L Sadoff
P Smith
Thomolsen

Curiosa

A Egan   T N Haviland   C J Sheiner

Dance

E Andrews
Ballet
Bks & Thngs-NYC
Broude Bros
W J Cassidy
Choreogr

Corner-NYC
Dance Etc
Dish Hollow
Footnote
G Javitch

C Kellinger
La Scala
L Loewenthal
J & J Lubrano
Lyrical Ballad

Maestro
Sand Dollar
Serpent & Eagle
R L Shep
Windage Farm

Decorative Arts

Anchor & Dol   Museum Gall   R L Press   T Trace

Delaware

Baldwin's Barn   Oz & Ends

Derrydale Press

| Angl & Shoot | P J Drabeck | Highwood | Remington's |
| Calderwoods | G L Estabrook | L L Razek | |

Desert

Assoc Bk Svc   Ishtar

Design

Mandrake   P Miller

Detective Fiction

Aardvark's-Orl	Bengta Woo	Boulevard	A Dumler
Abra Cadavar	Biblioctopus	Bryn Mawr-N Hav	Edtns Ltd
Action Bks	Blue Moon	Canterbury-Geo	L E Evans
J Addams	Bk Baron	Caveat Emptor	Fantasy
K Armens	Bk Sh-Ket	R Chalfin	D Fay
Attic	Bk Case-Pas	Chimney Sweep	Ferryman Ant
AVH Bkshop	Bk Treasury	Clipper Ship	First Impress
L J Bain	Bkery-Fai	Curious-Los G	E Fithian
Barjon's	Bkfndrs-Bol	Curious-East	Forest Park
M E Battersby	Bkshelf-El D	Debra	Francis & Yell
Beasley	Bkst-Mil	D Discher	G N Gabbard

C Garvin
P Greene
H Halbach
J Hansen
C Held
Hobby Hse
Hse Of Fict
P Hunt
Jack's Used
Janus-Tuc
Joyce
Keith & Martin
P Krapp
R Kristiansen
N L Laird
J Landau
E A Lehwald
Limestone Hills
R L Link

A B W MacEwen
McClintock
I Mendoza
Mermaid
J Meyerson
F Michelli-Nwk
F Michelli-Ogu
Mithras
Murray's
Mystery Hse
Mystery Manor
N'Woods Funnies
Oceanside
Okman's
E Olcott
P'back Exch
J L Parker
Pett & Lieber

T Phelps
L Pipes
J S Pipkin
J L Polley
D F Proctor
Ralston
K T Ransom
G J Rausch
Rodden's
Rue Morgue
T Rutherford
S & S
Sample-Sea
S F Mystery
Savran's
Shamus
T W Shaw
A Sherlock

Silver Door
Somerset
R Speray
P L Stern
Sykes & Fla
Sylvest & Orph
B Tauscher
S Temple
Terry's Better
Thomolsen
R Todd
Tri-Town
Vagabond
Waves
Weller Victoria
West's Agency
M C Wilson
C B Wimsey

Dictionaries

A C H
Bk Clearing
Bkmark-Pro
Bks Unltd-Nat

C Farkas
Gutenberg's
W S Heinman
Ivycrest

Landau
J J Lefebvre
Other
O Patterson

Reference
Revisionist
Secret Sharer
Theta

Documents

J Aldrich
T Alford
Alron
Amer So'West
C Appelbaum
B & B
R Batchelder
L Bowling

A G Clegg
E J Craig
H M Darvick
Fortunate Fnds
Guthman
D Harris
Hingham
Historic News

D B Howes
T Hughes
La Valois
Lion Heart
J Lowe
C E Miller
Mitch's
Old Prntd Word

Paper & Ink
O Patterson
K Prag
P C Richards
R H Richshafer
L Schulman
R Slifer

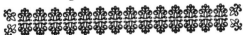

Dogs

Arabest
Bibliog Of Dog
Burt's
C Butcher
Canine Conn
Chestnut Ridge
Cortese

Dog Inc
A A Dunn
G L Estabrook
Eubiotics
G B I
Hobby Helpers
Hoffman Resch

Ken-L-Questor
R King
V Koppelman
N E Lyon
Old Dragon's
K Rais
L L Razek

C M Robinson
S R Smith
S Spindel
Sportsman's
P Sterne
Tan Bark

Doll Books & Paper Dolls

Mrs D Cook

Cypress-Park

J A Reisler

Mrs Thomason

Drama

Americanist
Bibliophile-NYC

Boulevard
Greenblatt

M Halpern

Theatrebooks

Drawings

Albion Graphics
Artcraft
Artistic End
B & B
Black Sun
Childs Gall

A P Collins
E Driscoll
B P Ferrini
D Frohnsdorff
G B I
L Goldschmidt

R J Kempe
B Leibowits
G R Minkoff
H S Mott
D F Proctor
P H Samuels

W H Schab
D Tunick
Unique Antiq
Valley-Say
P G Waite

Drug Culture

R Demarest   Earthworks   Jay's

Early Printed Books

Bromer   R L Collins

Economics & Business

Abbot	Computer Locate	Lincoln-O P	Revisionist
Amer Opinion	Educo	H J Mason	R H Rubin
M E Battersby	Folkways	Maxwell Sci	San Fernando
Biblio	J L Fraser	Merlin's	O Schreyer
W Bledsoe	Genessee	S Millman	M Tanditash
Bkpost-Dal	Hammer Mtn	J Norman	Urban
Bkst-Fai	Int Univ Bkslrs	J L Parker	Western Hemi
W J Cassidy	D & E Lake	Red Bridge	Ximenes

Education

Antiq Bks	Edison Hall	Marsh Farm	Sager's
Bk Barn-Bea	Guerin Editeur	F Metcalf	J G Schiller
Bkcell	Inn	Mt Falcon	L Smith
E K	M M Kraus		

18th Century Literature

Pacific Bk Hse   G Tramp

Emblem Books

A Fair   J Mancevice   W Salloch

Encyclopedias

Encyclopedias   Starr-Camb

English Literature

Bkfndrs-Mia	A Garnett	J O'Gara	Transition
J M W Borg	Hofmann & Free	Regent Hse	Van Norman
W T Clermont	Joseph Provider	Savoy	Vintage-Bost
Dauber & Pine	J & M Laurie	Starr-Bost	C B Wimsey
Debra	Lift Bridge-Fai	C A Stonehill	Woodspurge

Ephemera

J Addams	F A Berk	De La Pena	E Howe
Adrian's	C Blomgren	Dr Nostlgia	D B Howes
aGatherin'	Bohling	Drama	T Hughes
B Agranoff	Bk Bin-Dal	Drew's	Inland River
Air Age	Bk Mart	Drusilla's	Jean's
J Aldrich	L Bowling	A M Ellis	R J Kalanja
Allen	J & W Bursten	H R Emler	J & P Klemperer
Alta Calif	Carney	L H Finn	Kwasniewski
Ampersand	Carry Back	Fortunate Fnds	La Valois
Anacapa	R F Casavant	A & R Gardiner	Lambda Rising
Apothecary	B Cassidy	G F Glaeve	K Leach
Argus	Chapman & Berry	M Goldsholl	Lift Bridge-Fai
At The Sign	Chiswick	Grandpa's Hse	Lighthse
L Balish	Cinema-Sea	Gull	Little Hundred
P E Baracca	Common Reader	W D Hall	W Loewy
J R Becker	E J Craig	W H Helfand	L S Loomer
D B Belcher	Dana's Doorway	Hobby Helpers	MacDonald's Mil
M E Bennett	Dance Mart	Hsehold Words	R & A MacKay

Magazine
G H Mahfuz
J & L Mallis
Marg & Moss
Memory Box
C E Miller
A H Minters
D Miranda
Mitch's
W F Mobley
T T Moebs
W Monie
E Morrill
Murray
S & C Najarian
New Steamship

Northern Lights
Nutmeg
Oinonen Auct
Old Bk Sh-Morr
Old Curiosity
Old Bk St-Akr
Old Prntd Word
E Orth
Pages
Paper & Ink
Paper Peddlers
Pennyroyal
Performing Arts
W & L Pinkney
J S Pipkin

H J Popinski
K Prag
Prairie Archive
Print Dev-Arl
Ravine Cottage
S Resnick
Reston's
P C Richards
Richardsons
Riverow
C Ross
L Rostenberg
San Franciscian
Schoyer's
Shadow

Sindell Res
J M Skutel
J P Slattery
Spectrum
Stationarius
Sterling
Store
T Sullivan
R M Sylvester
H Tanner
F J Thomas
M L Tyrrell
Valley-Say
J Wade
Windage Farm

Erotica

Deskins/Greene
Elysian Fields
Kats

M M Kraus
C G Martignette
Old Bk St-Port

J Pollock
C A Rush

C J Sheiner
I Stormgart

Espionage

Bkphil

C C Davis

Elm

European History

Amer Bks
L Berliawsky

Q M Dabney
Hammer Mtn

Kalonbooks
J O'Gara

Red Bridge
Volkhoff & Von

Evolution

Scientia   Shaw-Banfill

Falconry

W J Bkhunter   Corner Shelf-Cul   P J Drabeck

Fantasy

Antiq Bkvestors   L Diehl   F M Halpern   Odyssey
Bailey Srch   P C Dillon   B R Levin   Old Glory
Bkwrights   A Egan   Longhorn   A Sherlock
C W Brooks   Francis & Yell   Midnight-Mar   W R Slater
Change Hobbit   J T Gatto   Mostly-Farm   R A Squires
G & H De La Ree   D & P Gilbert

Farming, Ranching, & Livestock

Amer So'West   T Durflinger   Mitchell's-San   J W Smith
Antiq Bks   O O Evans   Mt Falcon   Trotting
Backpocket   M Gibbs   Page One   R E Underhill
M E Battersby   Info   D Perier   Whitlock Farm
Bk Stall-Roc   H B Leech   Pomona Exch   G Wilson
Bkst-Fai   Marsh Farm   Wm Reese Co   E Woodburn
Broken Kettle   Mason's-Wab   Rupprecht's   C Wright
Chiricahua   Maxwell's   2nd Life   W L Zeigler
D N Dupley

Fiction

Abra Cadavar
Abraxas
Abreyde
Acres-Tre
Acres-Cin
Aesir
All B & P
Attic-Wins
atticus
AVH Bkshop
Back Row
L J Bain
Barn Sale
Bay Side
S C Bernard
Biblioctopus
Biermaier's
Big John's
Bigelows' Quill
Blue Eye
Blue River
Bk Bin-Kin
Bk Center-Ath
Bk End-Free
Bk Sh-Boise
Bk Sh-Ket
Bk Exch-Mis
Bk Fndr-Genev
Bk St-San
Bk World
Bkleggers
Bkman Arcady
Bkmark-Pro
Bks & Thngs-Boc
Bks For Every
Browsery
Bunker
Bunter
G F Bush
J R Butterworth
Cabin In Pines
A Carduner

Carmichael's
W Chadde
Chatham
Civic Center
Coach Hse
Cogitator
Columbia
Constant Reader
Country Connect
Coventry
Curiosity-Eau
Dakota
N Dame
Diff Drum-Wes
Dr Nostlgia
R P Dunaway
E & M Ediger
G F Edwards
Euclid
Floating Mtn
G B I
H Galewitz
L Galinsky
W C Gates
R G Gill
K Glackin
R Glassman
Grand
Griffin
Gull
J Hall
G S Herron
Hooked On
N T Hopper
Hse Of Fict
M Hudson
Invisible
Ithaca Hse
J D S
Janus-Tuc
Jennies
Joyce

D V Keck
T M Knaus
P Kufus
La Mesa
Lantern
Libra
R L Link
Little Prof
B Lysecki
M & M
R & A MacKay
Maelstrom
C Magee
G H Mahfuz
Main St
Maxwell's
B McBride
J McGovern
J S McKenna
A R Milkerit
Monroe
D Moore
J C Morel
C Morelle
Murray's
N R S
Nationwide
H Noble Jr
Nouveau
Old Bks & Coll
Old Favorites
Old Bk Rm-Gow
Our Heritage
M E Owen
Owl Pen
Ozark
T C Packard
E Panos
M R Parks
People's
Pett & Lieber

W Pierce
J L Polley
A & A Prosser
Quadrant
Quill & Brush
K Rais
Ralston
Randall Hse
Raymer's
Readmore
Renaissance-Mil
J B Reynolds
M B Robertson
B J Rule
L St Clair
Sangamon
7 Oaks
T W Shaw
W P Shepard
Sherlock
S Shmavonian
L Smith
Snowbound
P Sperling
Starr-Bost
Strand
Strawberry Hill
Strictly
Terry's Better
This Old Hse
Tri-Town
Turkey Hill
Valley-Amh
S Vogel-St L
Vol One Used
Wait Godot
J H Weinberg
A G Weindling
J Weiss
Wessex
Young Antiquar

Fine Arts

F A Bernett	Cyrano's	L McGilvery	No'West
Brillig Works	P D French	Museum Gall	R L Press
R K Brown			

Firearms & Weapons

J T Gatto	Riling Arms	Tan Bark

First Editions

A To Z	Bibliopolis-Cle	B Cassidy	Eagle's-Vero
Abra Cadavar	Black Sun	Castalia	Eagle's-Chel
Abraxas	R Bleiweiss	Caveat Emptor	C Elder
Academy-NYC	N Bond	Chafey's	Fant Archives
Action Bks	Bk Baron	Cherokee	Fantasy
Albatross	Bk Bin-Kin	Chloe's	J F Fleming
Aldine	Bk Barn-Sio	W T Clermont	A T Ford
Alphabet	Bk Harbor	Cogitator	Franklin
Anacapa	Bk Haven-Law	A Cohen	Fransen's
Ancient Cty Pr	Bk Mart-San	Colebrook	R Gardner
Andover Square	Bk Srch-Pit	Coll's List	A Garnett
Antic Hay	Bk Stop III	Coll's Bkcase	C Garvin
Antiquariat	Bkery-Fai	Common Reader	W C Gates
Antiquus	Bkmailer	Corner-Newp	Givens
C Appelbaum	Bksource	Cosmic Aero	L S Granby
Argosy	Bkstock	Country Lane	Grt So'West
Ark	Bkwrights	Court Place	Green Thought
G Armitage	V A Bradley	J Cummins	Grub St
Artifacts	M Braiterman	Curiosity-Eau	A Gud
Authors Of West	Bromer	Current	Gundy's
Back Tracts	Burke's	L W Currey	J H Hale
Barnstable	T W Burrows	Dan's	Hamill & Barker
Baron	H M Burstein	Danville	Hampton
C Baron	R H Cady	Dee Cee	Hartfield
Barrow	Canterbury-Chi	J A Dermont	W S Hay
D L Bauman	B C Carltiz	C Derowitsch	B J Hecht
J Bekker	Carrocell	R B Desmarais	Heritage-L A
S C Bernard	Carry Back	Detering	Hermitage
Biblioctopus	J Cashman	Don's	Hinds

Cj Hinke
Hobbit
Hobson's Ch
Hock-Hocking
Hoosier School
G Houle
Hummingbird
M Hunley
Hunted
I Am I
Inprint
Invisible
Isaiah Thomas
Jack London
D M Jacobs
J Appleseed
Johnson & O'D
T J Joyce
K Karith
K Karmiole
I Keats
C Kellinger
J K King
V Kraft
R Kristiansen
D & M Krueger
La Mesa
Lambda Rising
Leaves Of Grass
J G Leishman
B R Levin
London-Chi
London-Alb
Long's-Pen
J Lorson
R A Lowenstein
S Lupack
M & M
M & S

T MacAluso
R A MacKsey
G S MacManus
J Majer
Mansfield
Manuscript
Marion Antiq
Marshall Field
J W Martin
S Marx
D Mason
Maverick
B McBride
B E McCaslin
McClintock
M McCosh
J P McGahern
J O McMeans
Merlin's Closet
Midnight-Mar
A R Milkerit
Million Year
Monroe
Montrose
E Morrill
Mostly-Oma
B Mraz
Much Loved
Mystery Manor
D R Nelson
C A Noon
J Normile
P H North, Jr
Northeast
Norumbega
Nugent & Assoc
D L O'Neal
Ohio Bkhntr

E Olcott
Old Monterey
Old New York
Old Bk St-Akr
Our Heritage
J Owen
Owl Creek
P & H
Pacific Bk Hse
Pageant
Pan
R F Perotti
D Peterson
E Phalen
J L Polley
B Porter
K Rais
Rare Bk Co
E P Rich
Rockland
Ron-Dot
S-T
Sage
H & R Salerno
J R Sanderson
D Sauber
Saxifrage
M A Schaefer
2nd Life
W P Shepard
Silver Door
R B Sirrine
J A Smith
R W Smith
Somerset
South Bay
L Stamelman
P L Stern

Strictly
Suncircle
K W Sutcliffe
Sykes & Fla
Talbothay's
Temple Bar
Thelema
E C Thomas
Totteridge
Tower Hse
Towson
Tri-Town
P Tumarkin
Turkey Hill
Typographeum
Tyson
Vagabond
J Wade
D Ward
Warwick
Wayside
D Weiss
B Weiss
West L A Center
West's Agency
White's
Whitlock's
E C Williams
Wilson
Windhover
J M Winters
World Wide-NYC
Xanadu
Ximenes
H Yellin
Yesteryear-Atl
R Yorty
J T Zubal

First Editions, Modern

Aardvark-S F
Aardvark's-Orl
Able Beam
About
Alphabet
Ampersand
Antic Hay
Antiquus
P P Appel

Arcane
K Armens
Arts & Lett
Asian Amer
Associates
atticus
B Babcock
Bargain-San
Barnstable

Baron
C Baron
Baroque
Beasley
Belanske & Lev
R Bemis
D Benson
S C Bernard
P C Beyer

C Blomgren
Blue Moon
Bk Gall-Tac
Bk Attic
Bk Basement
Bk Dales
Bk Sail
Bk Gall-Gai
Bk Treasury

Bkery-Fai
Bkleggers
Bkpost-Dal
J H Burke
Burton's
J R Butterworth
Camelot
Carmichael's
B Cassidy
Castalia
Cathryn
B Chaney Jr
Chloe's
Clipper Ship
Coll's Ch-Wat
L Collins
Colophon
Corner-Newp
Coventry
B Dawson
W De Freitas
Debra
J A Dermont
R Diamond
D C Dickinson
Dictionary
Dinkytown
R E Donovan
P C Duschnes
Edison Hall
R M Eisenberg
C Elder
Euclid
L E Evans
Fain's First
First Impress
A S Fischler
Francis & Yell
German & Int'l
K Glackin
Gotham
Green Dolphin
P Greene
Greenwich
D Grossblatt

Gutenberg's
D Halloran
J Hansen
W S Hay
B J Hecht
Hermitage
Hirschtritt's
R Hittel
G Horowitz
Hse Of Bks Ltd
Hse Of Fict
Howe
Howland
P C Hull
L Hunegs
In Our Time
Jack's Used
Janus-Tuc
Jay's
Johnson & O'D
Jolly Roger
E M Katt
I Keats
B R Kemp
Y Kishi
P Krapp
B R Levin
Library-Dal
Lift Bridge-Bro
R L Link
Lion's Head
Looking Glass
K Lopez
Lorenz Books
J Lorson
R A Lowenstein
S Lupack
M & M
Maestro
Magic Mtn
Maiden Voy
Main St
D Mason
B McBride
W McDonnell

I Mendoza
Mermaid
R A Mezoff
J Michaels
A R Milkerit
H Miller
G R Minkoff
D Moore
J C Morel
B Morrow
B Mraz
Nationwide
M F Neville
North Shore
Nouveau
W T O'Malley
Okman's
E Olcott
Ottenberg Bks
Otzinachson
Out-Of-Prnt-NYC
S Penner
Pett & Lieber
Pharos
Phoenix
W & L Pinkney
L Pipes
N Potter
A & A Prosser
Quill & Brush
Ralston
K T Ransom
Resurrection
R Richards
Ridge
P R Rieber
C L Robinson-Ma
S-T
B Sackheim
A Sample
Sand Dollar
J R Sanderson
Sandpiper
H Satty
Savran's

B Scott
2nd Life
2nd Time Around
C Seluzicki
Serendipity
Sewards' Folly
J & V Shelton
J V Sichel
Signed Limited
Silver Door
Skeans & Cliff
F W Smith
R W Smith
K Starosciak
Strand-Rare
Strictly
Sylvest & Orph
M Tanditash
Temple Bar
S Temple
T W Tingle
R Todd
Transition
Treetops
Tri-Town
Vagabond
C J Vega
S Vogel-St L
Wait Godot
L A Wallrich
Waverly
Waves
Wayward
J H Weinberg
Weller Victoria
Wessex
West Side
Westmount
R Wilkerson
Windhover
Thomas J Wise
J Wobber
J H Woolmer
H Yellin
Young Antiquar

Fishing & Angling

Bryant's

G J M
I MacKenzie

Rising Trout
E Rovick

Titcomb's

Florida

R R Allen	Bk St-Nap	Mickler's	San Jose-Jack
Bk Shelf-Cle	Lighthse	E K Powell	San Marco

Folk Art

Bethlehem	Olana

Folklore

G E C Barnes	Fields	Obsolescence	Serpent & Eagle
Bk Land-Tor	Gateway	Paper & Ink	S R Shapiro
D Carbonneau	Horizon	Rivendell	A Sherlock
Colls' Cntr-Den	Info	I Rouse	Slavic Antiq
L Collins	E Klein	Sample-Sea	3 Geese
Darby	B Koenig's	Scarlet Letter	Twice Sold
Echo	Los Artesanos	S Scharoun	G Wilson
Facsimile	Legacy	K L Schwarz	

Fore-Edge Painting

Burkwood	J Levine ✓ 1/18/84	H J Shoebridge	Wake-Brook-Hyan
Carlos — 1/18/84	Remington's ✓ 1/18/84	Spector	L & H Weitz

Foreign Affairs

Amer Opinion	Cheng & Tsui	T Phelps	Scattergood
W Bledsoe	Lion Ent	L J Ryan	

ex libris

160A EAST 70 STREET NEW YORK 10021

Specialists in the Avantgarde Art Movements of the 20th Century

Foreign Languages

C Ackerman	H B Diamond	E Klein	Newcomb Hall
Adler's	Dragoman	M M Kraus	North Shore
Asian-Cam	German & Int'l	La Cite-L A	Pharos
Bk End-Mon	Gull	D Ladner	A J Phiebig
Brassers	B Hamel	Latin Amer	Seville
Carrocell	Hammer Mtn	D A Lawyer	B Wheel
Cheng & Tsui	W J Johnson	R A MacKsey	F J Wilhelm
Cypress-Park	Joyce	Miller-Fruchart	P L Jackson
David's			

C. S. Forester

Button	D & D

Freemasonry

C T Powner	R G Wilborn	A G Ziagos

French Books & Literature

J A Benoit	La Valois	M S Rosenberg	Transition
J Gagnon	Lib Quebecoise		

Fur Trade

Beaver	7 Seas	G Woolmer

Gambling

S Finer
Gambler's
Greet & Read

Gundy's
L Kohrs
Meyerbks

S Powell
M Roenick
Servant's Knowl

P Smith
World Wide-NYC
Yellow Press

Game Birds

G L Estabrook

O O Evans

Games & Pasttimes

Billiard
Meyerbks

Nickelodeon

Tree Hse

Yellow Press

Gardening & Horticulture

R E Abel
Anchor & Dol
Banyan
B L Bibby
Bk Chest
Bkmark-Pro
Bks-Gre
Bkstack-Elk
Bkst-Jenk
W F Broderick
H Clenick
Chimney Smoke
Chimney Sweep

Clark's
Copper Fox
Creedmoor
Dish Hollow
R M Eisenberg
E C Fales
G L Granger
N W Hoffman
Hortolus
Hurley
I Jackson
T M Knaus
Lincoln Hill

Lion's Head
T Mawson
M N McQuerry
B L Means
J J Nadolny
E Olcott
Orange Cat
Owl Pen
Pomona Exch
Question Mark
Raintree
C M Robinson
Rupprecht's

Science Bkshlf
2nd Life
J W Smith
Thomolsen
Toad Hall
R E Underhill
G Wayner
White's
R Wilkerson
Wine & Food
E Woodburn
Wooden Spoon

Geneaologies

Aceto
Adan
Appalachia
C V Barnes
Bk Fndrs-NYC
Brennan
Coll's Old
M L Cook

Estate
Genealogists
Goodsp'd's-Milk
Goodsp'd's-Beac
D Gratz
P Henderson
Heritage-Bow
G S Herron

Jennies
J J Lefebvre
Maverick
New Engl-Benn
Ostby's
N M Pawlett
Purple Bkcase
Sharp's

Slavic Antiq
D W Starry, Sr
T Sullivan
Townsends
Tuttle Antiq
Va Bk Co
Winter Farm
World Wide-NYC

General

About
Acorn
Adrian's
B Agranoff
Ahrens
Aldine
Aldredge
T Alford
Allen
R R Allen
S B Amdur
Amer Print
Ancient Cty Bk
Annie's-Act
Annie's-Nat
Annie's-Wes
Antiq Sh-Ste
Antiq Bksllrs
Applegate
Arctician
Argos
Arjay
R Asaro
Atherton's
Attic-Hodg
Attic
Attic-Wins
Ayrshire
Back Row
Backstage
J Bailey
P E Baracca
Bargain-Gran
Barn Sale

Barn Loft
G E C Barnes
Barrow
S N Bean
Bedford's
Berry Hill
E H Bevington
Bibliophile-NYC
Bibliophile-Pas
Biermaier's
Bird's Nest
Blors
Blue Eye
C J Boardman
Bob's-App
Bk End-Sta
Bk Baron
Bk End-Free
Bk Hse-Will
Bk Lady
Bk Stall-Cin
Bk Broker
Bk Buddy
Bk Case-Hou
Bk Case-Pas
Bk Cellar-Tem
Bk Connect
Bk Ends-Arl
Bk Fair-Eug
Bk Fndr-Genev
Bk Gall-Gai
Bk Haven-Law
Bk Hse-Pla
Bk Mark-Phil

Bk Srch-Pit
Bk Srvc-Ind
Bk Stop-Day
Bk St-Engl
Bk Friends
Bkfndr-Cut
Bkfndrs-Bol
Bkfndrs Unltd
Bkmailer
Bkman-Sed
Bks & Thngs-Boc
Bks Etc-Hast
Bks-Gre
Bks Unltd-Ind
Bkseller-Akr
Bkseller's Row
Bkstop-Laf
Borene
Boston Annex
Bradford
O H Brady
Brattle
Mrs L M Brew
Brick Hse
Bridgton
Broadfoot's
Broken Kettle
G D Brown
Browser's
Browsery
Bryn Mawr-Alb
Buckabest
Bullock's
Bunter

Burton's
G F Bush
Camden Hse
Cameron's
Carlos
Carney
Casperson
Catawba River
D Chapman
Chappaqua
Chicago
Choreogr
City Wide
Colebrook
Colgate
Coll's Libr
Computer Locate
Conversation
Corner-Newp
Corner-Cas
Corner Stone
Court Place
Cranbury
Creedmoor
Curious-Bost
Curious-East
D & D
Daedalus
Daly Coll
Dana's Doorway
David's
De Ville
Denbry

H O Dendurent
B Denver
Dictionary
Dish Hollow
Dobbs
Donaldsons
Dragon's Lair
Drew's
D N Dupley
E K
H H Eastman
Edison Hall
G F Edwards
Eight-Cent
R M Eisenberg
El Piasano
Elmcress
A Elsner
Erie
D J Ernst
Ex Libris-Ban
E C Fales
K & J Field
C G Fisher
Fletcher's
Fly Creek
Fox Hill
A Frisch
Frontier P'neer
Fuller's
H Galewitz
Galvez
Garciagarst
L Gereghty
Ghent Bkworm
Gilfillan
R G Gill
S Gilman
Givens
Golden Hill
Grand
Grandpa's Hse
Grt No'West
Greet & Read
K Grunewald
Guerin Editeur
Gull
Half Price
J Hall
M Halpern
Hamill & Barker
M Hammer
Hannelore
J W Harmand
Harold's
Haunted Bksh
Heinemann's

Hennesseys
Herp Exch
G S Herron
Hobbit
Hobby Hse
H'wood Bk Shop
Holmes-Oak
Holmes-S F
Homestead
N T Hopper
Horse In Attic
V Howard
R F Hutson
I Am I
Irene's
Isaiah Thomas
J & W
R W Jimerson
S Johnson's
Joyce
D V Keck
Kennedy's
J Klein
J & P Klemperer
Kneedeep
J Kuwalsky
Los Artesanos
Landscape
K Lang
R Lasley
Lennies
Libra
Librarium
Library Ltd
Lilac Hedge
E Llewellyn
Lobster Lane
Loft
Long's-Lin
Looking Glass
Lorenz Books
P M Lumb
B Lynch
Lyrical Ballad
B Lysecki
T MacAluso
R & A MacKay
Madonna Hse
Maelstrom
C Magee
Marion Antiq
S Marx
Mason's-Wab
Maxwell's
R W Mayer
McClintock
L H McGill

J McGovern
H McKee
J S McKenna
McLean
McMahon
B McMaster
H McMillen
Memorable
Metacomet
Michael's
F Michelli-Ogu
W Monie
Montgomery
C Morelle
Mosaic
Mostly-L A
Mother Tongue
Murray
Murray's
Needham
C A Noon
No Conway
Nutmeg
O'Conn Y'year
Oblong
Odds & Eads
Old Bk Sh-S F
Old Bk Sh-Morr
Old Bk St-Port
Old Bk & Cur
Old Bks-Brun
Old Delavan
Old Edtns
Old Favorites
Old Lou Books
Old Oregon
Old Verities
Orsay
G R Osgood, Jr
Otzinachson
M E Owen
Owl Pen
Oxford
Pacific Bk Hse
Page One
Page 2
P'back Paradise
P'backs Plus
Passaic
R A Paulson
Peninsula Antiq
People's
D Perier
Personal
D V Pfeifer
J Pitchforth
N Potter

R L Press
Purple Bkcase
I Quitzau
Quizzicum
Red Bridge
Renaissance-Mil
Renascence
Reston's
D Richards
Riverrun
R Robertson
H B Robinson
Rodden's
Rogers Park
C Ross
B J Rule
L St Clair
San Jose-San
M A Schaefer
S Schlossberg
L Schnell
Schoyer's
J F Schultz
J Scopazzi
Scribbling
2nd Fiddle
2nd Story
Shadow
T W Shaw
J & V Shelton
Shuey
R Shuhi
J V Sichel
Significant
R B Sirrine
Source
South Bay
South Side
L Stamelman
Stan's
Stanley
Starr-Bost
Starr-Camb
R B Stephenson
Sterling
P Stockman
Stonehill's
Store
Strand-Rare
Strand
Surrencys
Swiss Village
R B Taylor
Thrifty Reader
G Totty
Tower Hse
Tri-Town

Tryon Cnty
Tuttle Antiq
M L Tyrrell
Tyson
Unique Antiq
Univ Bk St-Man
Valley-Say

Village-Hud
Vol One Used
Von Blons
L A Wallrich
R S Walton
Wangner's
Wards Corner

Wayward
L Weidler
West L A Center
Whitlock Farm
Thomas J Wise
Womrath's
W P Wreden

Ye Olde Fan
Yesterday's-Hot
Yesterday's-Was
Yesterday's-Par
Yesteryear-Lin
S Yudkin

Genetics

W Dordick

Shaw-Banfill

Geography

Bygone
Fireside

R Fitch
Guerin Editeur

M Hudson
R C Scace

Ent Photo   0731

Geology

Allbks
Antiq Scientist
Bk Home
A G Clegg
Court Place
R & D Emerson

Estes Service
R Fitch
Geological
M Gibbs
R Hansen
H'wood Bk Shop

J Kidston
J G Leishman
B L Means
J J Nadolny
Pennyroyal

Peri Lithon
Prospector
R Robertson
L Sloan
J Woods-Yak

Georgia

H D Adams

Hound Dog

German Books & Literature

P T Fisher
Obsolescence

I Quitzau

M S Rosenberg

P Tumarkin

Golf

R E Donovan
Family

Hoffman Lane

P G Le Van

E Tatro

Graphic Arts

R H Adams	J Craig	L'estampe	Pansy Patch
Albion Graphics	Davis & Schorr	G Lange	Printery
Artcraft	Davison	Lee & Lee	Rinhart Gall
Artistic End	Ex Libris-NYC	Marg & Moss	Schuylkill
Arts & Lett	B Farnsworth	B McBride	Sebastopol
H J Besnia	L Fox	L H McGill	P A Stroock
Blue Rider	M Goldsholl	Memory Box	F J Thomas
Bk Block-Gree	L S Granby	Methodist	Waves
Bk Gall-Whit	L Herndon	Museum Gall	P Williams
Bks In Trans	Horchow	S N Halas	Wilsey Square
Christiania	E Howe	S Orr	Wittenborn
G J Cielec	R J Kempe		

Great Lakes

G D Brown

Call Me Ishmael

Erie

Goodwin & Zein

Greek & Latin Classics

E Andrews   H T Trueb

Greece & Turkey

Able Beam   W B O'Neill

Zane Grey

Cache   P & H   Pendleton Publ   J L Wheeler

Guns

D R Doerres   Highwood   Westfall Spring

Haggadot & Prayer Books

H Minkoff   Moriah

Hawaii

Aloha Bk   Chapman & Berry   Pacific Bk Hse   Sergio
Bkfndrs Hawaii   Jack London   Pacific Writers

Health

Arthritis   D A Lewis   Rittenhse   Vegetarian Soc
Holistic Health   Mayflower   Stryker's

Heraldry

Genealogists   J E Schober

Herbology & Herbs

Centauri   B Parrington   D E Whelan   R G Wilborn
F Goldman

Heritage Press

Bk Harbor   P C Hull

Herpetology

D E Hahn   Tolliver's

History

Abelard
Acorn
Acres-Cin
R Adamiak
J P Adzima
Alpha Omega
Anderson's
Andover Square
E Andrews
Antiq Bks
Articles Of War
Mrs A L Ashton
At The Sign
J Bambach
Baptist Bourse
J Bekker
Benjamin Autogr
C S Berkowitz
Bibliophile-NYC
Bloomsbury
Bk Fndrs-NYC
Bk Land-Tor
Bk Srvc-San
Bk Srvc-Ind
Bk St-San
Bks & Thngs-Boc
Bksource
Bound Pleas

Bullock's
Choctaw Traders
Christopher's
Clark's
T Coffman
Computer Locate
Copper Fox
Country Connect
Dakota
Dan's
Dauber & Pine
De Haviland
Delta
Diff Drum-Wes
R P Dunaway
Ex Libris-Ban
Fraser's
K G Gaisser
R Glassman
Global
Guerin Editeur
Hollands'
V Howard
L Hunegs
J D S
Jack's Used
Jennies
Kay's

T M Knaus
E Krebs
La Valois
D A Lawyer
H B Leech
J J Lefebvre
Lennies
Lib Quebecoise
Lincoln-O P
Loft
London-Chi
M A MacIntosh
Marlil
D Mason
R A Mezoff
Military
S Millman
D Moore
W D Nelson
New Engl-Benn
J O'Gara
W B O'Neill
Old Delavan
Old Edtns
Our Heritage
Out-Of-Prnt-NYC
Palma
Pangloss

J L Parker
N M Pawlett
Philosophical
Pomander
R & R
G J Rausch
Raymer's
Revisionist
B M Rieger
Rogers Park
Ross & Haines
L Rostenberg
San Marco
Scholar's
2nd Time Around
Slavic Antiq
Soldier
J Taylor
E C Thomas
Univelt
Used-West
J Weiss
Wings Of Eagle
D E Wojack

History, American

Abra Cadavar
Abraham Lincoln
Aceto
Acres-Tre
Adan
Amer Opinion
Amer Wrlds
Amer Mail Auct
Antiq Sh-Ste
Antiquariat
Argonaut
F Armstrong
K G Arthurton
Austin

J Bambach
Banyan
C V Barnes
Barnette's
Barrow
W E Beaver
Blue River
Bk Addict-Por
Bk Case-Hou
Bk Ends-Arl
Bk Mart-San
Bk Srvc-San
Bkmark-Pro
Bkphil

Cabin In Pines
A Carduner
Carolina
D M Chase
T Coffman
M L Cook
E J Craig
Crofter's
Curious-Bost
K Cutler
Darian
De Haviland
Diva
Don's

E F Dunlap
W A Graf
Grt Lake
Griffin
Gryphon's Lair
Guthman
R G Hayman
Heinoldt
Heritage-Bow
W W Hildreth
Horse In Attic
P C Hull
Indian Head
Inland River

J F F
J Appleseed
Kalonbooks
Knight's
E Krebs
K Leach
H B Leech
L N Lien
Lowe Antiques
Magnalia
F Mavis
M McCosh
Memorabilia

Military
S Millman
L A Moore, Sr
Morningside-Oak
Newcomb Hall
R G Newman
C A Noon
P H North, Jr
Old Lou Books
Ostby's
Ozark
T Phelps
Purple Bkcase

R & R
Rancho
Red Bridge
Regent Hse
Rendezvous
Rinhart Gall
H B Robinson
Rogers Park
J Rybski
Schroeder's
C Sessler
Sharp's
Starr-Bost

H Stevens Son
G Totty
Treasures
Tyson
Used-West
Village-Lit
Va Bk Co
D Ward
E C Williams
Winter Farm
D E Wojack
Wooden Spoon
Ye Olde Fan

History of Medicine & Science

Argosy
Arkway
Atlanta
Atticus-Tor
S D Beare

Biblion
Bk Stall-Oak
Bkery-Ith
Chirorgical
Corn Mill

W Dordick
P Dumas
W B Fye
Globe-L A
W H Helfand

Scientia
H L Stern
Tech Info-Doc
B Yolleck

Hobbies

Ginger   Pier

Holistic Health & Nutrition

East West   Orpheus   Sunny

Sherlock Holmes & A. Conan Doyle

W Berner
Bk Caravan

W De Freitas
D Doonan

H E Heinrich
Rue Morgue

J B Shaw
P L Stern

Homosexual & Gay Literature

Bk Stacks-Burl
Bks Bohemian
Corner-Cas

Deskins/Greene
Elysian Fields
Glad Day-Tor

Glad Day-Bos
Lambda Rising
Sisterhood

Walt Whitman
S Wetstone

Horology

Adams Brown

Bklyn Gall

William-Roberts

Horror

A Egan

Fantasy

Village-Mass

Horses

Aah!
Abbot
Arabest
Argus
Backpocket
Baird Press
Blue Rider

Bk Chest
Bkst-Vern
J Breen
C Butcher
Calderwoods
Chestnut Ridge
Craighse-Pat

Craighse-Mall
Elmcress
Ishtar
Ken-L-Questor
Lyrical Ballad
October Farm
Old Dragon's

Old Favorites
P M
Plane Tree
S R Smith
S Spindel
Trotting
A Vanasse

Horse Drawn Vehicles

G Snyder

Horticulture

Horticultural	M N McQuerry	Savoy

Hotels

M L Gore	Radio City	L W Smith	Wine & Food

Hudson River Valley

Bk Look-War	Croton	Pages	Purple Mtn
Coll's Crnr	Old Bk Rm-Cro	N & N Pavlov	Odd Bk

Humanities

Amer Wrlds	Delta	Hummingbird	Rogers Park
P P Appel	Detering	D Jaffe	Rosengren's
G Armitage	Elliot's	W S Johnson	J R Sanderson
D L Bauman	Farley's	M M Kraus	L W Smith
Bk Fndr-Genev	Ferryman Ant	Lion Ent	Tuckers
Bk Warehouse	G N Gabbard	Little Read	Wessex
Catawba River	R Gilbo	H J Mason	Word
Darby	J Hood	Period Ludw	

Humor

Eight-Cent	H Galewitz	Kardy's	Miller & Miller

Hunting, Fishing & Angling

R E Abel
Amer Eagle
Amer Bk & Gal
K Andersen
Angl & Shoot
Arctician
Atlantic
J W Beattie
Bicentennial
Bishop Of Bks
Blacktail Mtn
D Blomberg
Blue River
Bk & Tackle
Bk Chest
Bkfinders-Fair
Bks Black Bass
Bkstack-Elk
J Bowman
V Burgman
C Butcher
Cabinet Of
Calderwoods
Callahan & Co

Canterbury-Chi
Chestnut Ridge
Coll's Libr
Constant Reader
Cortese
Creedmoor
Mrs K R Dorn
P J Drabeck
A A Dunn
M Dunn
T Durflinger
E Enzler
G L Estabrook
Family
5 Quail
Fleuron
Gall Old West
Global
A M Griffiths
G Hall, Jr
D Halloran
E S Hickok
High Ridge

Highwood
R Hittel
Hoffman Lane
J Appleseed
J Juszyk
R J Kalanja
J J Keleher
M Kilen
Kneedeep
W Madden
M Marcher
Memory Aisle
R A Mezoff
I J Oelgart
Old Bkshed
Old Dragon's
Open Creel
P M
Peterson Bk Co
G Pettinger
Pisces & Cap
Print Dev-Arl
Prospector

L L Razek
Riling Arms
C M Robinson
E Rovick
E Short
R Shuhi
T Small
S R Smith
S Spindel
Sporting Biblio
Sporting
Sportsman's
P Sterne
G H Suhm
Tan Bark
Terramedia
Thunderbird
Unicorn-Eas
Village-Hud
S Vogel-St L
D Weiss
Westfall Spring
Wildwood

Iberia

Latin Amer

M A MacIntosh

Louis Icart

Floating Mtn

Icart Vendor

Ice Hockey

Book-Miss   Hall's Nostalg

Ichthyology

D E Hahn   S Stewart   Tolliver's

Idaho

Ute-Or-Ida   Yesteryear-Nam

Illinois

Goodwin & Zein   Leekley Srch   Prairie Archive   Stonehill's

IlluminatedManuscripts

P C Duschnes   L C Harper   W Loewy   Moriah
R O Estes, Sr   Johnson & Small   D M H Lowe   E K Schreiber
Family Album   S W Katz   G B Manasek   P A Stroock
D Gratz

Anthony P. Collins

BOOKSELLER

Rare Books, Fine Arts, Antiques,
Artifacts

Appointment Suggested

Franklin Avenue
Millbrook, New York 12545

(914) 667-9256

Illustrated Books

Aah!
B Agranoff
Albatross
Albion Graphics
Aleph-Bet
S Alsberg
Amer Frag
Antiquariat
Arkadyan
Ars Libri
Artistic End
Attic-Wins
Barn Sale
G E C Barnes
Bear
Belanske & Lev
D B Belcher
H J Besnia
Bishop Of Bks
Black Sun
H Black's
C Blomgren
Bk Block-Gree
Bk Dales
Bk Sail
Bk Cellar-Ful
Bk Haven-Law
Bk Hse-Arl
Bk Treasury
Bkcell
Bks In Trans
Bkwrights
E R Bowes
M Braiterman
Brentano's-NYC
M Breslauer
Bromer
C W Brooks
R K Brown
J Buck
K Buck
J Burger
Cabinet Of
Camelot
B C Carltiz
R F Casavant
M Castelli
S F Chapin
Cherokee
Chimney Smoke
Choreogr

Christoffersen
R W Clare
A Cohen
Coll's List
Coll's Ch-Wat
Coll's Crnr
Colls' Edtns
S F Cullins'
Colo Bkman
Columbia
Mrs D Cook
N Copeland
Cosmic Aero
J Criscione
J Cummins
Curiosity-St J
Curious-Bost
Curious-East
W & V Dailey
D Davis
Davison
B Dawson
De Victor's
De Victor's
G Deeds
B Denver
Detering
R Diamond
L Diehl
Diva
C Docheff
Donaldsons
Donegan
Dragon's Lair
Drusilla's
P C Duschnes
Echo
Electric Glory
H R Emler
Estate
L E Evans
A Fair
Family Album
B Farnsworth
A L Feldman
First Impress
Forest Park
A C Fox
L Fox
Froghollow
D Frohnsdorff

L Galinsky
W C Gates
D & P Gilbert
Glenn
J Goffman
J Goldman
L Goldschmidt
A Gud
Hacker Art
J H Hale
M Halpern
M Hammer
J Hansen
L C Harper
Harris Srch
B J Hecht
J S Helms
Heritage-L A
D Hirsch
Hirschtritt's
Hobbit
H'wood Bk City
Holy Land
J C Huckans
Illustrated Ant
J & C
J & J House
Janus-Hun
T J Joyce
K Karith
S W Katz
I Keats
R J Kempe
J K King
G Klemm
R Kristiansen
L'estampe
L La Berge
N L Laird
Las Lenguas
Lee & Lee
J Lehr
B Leibowits
H A Levinson
Littwin & Fel
E Llewellyn
W Loewy
Looking Glass
Lyrical Ballad
T MacAluso
Maelstrom

J Majer
J Makarewich
J Mancevice
Manning's
Mansfield
Marg & Moss
C G Martignette
Marvelous
T Mawson
L McGilvery
J S McKenna
B L Means
Memory Box
Merlin's Closet
J Michaels
Midway
Milestone-NYC
G R Minkoff
D Miranda
Mithras
Moe's
Much Loved
K Nebenzahl
D R Nelson
Nimue
H Noble Jr
N'Woods Funnies
Oceanside
Old Block
Old Bks & Coll
Old Glory
Olympia
Omega
S Orr
Ottenberg Bks
Out Of Prnt-Whi
Pan
E Panos
Pansy Patch
P'back Exch
Parker's
Peacock
S Penner
People's
R Perata
L Pipes
B Plant
Poor Farm
D F Proctor
Redford
J A Reisler

Renaissance-Lak
B Resnik
C L Robinson-Ma
H E Rohr
C A Rush
B Sackheim
Sail Loft-Summ
Sail Loft-Wint
Saxifrage
Scarlet Letter
J G Schiller
S Schlossberg
Schoyer's
K L Schwarz
J Scopazzi

B Scott
L Seeborg
J V Sichel
R B Sirrine
T Small
South Bay
Spector
Spectrum
D W Starry, Sr
G Steigerwald
Store
Sykes & Fla
V Tamerlis
Temares

Temple Bar
Terry's Better
F J Thomas
Titles
Totteridge
Transition
Treehorn
Twice Sold
Ursus
Victoria-NYC
S Vogel-San
P G Waite
Waverly
B Weiss

L & H Weitz
West Side
West's Agency
J L Wheeler
Wilsey Square
L Witten
Wittenborn
Wolf's Head
C B Wood III
Woodspurge
Yankee Peddler
Yesterday's-Wes
Yesteryear-Atl
I Zucker

Immigration

Austin

C A Noon

R Valdez

Imprints

Americanist

T G Boss

L Evans

Hurley

IncomeOpportunities & Self Help

S Apfelbaum

City Bk & Coin

Fortune Finders

Incunabula & Early Printing

W H Allen
Ars Libri
C V Barnes
P Berry

Biblion
Bibliopolis-Cle
M Breslauer
Bullock's

Castalia
Chamblin
R W Clare
R O Estes, Sr

Family Album
A C Fox
D E Guice
Hamill & Barker

L C Harper
Jenkins
H P Kraus
L La Berge

H A Levinson
B McKittrick
R A Palket
R H Redding

W Salloch
E K Schreiber
G Steigerwald
C A Stonehill

Tech Info-Doc
University Pl
L Witten

Indiana

Country Bkshlf

Hoosier School

J R Long

Industry & Labor

aGatherin'
Biblio
W Bledsoe

Bread, Wine
J L Fraser
M Gibbs

S Millman
R A Paulson

K W Sutcliffe
Treehorn

Inland Waterways

S E Blumenauer

Cantrells'

Source

Inscribed Books

Antic Hay
Camelot
Confederate
J A Dermont
Fant Archives
C Hamilton
W S Hay
S Heller

J S Helms
Hoosier School
Hse Of Bks Ltd
S Koschal
J Kuwalsky
B E McCaslin
M F Neville
North Shore

Norumbega
Nouveau
Quill & Brush
Rare Bk Co
Resurrection
P C Richards
J R Sanderson
B Scott

C Seluzicki
H J Shoebridge
Signed Limited
Theatrebooks
Towson
Wayside
J H Woolmer
J H Reuther

Iowa

Bkseller-Cher   D R Doerres   Source

Ireland & The Irish

Arcane	J M Hays	J P McGahern	W T O'Malley
Dwyer's	Keshcarrigan	J & J O'Donoghue	Sandpiper
Facsimile			

Irish & Scottish History

Dickson St   Facsimile   T M Knaus

Israel

Holy Land   Hyman & Son-Tor   Kats

Japan

| Bk Coll-Newt | East & West | J G Stanoff | Zita |
| Bks Embroid | Hirschtritt's | Ukiyo-E | |

Thomas Jefferson

Corner Shelf-Cul   Heartwood   E Musial

Jewelry

J E Arnay   Peri Lithon   Sisterhood

Judaica & Hebraica

K Appel	R L George	W Loewy	O Schreyer
Austin	German & Int'l	Memor Amer	Steinberg
G A Bernstein	Gierspeck & Rop	Memorabilia	Under Cover-Cle
A Bloom's	Y Goldman	Moriah	Under Cover-Sha
Bkie Joint	Holy Land	Paul's	Whistler's
H Clenick	Hyman & Son-Tor	M S Rosenberg	W P Wolfe
Christian-Mil	Judaica Bk Agy	A Schram	B Yolleck

Juveniles

Adventure	Cyrano's	Eagle's-Chel	Lantern
Bk Cellar-Fre	N Dame	Gierspeck & Rop	New Canaan
Bk Den East	Deeds	M Halpern	Old Bk Rm-Cro
Bk Srch-Pit	Dinkytown	N T Hopper	Oz & Ends
Bromer	Dish Hollow	Jean's	Pendleton Publ
R F Casavant	R Dworcyk	Jennies	P R Rieber
Country Bkshlf	Eagle's-Vero	P & D Kenyon	Sherlock

Kansas

Nemaha   Smoky Hill

Kennedy Assasinations

R J Kalanja   R & M Orner   D Spencer

Rockwell Kent

S E Rubenstein   Spector

Kentucky

Borderland   Craighse-Pat   E Davis   V Owens
Coll-Pad   Craighse-Mall   W C Gates   Pennyroyal

Labor History

Bkery-Ith   Crofter's   Urban

Lace

Bks Embroid   M Chapman-Coll

Landscape Architecture

Anchor & Dol   Landscape

Latin America

W H Allen
Bk Srch-Bro
Brick Row
M A Bromsen
Cape Cod-San
H B Diamond
El Cascajero

B Fein
M Ginsberg
J C Huckans
H Karno
Latin Amer
Libros Latinos
K Lopez

Mexbooks
On Paper
Pan-Amer
R C Ramer
W Reuben-NYC
W Reuben-Aus
Rosengren's

Ross Valley
J Rybski
Scharf Art
Sun Dance
C J Vega
Wahrenbrock's
C Wright

Law

R Adamiak
Amadeus
K G Arthurton
Austin
D L Bauman
P Berry
R Bleiweiss

W J Bkhunter
Claitor's
Q M Dabney
S W Katz
Koths
D & E Lake
Lake Law

Little Hundred
Magnalia
J R Mara
Meyer Boswell
New Jersey
K W Nims
Norumbega

Pacific Law
Pisces & Cap
R H Rubin
R L Sadoff
Schneemann
P Smith

Left Wing

Bay Side   R & M Orner   Scattergood

Libertarianism

P K Slocum   Used-Dye

Limited Editions Club

Bk Studio   P C Duschnes   Temares

Lincoln & Lincoln Assassination

Old Quenzel   Prairie Archive

Joseph C. Lincoln

Liberty Lore   J W Morritt   Wake-Brook-Ft L   Worldwide-Arl

Linguistics

Albion   Atlanta   Atticus-Tor

Literary Criticism

Amer Wrlds   Baldwin   Bk Sh-Sou   Bkmailer
P P Appel   Bear   Bk Srvc-Ind   Cathryn
Atticus-Tor   Brillig Works   Bked Up   Chatham

W T Clermont
Cogitator
Colonial
Constant Reader
Darby
H B Diamond
Drew's
R P Dunaway
Echo
Edgewood
Euclid

Fain's First
J Hood
Horizon
V Howard
L Hunegs
D Jaffe
W S Johnson
Jolly Roger
Kalonbooks
Library-Dal
Lincoln-O P

J W Martin
Martin's
Morrell's
W Nelson
Newcomb Hall
Ottenberg Bks
Palma
R A Paulson
K T Ransom
R H Redding
Regent St

Sangamon
Stanley
Suncircle
Talbothay's
T W Tingle
Valley-Amh
Weller Victoria
Wooden Spoon
Ziesing Bros
J T Zubal

Literature

Abelard
About
Abreyde
Academy-NYC
Acres-Cin
Aldine
Alicat
Allen
Alpha Omega
Alphabet
Alron
Amer Wrlds
Anderson's
H Anson-Cart
Antic Hay
Antiq Bksllrs
P P Appel
K Armens
G Armitage
Associates
Attic-Hodg
Attic-Wins
Authors Of West
Avocet
S Ballinger
P E Baracca
Barrow
Bay Side
Bear
Beasley
J Bekker
Belanske & Lev
Benjamin Autogr
L Berliawsky
S C Bernard
P C Beyer
Biblioctopus

Bibliophile-NYC
Biermaier's
Bigelows' Quill
Brillig Works
Bishop Of Bks
H Black's
Bloomsbury
Bk End-Mon
Bk Habit
Bk Lady
Bk St-Oly
Bk Cellar-Brat
Bk Fndrs-NYC
Bk Land-Tor
Bk Mark-Phil
Bk Srvc-San
Bk Srvc-Ind
Bk Warehouse
Bked Up
Bkie Joint
Bkleggers
Bkmailer
Bkman Arcady
Bks & Thngs-NYC
Bkst-Len
T G Boss
Boston Annex
Brentano's-NYC
Brick Row
Browsery
T W Burrows
J R Butterworth
A Carduner
J Cashman
M Castelli
Cathryn
W Chadde

Chafey's
B Chaney Jr
Chatham
Chloe's
Choreogr
W T Clermont
College Nook
Colonial
Country Connect
Coventry
Creative Arts
Curious-Bost
Current
J P Custis
Darby
B Dawson
Deeds
H O Dendurent
R B Desmarais
H B Diamond
Dickson St
Dinkytown
P Dumas
R Dworcyk
Dyment
Edgewood
C Elder
Bkman-Gran
Ex Libris-Ban
A Fair
C Farkas
D Fay
Ferryman Ant
Find A Bk
Folger
Fraser's
Froghollow

K G Gaisser
Genessee
George Sand
R Gilbo
R Glassman
Gotham
Greenblatt
Y W Griffin
Guerin Editeur
M Hammer
Hannelore
Haunted Bksh
Heartwood
Hermitage
D Hirsch
W Hoffer
Hollands'
Horizon
Hse Of Fict
Howe
M Hudson
Hummingbird
Huntley
Invisible
Irene's
D Jaffe
B A James
Janus-Tuc
Jenkins
W S Johnson
Joseph Provider
Kalonbooks
Kay's
J K King
E Krebs
R Kristiansen
D & M Krueger

K Leach	R A Mezoff	J L Polley	W T Taylor
Liberty Rock	Midway	Pomander	Temple Bar
Libra	A H Minters	A & A Prosser	S Temple
Librarium	W Monie	R H Redding	T W Tingle
L N Lien	Montrose	B M Rieger	Treetops
Lighthse	Mostly-Oma	Rogers Park	Typographeum
Lilac Hedge	H S Mott	I Rouse	Vagabond
R L Link	W D Nelson	Russica	Valley-Amh
Little Read	New Engl-NYC	S-T	S Vogel-San
Littwin & Fel	Newcomb Hall	Sangamon	Wait Godot
Loft	H Noble Jr	S Scharoun	L A Wallrich
London-Chi	No Conway	S Schlossberg	Warwick
K Lopez	Norumbega	Scholar's	Waves
D M H Lowe	Nouveau	Schoyer's	J H Weinberg
C Lowenberg	Novel Exper	Scribbling	Wessex
M & M	F M O'Brien	Secret Sharer	West L A Center
M & S	Old Bks-Brun	7 Oaks	Westmount
G S MacManus	Old Bk St-Akr	Seville	J L Wheeler
Maelstrom	Old Verities	J & V Shelton	Whistler's
Magic Mtn	Ottenberg Bks	R Shuhi	R Wilkerson
T D Mahoney	Out-Of-Prnt-NYC	Sidney's	Wings Of Eagle
Maiden Voy	Oxford	L Smith	Thomas J Wise
Main St	Pageant	R W Smith	J Wobber
J Makarewich	Pangloss	Smith's-Brew	J H Woolmer
J W Martin	P'back Paradise	P Sperling	Word
D Mason	S Penner	P L Stern	W P Wreden
R W Mattila	R F Perotti	Suncircle	Ximenes
M McCosh	Pett & Lieber	Sylvest & Orph	Yesterday's-Ash
L H McGill	Philosophical	Talisman	Ziesing Bros
J O McMeans	P J Pirages	M Tanditash	J T Zubal
Merlin's Closet			

Literature in English Translation

M McCosh	Riverrun	S Temple	Weller Victoria

Little Magazines & Literary Small Presses

Ampersand	V Burgman	Euclid	Gotham
atticus	Camelot	Ex Libris-NYC	Grolier
Beasley	J S Canner	First Impress	International
Bk Stacks-Burl	Chloe's	George Sand	R A MacKsey
Bkst-Len	J A Dermont	Goodwin & Zein	Magazine Center

H Miller
W Nelson

Ridge
Sand Dollar

P Stockman

J H Weinberg

Local History

Albert
Antiq Michiana
Baldwin's Barn
H O Berg
Bk Keeper-Mit
Bunkhse

J E De Turck
L Evans
Genealogists
Genessee
P Henderson
Kardy's

London-Alb
Memory Aisle
H N Ottaway
I M Roth
H V Ryan
Source

Tan Bark
Thoreau Lyceum
Titcomb's
Townsends
Tuttle Antiq
A G Ziagos

Locks

C Chandler

D R Doerres

Logging

M Kilen

D A Lawyer

Logic

Arc Bks

A Cheslock

C C Davis

Jack London

Diablo
Jack London

S Noto

Perry's Antiq

B Yolleck

Louisiana

Ark-La-Tex   Beckham's   Red River

Loyalists

L Hill   C A Noon

Magazines

S Alsberg	City Wide	Magazine	Reedmor
Bee Gee's	P Kufus	Old Bk St-Port	L Stamelman
Bk Den-San	Longhorn	Omega	J M Winters
Cameron's			

Magic

B & G   Bk Studio   L Kohrs   Meyerbks

Maine

Bedford's	Ex Libris-Ban	F M O'Brien	Old Bk Sh-Ken
Cross Hill	D Isaacson	M Ockett	Winter Farm
H O Dendurent	A B W MacEwen	Old Bks-Brun	F P Wood
H H Eastman			

Maine Authors

Bk Cellar-Fre	J B Keeler	Old Bk Sh-Ken	Snowbound
Bunkhse	M Ockett		

Mammalogy

Corn Mill	D E Hahn	P Howard	Tolliver's

Manuscripts

aGatherin'	H M Darvick	Joseph Provider	W Reuben-Aus
T Alford	E Driscoll	S Koschal	P C Richards
Alron	Bkman-Gran	L La Berge	B & L Root'berg
Amer Mail Auct	E C Fales	W B Liebmann	J Rubinfine
Americanist	Fant Archives	Lion Heart	Sandpiper
C Appelbaum	B P Ferrini	Little Hundred	Schuylkill
B & B	J F Fleming	J Lowe	B Scott
R Batchelder	A Goodman	G S MacManus	Scriptorium
Biblioctopus	Goodsp'd's-Beac	B Morrow	C Seluzicki
Black Sun	Goodsp'd's-Milk	R G Newman	A Sosenko
V A Bradley	Green Thought	P H North, Jr	C A Stonehill
M Breslauer	C Hamilton	Oinonen Auct	Tech Info-Doc
M A Bromsen	D Harris	K C Owings Jr	Va Bk Co
W J B Burger	Hofmann & Free	P J Pirages	Volkhoff & Von
B C Carltiz	G Horowitz	Ravine Cottage	G E Webb, Jr
Carnegie	El Dieff	Rendells	D Weiss
B Cassidy	J Howell	S Resnick	J H Woolmer
Clipper Ship	J C Huckans	W Reuben-NYC	W P Wreden
E J Craig	B A James		

Manuscripts, Medieval & Illuminated

D Gratz	H A Levinson	Rendells	L Witten
Hofmann & Free	G B Manasek	B M Rosenthal	J Woods-Yak
H P Kraus	Philos Bk Ser	E C Williams	

Manuscript Logbooks

Caravan-Marit   C Hinchliffe

Maps, Atlases, & Cartography

H D Adams
R H Adams
S Alsberg
Amer Frag
Amer So'West
Amer Mail Auct
Antiq Bks
W G Arader III
Arctician
Argonaut
Argosy
Arkadyan
Arkway
Barra
J N Bartfield
M B Beal
W E Beaver
R V Boswell
Branford
H W Brewer
Broadfoot's
B C Carltiz
Cartographics
J & R Casten
T Clark
N Copeland

Drew's
E F Dunlap
C G Fisher
R Fitch
Forsyth Travel
Fortunate Fnds
A & R Gardiner
W T Gavin
G F Glaeve
Globe-Chic
Goodsp'd's-Milk
Goodsp'd's-Beac
A Gutkin
A J Gutman
J H Hale
W E Hallberg
M Hammer
J Harder
H C Hensel
High Ridge
Historic News
Holy Land
M Hudson
Indolent Antiq
R T Kennedy
H P Kraus

La Cite-L A
Lamp
H B Leech
E J Lefkowicz
Little Hundred
I MacKenzie
Magnalia
G B Manasek
Maps & Bks
Marshall Field
Miller's
Mooers
A Mueller
'neath The Elms
K Nebenzahl
S N Halas
New Albion
Nutmeg
Oblong
Observatory
Old Bk Sh-S F
Old Print Sh
Old Print Gall
Old Prntd Word
Our Heritage
K C Owings Jr

Pageant
Parker's
N & N Pavlov
Remington's
W Reuben-NYC
W Reuben-Aus
P A Rousssel
J Scopazzi
Sergio
C Sessler
R Slifer
R W Spellman
H Stevens Son
Store
G P Szontagh
Talisman
H Tanner
Tappin
Tattered Cover
Tech Info-Doc
Travellers'
Tuttle Antiq
William-Roberts
Winter Farm
Yesterday's-Wes

Marine Biology

Kingfisher   Seashell Treas

Marxism-Leninism & Communism

All Pts View   Scattergood

Maryland

Deeds   Kardy's   Remington's   Unicorn-Eas
A J Gutman   Old Quenzel

Mathematics

Antiq Scientist	A Cheslock	J R Goodwin	Maxwell Sci
Astronomy	College Nook	D E Guice	Merlin's
Bk Stall-Oak	E K	Hawley's Island	Scientia
Bk Traders	Elgen	Hinds	Vintage-St P
J C Bryan	E V Glaser	J R Levien	

Mechanical Musical Instruments

W H Edgerton   M Roenick

Medals (books on)

L H Finn   J L Lepczyk

Medical & Medicine

K T Adamson	G Houseman	Medical	R L Sadoff
W G Bazan	D A Lewis	Old Hickory	W H Schab
T N Haviland	Maxwell Sci	Rittenhse	

Medicine & Science

Aardvark-S F	R W Clare	J A Hill	Old Galen's
Antiq Scientist	College Nook	Hinds	Old South
The Antiquarium	Cornhill	Holistic Health	Palinurus
Apothecary	H C Daitz	Indolent Antiq	Print Dev-Arl
Ark	W Dordick	Int Univ Bkslrs	Question Mark
Astronomy	Elgen	W J Johnson	Regent St
Autos & Autos	R & D Emerson	Junius	C L Robinson-Ma
W G Bazan	Fain's First	S W Katz	B & L Root'berg
Bick & Barc	Folkways	J R Levien	R L Sadoff
Blors	Folkways	H A Levinson	Sager's
Bk & Tackle	W B Fye	M & S	A D Santomasso
Bk Clearing	Geological	C Magee	K Schick
Bk Fndrs-NYC	L Ginsberg	G B Manasek	O Schreyer
Bkcell	E V Glaser	J Mashman	Science Bkshlf
Bks Unltd-Nat	D E Guice	W McDonnell	Scientia
Bread, Wine	Hamill & Barker	McDuffies	Sebastopol
British Stamp	L C Harper	B McKittrick	Significant
B C Carltiz	Hawley's Island	Medical Manor	Volkhoff & Von
Cathryn	F T Heller	J Norman	Warwick
Celestial	Hemlock	E Offenbacher	Ximenes
H Clenick	W W Hildreth	Old Bks & Coll	M Zervas
Chatham			

Memory & Mnemonics

C V Barnes	M N Young

H. L. Mencken

A J Gutman   Unicorn-Eas

Mennonites

D Gratz   J W Smith

Metaphysics

Brillig Works	Globe-L A	Metaphsic-L A	H T Trueb
Bk Harbor	Mason's	Orpheus	Valley Bk City
City Bk & Coin	Mayflower	Raymer's	Ye Olde Fan

Methodism

Methodist   Stroud

Mexico

Alcazar	Bisbee	De La Pena	D M Sanchez
Alta Calif	Brick Row	M S Lambeth	Tolliver's
Assoc Bk Svc	Cole's-La J	J B Nomland	R Valdez

Michigan

Argos	Bk World	Diff St	Memory Aisle
Bicentennial			

Middle Ages

Albion	Christopher's	Krown & S'man	J Woods-Yak
J Bambach	G N Gabbard	B M Rosenthal	M D Zambelli
Bloomsbury	P Krapp	W Salloch	

Middle East

K Appel	Bkphil	McBlain	R L Press
Asian-Cam	East & West	W B O'Neill	Terramedia
Asian-NYC	P R Feltus	Paragon Gall	Witherspoon
Baird Press	M A MacIntosh	Plane Tree	Worldwide-Arl
G A Bernstein			

Middle West

Albert	Andromeda	Blue River	Van Norman

Militaria

Again	Mrs A L Ashton	Barber's	Bk Attic
Air Age	Atlantic	Battery	Bk Sh-Sou
Amer Bk & Gal	Auslender	K Benson	Bk Hse-Arl
Antheil	B & G	Bicentennial	Bk Mart-San
Articles Of War	Balaclava	H Black's	Bk Stop-Day

Bkfinders-Fair
Bkphil
Bkseller-Akr
Bunkhse
Campbell's
Cherokee
Colleen's
A P Collins
Comstock's
Conrad's
Court Place
Croton
Q M Dabney
Darian
J C Daub
Delta

J A Desch
Dugout & Depot
T Durflinger
Eagle
E & M Ediger
K & J Field
Fransen's
K G Gaisser
I Galis
Global
A Goodman
W A Graf
R Greenwood
Guthman
G Hall, Jr
J Harder

P Hunt
Int'l Hobbies
J F F
P L Jackson
A Maita
Mason's-Wab
Mil-Air
Military
E Morrill
W R Orbelo
J E Pearson
B E Pingenot
H J Popinski
E P Rich
Ross & Haines

R Shuhi
Sky Bks Int
Snowbound
Soldier
Strictly
Talbothay's
J D Terry
L Thompson
Thunderbird
Tucson
Valley Forge
H Volker
D E Wojack
Womrath's
Yesteryear-Atl

Military (World War II)

Battery

A Jacobs

Miniature Books

D Benson
Blue Eye
Bk Habit
Bromer
Coll's Crnr
J E Conner

Dawson's
Donegan
A L Feldman
Fly Creek
A T Ford
M Frazier

D Frohnsdorff
K Gregory
Illustrated Ant
Greame Kelley
J R Levien
J Lorson

R L Merriam
D Peterson   4-5-83
Mrs Thomason
Victoria-NYC
Wake-Brook-Ft L
Wake-Brook-Hyan

Minnesota

E L Anderson
Harold's

J & M Laurie

Northern Lights

Once Read

Mining & Metallurgy

Examino   Peri Lithon

Mississippi

Choctaw Traders

Mississippi River

Choctaw Traders ✓   Northern Lights

Missouri

C Payton

Modern Library (Publishers)

R Glassman   N R S

Mollusks

B E Cassie   Seashell Treas

Montana

Gall Old West   T Minckler

Mormons

Cosmic Aero   Kats   J H Reuther   Ute-Or-Ida
Darian   W Lillywhite

Mountaineering

K Andersen   Comstock's   J R Goodwin   Pacific Writers
Angel's   L Cross   D Gratz   J C Rather
Bk Addict-Albu   Dawson's   V Howard   E Short
Bk Bin-Kin   M Dunn   Mtn Travel   Sportsman's
Bk Stall-Oak   Gene & Kit's   Ottenberg Bks   T Williams

Movie & Fan Magazines

Bk City Coll   San Franciscian   Scriptorium   W P Shepard

John Muir

Diablo   S Noto   D Peterson

Frank L. Munsey

Fraser's   P F Miller

Music

Amadeus	L Bowling	H Goodkind	Paper Person
E Andrews	Broude Bros	R Graham	N Potter
Anglican Bib	Bryn Mawr-Alb	Y W Griffin	A Schnase
Bel Canto	Cadenza	La Scala	O Shapiro
Benjamin Autogr	W H Edgerton	J & J Lubrano	M A Silver
L Berliawsky	D Elsberg	T L McCook	Vi & Si's
Bk Bazaar	Firstborn	J B Muns	G E Webb, Jr
Bk Srch-Avon	Footnote	Nickelodeon	J Wobber
Bkfndrs-Mia	Fraser's	Old Tyme	Zita

Musical Instruments

Amadeus	J H Reuther	O Shapiro	Vi & Si's
Organ Lit			

Mushrooms

J T Gatto   Ken-L-Questor

Mystery Fiction

J G Amadeo	D Discher	Janus-Tuc	Mystery Hse
Bk Habit	Ex Libris-Ban	J Klein	Mystery Manor
P C Dillon	D & P Gilbert	A B W MacEwen	J & J O'Donoghue

Oceanside	I Rouse	S F Mystery	S Wetstone
Odyssey	Rue Morgue	Wayside	Yellowstone
Passaic			

Myths

Rivendell	Serpent & Eagle	3 Geese	D E Whelan

Napoleon

D W Goudy	P L Jackson	I MacKenzie

National Geographic Magazine

O O Evans	R T Kennedy	D Smith	Wake-Brook-Ft L
O J Imel	R MacDougall		

Natural Healing

H Clenick	Stryker's

Natural History

Adventure	W G Arader III	B L Bibby	Bk Addict-Por
Allbks	Armchair Sailor	Big John's	Bk Caravan
Amer Frag	Audubon	D Blomberg	Bk Chest
K Andersen	Avocet	Blue Jay	Bk Home
Antiq Scientist	Banyan	Blue Eye	Bk Hse-Arl
The Antiquarium	J N Bartfield	Bk Addict-Albu	Bkcell

W J Bkhunter
Bks-Gre
Bkstack-Elk
J Bowman
H W Brewer
W F Broderick
J Buck
K Buck
Buteo
Cabinet Of
Callahan & Co
B E Cassie
H Clenick
Chamblin
Chickadee
Chimney Smoke
T Clark
Colo Bkman
Cortese
Country Craft
Country Lane
Cyrano's
Davis & Schorr
J E De Turck
Debra
G Deeds
M C Dooling
Mrs K R Dorn
A A Dunn
R M Eisenberg
E Enzler

Estate
Estes Service
C G Fisher
Floating Mtn
Forest
Fox & Suther
W T Gavin
Geological
R Glassman
A Gutkin
H W K
D E Hahn
Happy Source
J Harder
T Harper
T N Haviland
Hawley's Island
J S Helms
Herp Exch
Hingham
M S Hollander
Horticultural
Indolent Antiq
J & J House
J Johnson
J Juszyk
R J Kalanja
J B Keeler
J J Keleher
P Ledlie
J G Leishman

Limestone Hills
Lion's Head
P M Lumb
W Madden
M Marcher
J O McMeans
M N McQuerry
Milestone-NYC
E Moran
B Mraz
J J Nadolny
K Nebenzahl
New Steamship
Nimue
J Norman
I J Oelgart
Old Bks & Coll
Old Bkshed
Pacific Writers
Page One
Peterson Bk Co
A Philpott
Pomona Exch
Prospector
Wm Reese Co
R R Rhoads
P R Rieber
R Robertson
A G Robinson, Jr
H B Robinson
Rockland

R W Sabbot
Sail Loft-Summ
Sail Loft-Wint
Saxifrage
Science Bkshlf
Scientia
2nd Fiddle
Shorey
R Shuhi
Significant
T Small
Smith's-Brew
Sporting Biblio
Sporting
Sportsman's
Stinson Hse
Stuart's
G H Suhm
Sykes & Fla
Tan Bark
Thoreau Lyceum
R E Underhill
G Wayner
Whitlock Farm
Wildwood
J Woods-Yak
Yesterday's-Wes
B Zaremba
Zeitlin & Ver B
I Zucker

Nautica

Caravan-Marit
Cross Hill

History House
Int'l Hobbies

Jolie's
Mariner's Unltd

Odd Bk

Naval & Marine

Again
Albatross
Amer Bk & Gal
Anderson's
Antheil
Armchair Sailor
Articles Of War

Atlantic
Auslender
Balaclava
Banyan
Bayview
Bedford's
Boardwalk

Bk & Tackle
Bk Den East
Bk Ranger
Bkfinders-Fair
Bks Unltd-Nat
Bryant's
J Burnett

Caravan-Marit
J Clinton
Colleen's
Comstock's
N Copeland
Crofter's
Cross Hill

Current	C Hinchliffe	E Moore	Sky Bks Int
O Davies	Homestead	E Morrill	Soldier
Elmcress	K Huntress	Nautica	Tappin
Estate	J D S	'neath The Elms	10 Pound
B Finch	J F F	D R Nelson	D Tessier
I Galis	B A James	New Steamship	L Thompson
A Goodman	E J Lefkowicz	Old Mystic	Thunderbird
Grt Lake	J Levine	Ostby's	Titcomb's
Green Dolphin	Lowe Antiques	J Owen	Tucson
Gryphon's Lair	R F Lucas	A W Paine	H Volker
Guthman	Magnalia	Parnassus Svce	Wayside
W D Hall	Mariner's Unltd	Peninsula Antiq	West Side
J & J Hanrahan	B McBride	Pier	Whaling
H C Hensel	S McIntyre	Prospector	White's
High Ridge	Mil-Air	Seabook	E C Williams
W W Hildreth	Military	C Sessler	Womrath's

Nebraska

D N Dupley	Mostly-Oma	O E Warrick

Needlework

Bks Embroid	M Chapman-Coll	B Parrington	L St Clair
Mrs L M Brew			

Neurosciences

W B Fye	J Mashman

Nevada

Unique Stall

New Books

About Music
Ainslie
Articles Of War
Bigelows' Quill
Blors
Bk Barn-Bea
Bk Bin-Dal
Bk Center-Ath
Bk End-Free
Bk Peddlers
Bk Sh-Boise
Bk Fair
Bkends-Napa
Bkfnder-Pen
Bkmark-Sto
Bkshelf-Cla

Bkst-Mil
Carmichael's
Centauri
Change Hobbit
Chickadee
Corner-Cas
Court's
N Dame
G F Edwards
Fantasy
Floating Mtn
Givens
Greet & Read
Homesteader
Inn

La Mesa
Lantern
Lift Bridge-Bro
Lion's Head
Maverick
Metaphysic-Por
Midvale
Miller's
Mostly-Farm
N R S
New Canaan
Nugent & Assoc
Oxford
P'backs Plus
Peggatty

Red Bank
Rosengren's
Royal Oak
R W Sabbot
Savran's
J & V Shelton
Spencer
Strawbridge
L Tebbetts
R E Underhill
Univ Bk St-Man
S Wetstone
Whistler's
Williams
Womrath's

New England

Barn Loft
S N Bean

J & J Hanrahan
Hingham

Howland
Kalonbooks

No Conway
F P Wood

New Hampshire

Stinson Hse

Village-Lit

New Jersey

Coll's Crnr
Escargot

J J Felcone
B Godshall

H Nestler
Old Bk Sh-Morr

Paper & Ink
Past History

New Mexico

Alcazar   De La Pena

New York Metropolitan Area

M E Bennett   Harbor Hill   Jeltrups'   N Y Bound
Cityana Gall   History House   J & P Klemperer   Old Bk Rm-Cro

New York

Berry Hill   Bkery-Ith   E Monarski   W & L Pinkney
E G Blankman   R Butterfield   N Y Bound   With Pipe
C J Boardman   Harbor Hill   Old Bk Rm-Cro   Yankee Peddler

Newspapers

S Alsberg   Harrington's   S & C Najarian   R W Spellman
Bk Bin-Dal   Historic News   W P Northrop   G Totty
J Cashman   T Hughes   J B Reynolds   F J Wilhelm
Civic Center   F Metcalf   R H Richshafer   Yellow Press
A & R Gardiner   Mooers

19th Century Literature

S D Beare   Heartwood   Jack London   Pogonia
P Greene   Hirschtritt's   Limestone Hills

19th Century Periodicals

Methodist   Pogonia

North Carolina

Bird & Bk   Bk Mart-Ash   Carolina   Grandpa's Hse
Bk Basement   Bk Trader-Fai   Cyrano's   Keith & Martin

North Dakota

H O Berg

Northwest

Barjon's   Diff Drum-Sea   R W Mattila   D Perier
Bk St-Oly   Green Dolphin   Old Oregon   Ute-Or-Ida

Nostalgic Fiction

Bk Cellar-Fre   People's   J M Winters

Numerology & Tarot

Mason's   Mayflower

Numismatics

S Apfelbaum   Bklyn Gall   G F Kolbe   J L Lepczyk
J R Becker   L H Finn   F L Kovacs   San Fernando
C S Berkowitz   W R Harris

Occult & Metaphysics

D J   R Greenwood

Ohio

Bloch & Co   P H North, Jr   I M Roth   Trans Allegheny
Bkseller-Akr   Ron-Dot

Oklahoma (& Indian Territory)

A Pts Northe   Michael's   Red River   Von Blons
R Bever   C Payton   Smoky Hill

Olympic Games

H Abrams-Sta   A Iuspa   Northwoods   E Tatro

Opera

Ballet   H R Emler   Jenny Lind   Opera Box
Bel Canto   Footnote   La Scala

Optics

Celestial   J P Leeds   H A Luft   Willmann-Bell

Orientalia

Abbot   East West   Joyce   C A Rush
Academy-Hon   J S Edgren   Keramos   Scharf Art
Allbks   P D French   Y Kishi   K L Schwarz
Asian Amer   Gull   P Lozinski   Sebastopol
Asian-Cam   W S Hay   McBlain   J G Stanoff
Asian-NYC   Hermeticus   Paragon Gall   Terramedia
Brennan   M S Hollander   B Parrington   G Vanderstoel
Cheng & Tsui   L Hunegs   A J Phiebig   S Weiser
Danville   H Johnson   Plane Tree   World Wide-NYC
Dawson's   W S Johnson   S E Rubenstein   Worldwide-Arl
East & West

Original Art of Book Illustrations

Bk Roundup   Comic Art   H E Heinrich   D Hirsch

J A Reisler   J G Schiller   Victoria-NYC   Zita
Rockaway   L Seeborg

Out of Print, with Stock

Aardvark-S F
Abbies
About Music
Acoma
Acorn
Acres-Tre
J Addams
Ahrens
Ainslie
Albatross
Aldine
All B & P
All Photo
All Pts View
Allbks
Allen
Amer Print
Ancient Cty Bk
Anderson's
Anglican Bib
H Anson-Cart
Antiquariat
Antiquus
Appalachia
P P Appel
Appleland
Argosy
K Armens
F Armstrong
Arnold's
Art Catalogues
Articles Of War
Astronomy
Atlanta
Atlantic
Attic
B & G
Back Row
Back Tracts
J Bailey
Bargain-Gran
Barnette's
Beaufort
Ben Franklin
Bengta Woo
D Benson

H O Berg
Bibliophile-Pas
Bird's Nest
Bisbee
Blacktail Mtn
Blitz
Bk Addict-Albu
Bk Attic
Bk Baron
Bk Bin-Dal
Bk Barn-Sio
Bk Dispensary
Bk Lady
Bk Sh-Boise
Bk Stall-Cin
Bk Stop-Tuc
Bk Case-Pas
Bk Cellar-Tem
Bk Cellar-Brat
Bk Coll-Newt
Bk Cottage
Bk Ends-Arl
Bk Exch-Mis
Bk Fndr-Genev
Bk Fndrs-NYC
Bk Look-War
Bk Place-Col
Bk Ranger
Bk Srvc-Ind
Bk Stall-Roc
Bk Stop-Day
Bk Stop III
Bk St-West
Bk St-Engl
Bk Trader-Fai
Bk Friends
Bkfndr-Cut
Bkfnder-Pen
Bkfndrs-Bol
Bkhaven-Spr
W J Bkhunter
Bkmailer
Bks & Thngs-Boc
Bks By Mail
Bks On File-Uni
Bks Then & Now

Bks Unltd-Ind
Bkseller's Row
Bksh-War
Bkstack-Elk
Bkstock
Bkst-Fai
Boston Annex
R V Boswell
Bradford
O H Brady
Brainard
Brassers
Brennan
Browser's
Browsery
J M Bruna
J C Bryan
J H Burke
Burke's
Burton's
Bygone
Cache
Call Me Ishmael
Campbell-Camp
Canterbury-Chi
Cape Cod-San
Carolina
Catawba River
Cath Bk Coll
Caveat Emptor
Change Hobbit
Chantiicleer
Chicago
Chickadee
Christian-Mil
Cinema-Sea
Cipriano's
Cogitator
Colebrook
Colleen's
College Hill
Colonial
Common Reader
Computer Locate
Comstock's
Conversation

Corner-Newp
Country Connect
Country Craft
N Cowen
Crabtree
Curious-East
Cyrano's
D J
H C Daitz
Darby
Davis & Schorr
Day's
R Demarest
H O Dendurent
M H Detweiler
Diamond-Mon
Diff St
Diva
Dolphin-NYC
Donaldsons
Donan
Mrs K R Dorn
J Dowd
Dragoman
Drama
Drusilla's
M Du Priest
R P Dunaway
D N Dupley
E K
Eagle
Edenite Soc
Educo
G F Edwards
Eight-Cent
Elliot's
Ethnograph Arts
Fant Archives
Fantasy
B Farnsworth
K & J Field
Fields
Fireside
First Impress
Firstborn
E Fithian

Forest Park
Fransen's
Fuller's
G F S
Garciagarst
C E Gardiner
Gateway
Ghent Bkworm
Gierspeck & Rop
Givens
J R Goodwin
Grand
Grandpa's Hse
Grt No'West
Gundy's
C Hacker
G Hall, Jr
D Halloran
T Harper
Haunted Bksh
F Hawkins
Heinemann's
S Heller
H C Hensel
Heritage-Son
Hermeticus
Holistic Health
H'wood Bk Shop
Holmes-Oak
Holmes-S F
Homesteader
L Honan
J Hood
N T Hopper
Hummingbird
Hunted
A C Hunter
I Am I
Inprint
Invisible
Isaiah Thomas
A Jacobs
K Karith
Kay's
D V Keck
J B Keeler
Keith & Martin
B R Kemp
Kennedy's
Kestrel
J K King
E Klein
T M Knaus
Kneedeep
B Koenig's
E Krebs
D & M Krueger

J Kuwalsky
Lambda Rising
J Landau
C Larson
R Lasley
Latin Amer
Leekley Srch
Lennies
Liberty Rock
Libra
Lighthse
Lilac Hedge
W Lillywhite
Lion's Head
Literary Seal
Looking Glass
P Lozinski
P M Lumb
B Lynch
B Lysecki
Maelstrom
Main St
A Maita
Manuscript
Marion Antiq
S Marx
T Mawson
A E Maxted
Maxwell's
L H McGill
H McKee
Merlin's Closet
Metaphysic-Por
J Meyerson
Michael's
J Michaels
F Michelli-Nwk
F Michelli-Ogu
Midvale
Midway
E Miller
K Mitchell
Moe's
E Monarski
Monroe
Montrose
C Morelle
Morningside-Oak
Mostly-Oma
Murray's
Nautica
'neath The Elms
Nemaha
Novel Exper
Nugent & Assoc
Nutmeg
S T Oakley, Jr

Observatory
Obsolescence
Oceanic Primitive
Old Bks-Brun
Old Corner
Old Delavan
Old Favorites
Old Monterey
Old Verities
Ollies
Orsay
S Ottenberg
J Owen
Ozark
Pages
Paper Chase Sch
Paper Peddlers
P'back Paradise
Papermill
Paragon Gall
M R Parks
E Pasoti
Peggatty
Peninsula Antiq
Perception Plus
Performing Arts
Period Ludw
D V Pfeifer
W Pierce
Pomona Exch
H J Popinski
B Porter
Prairie Archive
D J Preece
Princeton Antiq
A & A Prosser
Quadrant
G J Rausch
Raven
Readmore
Redford
Reliable
Renaissance-Mil
Rendezvous
M B Robertson
Rockland
M S Rosenberg
Royal Oak
B J Rule
S & S
C F Safir
Sage
Sail Loft-Summ
Sail Loft-Wint
H & R Salerno
Sand Dollar
L Schnell

W E Schroeder
Science Fantasy
Sci Fict
Srch Srvce-Wau
2nd Story
Servant's Knowl
B Shaler
T W Shaw
Sign Of Unicorn
Significant
Silver Door
D Sloan's
South Side
R Speray
Stanley
Sterling
I Stormgart
Strawbridge
P A Stroock
Stuart's
T Sullivan
K W Sutcliffe
Tainters
Taos
B Tauscher
L Tebbetts
Temares
Theatrebooks
E C Thomas
Thrifty Reader
Tower Hse
Trackside
Trail To Y'day
Treasures
Tuckers
G H Tweney
Used-Dye
Used-West
H J Vickey
Wake-Brook-Hyan
Wards Corner
Waves
Wayward
L Weidler
Wessex
Whitlock's
Whitlock's
E C Williams
T Williams
Wine & Food
Wings Of Eagle
With Pipe
Witherspoon
Wolf's Head
C Wright
Xanadu
Yesterday's-Hot

Yesterday's-Ash   Yesterday's-Par   R Yorty

Out of Print, without Stock

Aide	Cortese	Herp Exch	Print Dev-Mil
Ambelrs	Court's	Hobby Hse	S & S
Blors	Coventry	Jolly Roger	Sage
Bk Dispensary	De Ville	R T Kennedy	Savran's
Bk Fiend	Donan	J Kidston	M A Schaefer
Bk Hse-Pla	Edgewood	R A Lowenstein	B Shaler
Bk Nook	Forest	M & M	Super
Bkmark-Sto	Fox & Suther	C Magee	R B Taylor
Bks By Mail	R G Gill	Midvale	D Testa
B Boss	K Glackin	Nationwide	13 Colonies
Boston Annex	Grt Lake	Old Curiosity	R E Underhill
Bunter	Greet & Read	Out Of Prnt-Whi	Whistler's
Centauri	Harris Srch	Peninsula Bksch	Williams
G J Cielec	Heritage-Son	Perryman	Wurlitzer-Bruck

Outlaws & Rangers

Aah!	D M Chase	Y Kishi	So By S'West
Aardvark-Tuc	Chiricahua	Los Artesanos	J D Terry
Amer So'West	A H Clark	Mitchell's-San	R Todd
H R Andrews	Dakota	Nemaha	Trackside
F Armstrong	J Dykes	Princeton Antiq	Trail To Y'day
K G Arthurton	M Gibbs	Red River	Valley-Gal
Asian Amer	D Grossblatt	J E Reynolds	R M Weatherford
Bk Mart-San	Heinoldt	J D Rittenhouse	C Wright
Bk Mart Anx-San	S L Heritage	Rosetree Inn	

Overland Narratives

Barnette's	D Harris	Rancho	Sun Dance
D Blomberg	Heinoldt	Wm Reese Co	H Tanner
Chiricahua	J & J House	Rendezvous	G H Tweney
C Dvorak	S C Lunsford	J E Reynolds	Valley-Gal
L Ginsberg	Mitch's	J D Rittenhouse	R M Weatherford
M Ginsberg	Ostby's	Sage	Zeitlin & Ver B
R Hansen	Raintree		

Ozarks

Dickson St   C Payton

Pacific Region

Aardvark-Tuc   Delta   Magazine   Pacific Bk Hse
Academic   I Ehrlich   J Makarewich   Pacific Writers
Academy-Hon   Ethnograph Arts   F Mavis   Pacificana
R H Adelson   F & I   Maxwell's   A W Paine
Aloha Bk   A Hills   R A Mezoff   D Peterson
H R Andrews   W Hoffer   S N Halas   J E Reynolds
Asian Amer   Hollands'   J Normile   M B Robertson
Bkfndrs Hawaii   N T Hopper   Oceanic Primitive   J Rybski
Broken Kettle   Info   Okanagan   Scotia
Cellar   D Jaffe   Old Mill   S Shmavonian
Chapman & Berry   E J Lefkowicz   Orange Cat   Sun Dance
Cheng & Tsui   R F Lucas   Ostby's   tusitala
A H Clark   S C Lunsford

Paintings

R H Adams   A P Collins   Johnson & Small   P H Samuels
Artcraft   J S Edgren   R J Kempe   Spectrum
Artistic End   G B I   Maestro   K Starosciak
Bk St-San   J Goffman   P H North, Jr   Unique Antiq
M A Bromsen   J & J Hanrahan   O'Neills   Valley-Say
W J B Burger   D B Howes   Reston's   S Vogel-San
T Clark   Illustrated Ant

Paintings (books about)

Museum Gall   Olana

Paleontology

Geological	J J Nadolny

Panama & Panama Canal

J Burnett	P Howard

Paperbacks (new)

A To Z	Bkery-Fai	G B I	Miller's
Abra Cadavar	Bkfnder-Pen	G N Gabbard	Million Year
Adams	Bkfinders-Fair	Garciagarst	K Mitchell
Aesir	Bkhaven-Spr	Grand	N'Woods Funnies
All B & P	Bkie	Greet & Read	Nugent & Assoc
Annie's-Act	Bks For Every	Gundy's	Oblong
Annie's-Nat	Bks Unltd-Ind	H Halbach	Old Corner
Annie's-Wes	Bks & Thngs-Ter	Half Price	T C Packard
Argos	Bkshelf-El D	J Hall	P'back Exch
As You Like It	Bkshelf-Cla	Heinemann's	Paperback Jack
Attic	Bkst-Len	Hooked On	P'back Paradise
Avocet	Bkst-Mil	Hse Of Fict	O Patterson
Back Row	Bk Traders	P Hunt	Peggatty
Barjon's	Brassers	I Am I	Pel's
Barn Sale	Bread, Wine	Imagine That	H J Popinski
Bee Gee's	Bryn Mawr-N Hav	Jack's Used	Print Dev-Mil
Ben Franklin	Burton's	Keith & Martin	Raintree
Bengta Woo	Cache	M M Kraus	Readmore
Bigelows' Quill	A Carduner	Lambda Rising	Red Bank
Bk Center-Ath	W Chadde	J Landau	Redford
Bk End-Free	Change Hobbit	Lantern	J B Reynolds
Bk Peddlers	City Bk & Coin	E A Lehwald	Ridge
Bk Cellar-Tem	City Wide	Little Read	C M Robinson
Bk Connect	Civic Center	Longhorn	Rockaway
Bk Cottage	Confederate	B Lysecki	Rodden's
Bk Exch-Mis	Copper Fox	G H Mahfuz	Ron-Dot
Bk Fair	David's	McClintock	Royal Oak
Bk Fndr-Genev	J A Desch	Mermaid	Sangamon
Bk Mart	Dragon's Lair	Mexbooks	W E Schroeder
Bk St-San	G F Edwards	J Meyerson	Science Fantasy
Bkends-Napa	Frontier P'neer	Michael's	Shamus

W P Shepard	Stan's	Thrifty Reader	Wards Corner
Sidney's	Sterling	Tri-Town	Thomas J Wise
L Smith	Suncircle	Univ Bk St-Man	Womrath's
Spectrum	K W Sutcliffe	Valley-Amh	Word
R Speray	Terry's Better	Vol One Used	World Wide-NYC

Paperbacks (early & collectible)

Bk Case-Pas	Greenblatt	J L Wheeler

Papermaking & Marbling

Enterprise	R J Hoffman	N T Smith	Wilsey Square
Eu Be Co	Midnight-West	Steinberg	

Parapsychology

E Jaksto	Mason's	Unicorn-Chi

Parenting

Bk Barn-Bea	E R Bowes	Tree Hse

Pennsylvania

Baldwin's Barn	R J Kalanja	Otzinachson	W Thomas
J E De Turck	Obsolescence	D W Starry, Sr	D Weiss
D J Ernst	Old Bkshed	T Sullivan	Zellner's
B Godshall			

Performing Arts

About Music
Academy-NYC
Aldine
D C Allen
Amadeus
G Armitage
Backstage
Blue Moon
Bk Srvc-San
Bk St-San
Bks & Thngs-NYC
Buckabest
A Carduner
Cathryn

Cinema-Sea
Civic Center
Common Reader
Dance Mart
Drama
A M Ellis
L Fox
H Galewitz
George Sand
R G Gill
Gotham
Griffin
W F Hale
Harris Srch

Horchow
International
Jolly Roger
E M Katt
L Laws
Libra
J & J Lubrano
Maestro
G H Mahfuz
T L McCook
North Shore
Okman's
On Paper
Other

Perception Plus
Performing Arts
R L Press
Ridge
Savran's
2nd Debut
R L Shep
A Sosenko
Theatrebooks
Vagabond
Village-Hud
Words Worth
Wurlitzer-Bruck

Periodicals

A M S
Academic
Adan
S Alsberg
Amer Print
Argos
G H Arrow
AVH Bkshop
Back Number
Back Row
Bick & Barc
P H Bliss
Bk End-Free
Bk Exch-Mis
Bk Srch-Bro
Bk Stall-Roc
E D Bullian
Bunker
V Burgman
A Buschke

J S Canner
J Cashman
L Diehl
Diva
Dragon's Lair
Drama
Educo
Forsyth Travel
Fortune Finders
Grand
Grandpa's Hse
J Hansen
Historic News
T Hughes
P Hunt
Int Univ Bkslrs
W J Johnson
R T Kennedy
L Laws

Little Prof
L S Loomer
Magazine Center
Magazine
Mariner's Unltd
H J Mason
B McBride
P F Miller
A H Minters
Mostly-Farm
J C O'Connor
Oxford
Page One
Paperback Jack
Period Ludw
A J Phiebig
Phoenix
B Plant
B Resnik

Rodden's
San Marco
Scarlet Letter
A Schnase
L Schnell
W E Schroeder
L Schulman
Science Fantasy
Shamus
W P Shepard
Spectrum
S Stewart
Theta
Western Hemi
F J Wilhelm
W P Wolfe
Yellow Press
Zeitlin Period
J T Zubal

Petroleum

Barber's	Erie	E C Miller	Red River
Donegan	Geological		

Philately & Philatelic Literature

aGatherin'	Bk Studio	C Hacker	A Lutz
S Apfelbaum	Bklyn Gall	W R Harris	Philatelic
B & K Stamps	P R Feltus	H Herst, Jr	

Philosophy

Abelard	Christopher's	Huntley	Renaissance-Lak
Academy-NYC	Diff Drum-Wes	W M Hutter	B & L Root'berg
R Adamiak	Dyment	J & C	Sangamon
Albion	E K	J & J House	K Schick
E Andrews	East West	D & E Lake	Schneemann
Atticus-Tor	Edenite Soc	Lion Ent	Scholar's
Baker	Epist Scholar	Mandrake	2nd Time Around
Bay Side	Estes Service	R W Mayer	Starr-Camb
Bibliophile-NYC	Fox & Suther	Mayflower	J Taylor
Bk Exch-Corn	Fraser's	Metaphysic-Por	Theoria
Bk Harbor	K Grunewald	F Metcalf	H T Trueb
Bk Nook	Hermeticus	Philos Bk Ser	Volkhoff & Von
Bkery-Ith	Hollands'	Philosophical	S Weiser
J C Bryan	J Hood	Pomander	J Weiss
Cartesian	Hummingbird	Print Dev-Mil	M D Zambelli
Celtic Cross			

Phonograph Records

Bryn Mawr-Alb	Imagine That	Mermaid	Tree Hse
Corner Stone	R T Jordan	Old Tyme	Vi & Si's
Cosmopolitan			

Photography

All Photo
Alta Calif
Ars Libri
J R Becker
D B Belcher
Bick & Barc
D Blomberg
C Blomgren
A Bloom's
Blue Rider
Bk Gall-Whit
Bk City Coll
Bk Warehouse
J & W Bursten
Carry Back
Choreogr
G J Cielec
Coach Hse
Colls' Edtns
Colo Bkman
Cornwall Hse
J Craig
H C Daitz
R Dean
D Doonan

Ex Libris-NYC
H Feldstein
Find A Bk
S Finer
Fox & Suther
Fron Amer
V Germack
M Goldsholl
E Gordon
L S Granby
Grub St
W F Hale
C F Hamsa
J A Hess
Hock-Hocking
M S Hollander
H'wood Bk City
K Karith
E F Keenan
Kwasniewski
Lee & Lee
J Lehr
Leiden
L Loewenthal
W Loewy

J Lowe
MacDonald's Mil
Manning's
Marg & Moss
J Michaels
A H Minters
J B Muns
Neikrug
S N Halas
R Norton
Old Bkshelf
Old Delavan
Old Prntd Word
K C Owings Jr
Pan
Perception Plus
Pharos
Photog's Place
J Pollock
N Potter
D F Proctor
J C Rather
R H Richshafer
Rinhart Gall
H & R Salerno

San Franciscian
A D Santomasso
H Schickler
S Shuart
Sindell Res
J P Slattery
T Small
R W Smith-N Hav
Spiratione
K Starosciak
Talisman
D Testa
F J Thomas
Titles
C K Travis
Valley Bk City
S Vogel-San
Waverly
West Side
Wildwood
Williams
Witkin
C B Wood III
Wurlitzer-Bruck
Yankee Peddler

Physical Education

H Abrams-Sta

Nickelodeon

Old Bkshed

Physics

Bk Stall-Oak

Celestial

Maxwell Sci

M Waldstein

Playing Cards

| De Haviland | K Gregory | H Halbach | U S Games |
| Estes Service | | | |

Poetry

A To Z	M Castelli	Hobson's Ch	J B Nomland
Abreyde	Cathryn	Hock-Hocking	Pett & Lieber
Al's	Chloe's	W Hoffer	Pharos
All B & P	Clark's	Horse In Attic	A Philpott
Alphabet	Coach Hse	Hse Of Bks Ltd	Phoenix
Americanist	Coll's List	Invisible	Raven
Anacapa	Core Coll	Ithaca Hse	Ridge
Mrs A L Ashton	Country Connect	Janus-Tuc	I Rouse
atticus	David's	Jennies	Sand Dollar
Authors Of West	J A Dermont	Jolly Roger	Sangamon
Baptist Bourse	Deskins/Greene	J Kuwalsky	Serendipity
Bay Side	D C Dickinson	Las Lenguas	Sylvest & Orph
Beasley	Diff Drum-Wes	Library-Dal	M Tanditash
Belanske & Lev	C Elder	R L Link	Tattered Cover
Brillig Works	Euclid	Lion Ent	J Taylor
A Bloom's	Facsimile	L Loewenthal	S Temple
Bk Caravan	C L Feick	Looking Glass	Trebizond
Bk Cellar-Brat	Fly Creek	S Lupack	Turkey Hill
Bk Srvc-San	Froghollow	Martin's	Wait Godot
Bk Stacks-Burl	L Galinsky	Maverick	B Weiss
Bkman Arcady	George Sand	F Michelli-Nwk	West L A Center
Bks & Thngs-NYC	Gotham	F Michelli-Ogu	Williams
Bkst-Len	R Graham	H Miller	J Wobber
Bread, Wine	Griffin	D Moore	Word
J H Burke	Grolier	J C Morel	H Yellin
G F Bush	H Halbach	New Engl-NYC	Yesterday's-Hot
Campbell-Camp	Hartfield	Newcomb Hall	Ziesing Bros

Political Science & Theory

Acres-Tre	Amer Opinion	Dee Cee	Fraser's
R Adamiak	Angriff	Dyment	Hive
All Pts View	W Bledsoe	Folkways	Huntley
Alpine	Bk Srch-Bro	Franklin	Lincoln-O P

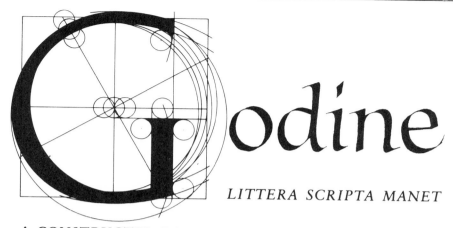

LITTERA SCRIPTA MANET

A CONSTRUCTED ROMAN ALPHABET by David Lance Goines

Master calligrapher, graphic artist, and printer, Goines has spent years creating geometric constructions of the Roman alphabet, including Greek characters and Arabic numerals. A stunning book, printed letterpress with letters printed offset in two colors. Hardcover edition of 2,000. Limited edition of 350, signed and numbered, bound in quarter-leather and slipcased, with an extra set of the letters.

192 pages. 8 x 12″. 53 full-page, 2-color letters. ISBN -375-3 HC, -376-1 LTD. $40.00 hardcover, $150.00 limited

SCRIBES & SOURCES
Handbook of the Chancery Hand in the Sixteenth Century
selected, introduced and translated by A. S. Osley
'A beautiful, invaluable reference for anyone who is in any way seriously interested in the italic hand.' – Publishers Weekly

272 pages. 7 x 9¼″. 22 full-page illustrations, over 500 examples of lettering. ISBN -297-8. $25.00

Now in paperback:
A SHORT HISTORY OF THE PRINTED WORD
by Warren Chappell
An admirable survey of the evolution, impact, and importance of the printed word, produced with a sewn binding in the same elegant style as the original hardcover.

288 pages. 6⅛ x 9¼″. 200 photographs and illustrations. ISBN -312-5. $9.95 paperback

STEEL-ENGRAVED BOOK ILLUSTRATION IN ENGLAND
by Basil Hunnisett
'. . . a pioneering work of high scholarship, destined to become a standard in its field.' -- American Book Collector

288 pages. 7 x 10″. 65 full-page plates, many other illustrations. ISBN -322-2. $40.00

SLAVE TO BEAUTY
The Eccentric Life & Controversial Career of F. Holland Day: Photographer, Publisher, Aesthete
by Estelle Jussim
'Jussim combines dazzling scholarship with meticulous organization and book design to tell an amazing story.' – Publishers Weekly

320 pages. 7½ x 10¼″. 59 duotone plates, 193 black and white photographs. ISBN -346-X. $35.00

Godine now distributes two St. Heironymous Press books, *An Introduction to the Elements of Calligraphy* and *A Basic Formal Hand.*

David R. Godine, Publisher, Inc.

 306 Dartmouth Street
Boston, Mass. 02116 U.S.A.
(617) 536-0761

Please write for our complete catalog.
Godine ISBN prefix: 0-87923-

Lion Ent	R H Rubin	K W Sutcliffe	Volkhoff & Von
T Phelps	H V Ryan	Urban	White Hse
L Rostenberg	P K Slocum		

Political, Social, & Cultural History & Thought

All Pts View	Dyment	J & L Mallis	L J Ryan
Alpine	Hammer Mtn	H J Mason	A Sample
Angriff	R G Hayman	Memorable	Scattergood
Baldwin	Hollands'	C A Noon	L Smith
P E Baracca	Knight's	G R Osgood, Jr	R Spafford
W Bledsoe	J J Lefebvre	T Phelps	Strawberry Hill
Bk Srch-Bro	London-Chi	R & R	Treehorn
R Butterfield	M & S	R H Rubin	G Wilson
Dan's	C Magee		

Popular Culture

J T Gatto	Legacy	J L Wheeler

Postcards

Bks & Thngs-NYC	R & A MacKay	Old Bk Sh-Morr	I M Roth
S S Carver	D Miranda	H N Ottaway	San Franciscian
Fortunate Fnds	Northwoods	Paper & Ink	Yesteryear-Nam
J & P Klemperer			

Posters

Autobks E	Ex Libris-NYC	J & P Klemperer	Omega
R K Brown	J Giller	B Leibowits	B Resnik
Colls' Edtns	Icart Vendor	W F Mobley	I M Roth

| San Franciscian
Shamus | Sisterhood | Stonehill's | P Williams |

Presidents

Abraham Lincoln	W T Gavin	S Koschal	R G Newman
B & B	J Granat	J Lazarus	R & R
J Bambach	D Harris	B E McCaslin	Rinhart Gall
Benjamin Autogr	Hoosier School	Memor Amer	Village-Hud
A M Ellis	J F F	W Monie	White Hse
I Galis			

Press Books & Fine Printing

C Ackerman	J Cummins	L S Granby	Midnight-West
Albatross	L W Currey	Grt So'West	G R Minkoff
E L Anderson	W & V Dailey	R D Greenlee	Montrose
Antiquariat	R B Desmarais	A Gud	B Morrow
Argonaut	Detering	D Halloran	Much Loved
Back Tracts	R Diamond	J S Helms	New Engl-NYC
P E Baracca	M Du Priest	Heritage-L A	J Norman
G E C Barnes	P C Duschnes	R Hittel	W T O'Malley
Belanske & Lev	Dwyer's	Hobson's Ch	D L O'Neal
P Berry	Bkman-Gran	G Houle	Oak Knoll
H J Besnia	Electric Glory	E Howe	Ohio Bkhntr
P C Beyer	Elmcress	Hurley	Out Of Prnt-Whi
Black Sun	R & D Emerson	Illustrated Ant	Parker's
R Bleiweiss	Et Cetera	In Our Time	S Penner
Bk Block-Gree	Euclid	Ivycrest	R Perata
Bk Mart Anx-San	B Farnsworth	T J Joyce	A Philpott
T G Boss	A L Feldman	K Karmiole	P J Pirages
M Braiterman	A S Fischler	I Keats	Poor Farm
Brentano's-NYC	Fly Creek	Greame Kelley	I Quitzau
Bromer	Folger	B R Kemp	Rancho
J H Burke	A C Fox	Kestrel	Randall Hse
R H Cady	M Frazier	L'estampe	K T Ransom
Calderwoods	Fron Amer	G Lange	J E Reynolds
Camelot	A Garnett	J & M Laurie	Rockland
Chiswick	C Garvin	Leaves Of Grass	Sandpiper
Chloe's	Ginger	J Levine	J Scopazzi
Christoffersen	Glenn	W B Liebmann	B Scott
Cogitator	J Goldman	R L Link	C Seluzicki
Colls' Edtns	L M Gottlieb	J Lorson	Serendipity
S F Cullins'	C P Gould	Magic Mtn	S R Shapiro
Colophon	Graedon	Manuscript	H J Shoebridge
Cornwall Hse	W A Graf	B E McCaslin	J V Sichel

T Small	Taurus	Under Cover-Sha	B Weiss
N T Smith	W T Taylor	Under Cover-Cle	Wilsey Square
South Bay	F J Thomas	R L Veatch	Wilson
Stationarius	Titles	Wayside	W P Wreden
G Steigerwald	Transition	Wayward	Zeitlin & Ver B
Sylvest & Orph	O W Tuthill		

Primitive & Pre-Columbian

M S Lambeth   J Normile   Oceanic Primitive

Printing & Printing History

R E Abel	J E Conner	G L Granger	E Offenbacher
L Balish	J Criscione	J A Hill	Rancho
Bennett & Marsh	Dawson's	R J Hoffman	A Saifer
P Berry	De Simon	Homestead	S O Saxe
P C Beyer	Dwyer's	E Howe	J E Schober
Bks In Trans	Bkman-Gran	Indolent Antiq	K L Schwarz
M Braiterman	Elmcress	Ivycrest	Stationarius
Brownstone	Enterprise	Jean's	G Steigerwald
Bryn Mawr-Alb	A L Feldman	K Karmiole	Steinberg
K Buck	Fir Tree	D Ladner	V Tamerlis
Chiswick	A C Fox	G Lange	Taurus
Christiania	Glenn	D L O'Neal	D Testa
S F Cullins'	J Goldman	Oak Knoll	R L Veatch
Colophon	L M Gottlieb		

Printing in Canada

J Burtniak   A W Paine

American Book Collector has computerized all the names, addresses, and book specialties for the 3,000 dealers found in this directory and for a growing list of dealers who will appear in subsequent editions. We can provide mailing labels for these dealers, selected by specialty if you wish, at reasonable cost. Write for our price schedule. *ABC,* 274 Madison Avenue, New York, N.Y. 10016.

Prints

H D Adams
R H Adams
Albion Graphics
Amer Frag
Amer Print
Apothecary
Arkadyan
Audubon
H J Besnia
Bloch & Co
Bk Bin-Dal
Bk Cottage
Broadfoot's
J Buck
W J B Burger
A Buschke
Cartographics
Childs Gall
Cityana Gall
A P Collins
Cornwall Hse
W & V Dailey
Dance Mart
De Victor's
Drew's
H H Eastman
Edenite Soc
B P Ferrini
Fir Tree
R Fitch

Folger
P D French
G B I
J Giller
G F Glaeve
Goodsp'd's-Beac
Goodsp'd's-Milk
M Gordon
K Gregory
A Gutkin
W E Hallberg
J & J Hanrahan
J W Harmand
Historic News
H'wood Bk City
J Howell
Inland River
E F Keenan
R J Kempe
V Kraft
L'estampe
Lamp
D L Larson
R E Lewis
Little Hundred
L S Loomer
R A Lowenstein
R & A MacKay
I MacKenzie
T D Mahoney

J Majer
G B Manasek
Maps & Bks
Marg & Moss
Marshall Field
Memory Box
W F Mobley
Mooers
A Mueller
S N Halas
Nimue
Nouveau
O'Neills
Old Bk Sh-S F
Old Print Sh
Old Print Gall
Old Prntd Word
Pageant
Pages
Pansy Patch
N & N Pavlov
Period Ludw
B Porter
Print Portfolio
Printery
Quill & Brush
B Resnik
Reston's
H E Rohr

Royal Oak
B Sackheim
San Franciscian
Scarlet Letter
W H Schab
Sergio
C Sessler
G Snyder
Spectrum
R W Spellman
Stonehill's
Store
G P Szontagh
V Tamerlis
13 Colonies
3 Arts
D Tunick
Unique Antiq
Ursus
Valley-Say
S Vogel-San
J Wade
Wildwood
P Williams
Woodspurge
Wurlitzer-Bruck
Yesterday's-Wes
R Yorty
S Yudkin

Psychiatry, Psychology, & Psychonanalysis

Academy-NYC
Adan
Aide
Albion Graphics
Antiques-Hil
Atlanta
Atticus-Tor
Bibliophile-NYC
Bk Stop III
Bkfndrs-Mia

Bkpost-Card
Bkpost-Card
Bryn Mawr-N Hav
Chappaqua
Christian-Mil
College Nook
Cosmopolitan
G De Chene
De Haviland
Diva

M C Dooling
W Dordick
Dyment
East West
Epist Scholar
Ex Libris Mazel
Fields
Find A Bk
Folkways
Folkways

G J M
J Gach
L Goldschmidt
Happy Source
F T Heller
Hoffman Resch
Holistic Health
L Kohrs
M M Kraus
R MacKendrick

Mandrake
J Mashman
R W Mayer
J O'Shea
Old Galen's

Philos Bk Ser
Philosophical
Print Dev-Mil
Red Bridge
Regent Hse

Regent St
Riverside Mail
R L Sadoff
K Schick
O Schreyer

B Shaler
C Steir
Tattered Cover
White's

Psychopharmacology

R Demarest   D Fay   G E Webb, Jr

Publishing History

Acoma   Colebrook   K Lang   Pogonia

Pulps

Bailey Srch
Bee Gee's
Bk Mart

G & H De La Ree
A Egan
Hooked On

N T Hopper
N'Woods Funnies
Rockaway

W P Shepard
Village-Mass

Puppetry & Marionettes

M M E Maxwell   Meyerbks

Puzzles, Contests, & Games

P & D Kenyon   N'tl Libry

Railroads

A C H
Aardvark-S F
Again
Albert
Antiq Sh-Ste
S Arden
F Arone
Biblio
Bk Barn-Sio

Bk Mart Anx-San
Bkpost-Dal
O Davies
Diablo
D R Doerres
Dugout & Depot
P Ellis
C E Gardiner
Green River

P Hunt
S McIntyre
C E Miller
E Moore
T C Packard
J E Pearson
Pennyroyal
B E Pingenot

K Prag
Prospector
R M Smythe
Strictly
Trackside
Valley-Gal
Von Blons
Wantagh

Rare Books

Aardvark-S F
Aardvark-Tuc
Adan
All Photo
W H Allen
Ancient Cty Pr
Ancient Cty Bk
Antiq Bksllrs
The Antiquarium
Appelfeld
Arcane
Argonaut
Ark
Arnold's
Ars Libri
As You Like It
Mrs A L Ashton
Audubon
B Babcock
Barnstable
Barra
D L Bauman
M B Beal
D B Belcher
P Berry
Biblion
Bibliopolis-Cle
Black Sun
H Black's
Blors
Bk Gall-Tac
Bk Barn-Sio
Bk Sail

Bked Up
Bkfndr-Cut
Bkhaven-Spr
W J Bkhunter
Bkmark-Sto
Bkstock
Bkwrights
R V Boswell
H W Brewer
Bryn Mawr-Alb
Burke's
T W Burrows
H M Burstein
A Buschke
Caravan-L A
Carlos
Carnegie
Castalia
J & R Casten
Celestial
Chafey's
Chatham
Chiswick
Christian
Christoffersen
Cityana Gall
R W Clare
A Cohen
A P Collins
Copper Fox
Cornwall Hse
Crabtree
J Criscione

Curiosity-St J
Curious-Los G
Current
L W Currey
K Cutler
W & V Dailey
Dakota
Dance Mart
Darian
Detering
Dragoman
M Du Priest
C Dvorak
Eagle
J S Edgren
Edison Hall
C Elder
R & D Emerson
Escargot
A Fair
Family Album
B P Ferrini
J F Fleming
A T Ford
D Frohnsdorff
J Gach
K G Gaisser
C Garvin
W T Gavin
L Ginsberg
Givens
Y Goldman
A Goodman

L S Granby
Grandpa's Hse
Grub St
K Grunewald
D E Guice
Gull
Gundy's
Hamill & Barker
J & J Hanrahan
J W Harmand
T Harper
W R Harris
Hartfield
Haunted Bksh
R G Hayman
Heinemann's
Heritage-L A
Hermeticus
D Hirsch
Hist Real
Hock-Hocking
Holmes-Oak
Holmes-S F
Holy Land
D Hood
El Dieff
J Howell
J C Huckans
M Hunley
W M Hutter
Invisible
Isaiah Thomas
D M Jacobs

B A James
Jay's
Jenkins
P Jenkins
J Appleseed
Johnson & Small
J Johnson
Johnson & O'D
Jolie's
Joyce
T J Joyce
K Karith
K Karmiole
S W Katz
D V Keck
Kennedy's
P & D Kenyon
Keramos
Kestrel
R King
S Koschal
V Kraft
Krown & S'man
D & M Krueger
J Kuwalsky
L La Berge
La Valois
D & E Lake
G Lange
Lantern
R Lasley
K Leach
Leaves Of Grass
Liberty Rock
Lib Quebecoise
W B Liebmann
L N Lien
E Llewellyn
L S Loomer
J & J Lubrano

M & S
T D Mahoney
Maiden Voy
J & L Mallis
J W Martin
McClintock
J P McGahern
L H McGill
B McKittrick
Meyer Boswell
Midvale
Milestone-NYC
K Mitchell
E Monarski
Monroe
Montgomery
Montrose
Mooers
E Moran
B Morrow
A Mueller
Murray
Nationwide
'neath The Elms
K Nebenzahl
New Engl-NYC
J Norman
Northern Lights
Norumbega
D L O'Neal
W B O'Neill
Observatory
E Offenbacher
Oinonen Auct
Old Lou Books
Old Monterey
Old Oregon
Old Prntd Word
Our Heritage

Out-Of-Prnt-NYC
Pageant
J L Parker
Parker's
N & N Pavlov
Peggatty
Performing Arts
R F Perotti
P J Pirages
H J Popinski
Question Mark
Quill & Brush
Randall Hse
Ravenstree
R H Redding
S Resnick
E P Rich
R H Richshafer
J D Rittenhouse
H E Rohr
B & L Root'berg
C Ross
L Rostenberg
Russica
S-T
W Salloch
J R Sanderson
D Sauber
Savoy
K Schick
E K Schreiber
O Schreyer
Schuylkill
Science Fantasy
Sci Fict
2nd Story
Sewards' Folly
S R Shapiro
R W Smith

G Steigerwald
H L Stern
H Stevens Son
I Stormgart
Strand-Rare
Strictly
R M Sylvester
Symposium
L Tebbetts
Thelema
E C Thomas
Titles
Towson
Trebizond
P Tumarkin
Typographeum
Ute-Or-Ida
Victoria-NYC
Volkhoff & Von
J Wade
Wahrenbrock's
P G Waite
M Waldstein
F G Walett
Wantagh
Wards Corner
Warwick
G Wayner
Windhover
Witherspoon
W P Wolfe
W P Wreden
Wurlitzer-Bruck
Yesterday's-Was
Yesteryear-Atl
R Yorty
M Zervas
A G Ziagos
I Zucker

Reference

Adan
The Antiquarium
Bk Clearing
Bkshelf-Cla
L Bowling
Bunker
H M Burstein
J S Canner

Cath Bk Coll
Core Coll
M R Cutler
De Simon
G Deeds
D Discher
M W Dowhan
C Farkas

R Fitch
Gem Antiq
E Gordon
M Gordon
D Hirsch
Jokal
R T Jordan
Landmark

Library-Dal
W Lillywhite
Little Prof
Loft
M McCosh
K Mitchell
D Moore
N'tl Libry

S Orr	O Patterson	Russica	Theoria
G R Osgood, Jr	Reference	Scribbling	Univelt

Religion & Theology

ABC Theological	Cath Bk Coll	Hurley	R O Roberts
A C H	Celtic Cross	L S Kaiser	Rogers Park
Abelard	Chimney Sweep	E Klein	L J Ryan
Abreyde	Christian-Mil	Kregel's	Schneemann
Aide	Christian	Liberty Rock	Scholar's
Albion	Christiania	W Lillywhite	2nd Debut
Alicat	Christopher's	Madonna Hse	2nd Time Around
Allenson-Breck	Constant Reader	H McKee	Seminary
Amer Opinion	Conversation	Metaphysic-Por	B Shaler
Anglican Bib	Corner Stone	W Monie	Sharp's
K Appel	Country Connect	Morrell's	Sidney's
Baker	Cumberland	New Engl-Benn	D Sloan's
Baptist Bourse	Darian	Noahs Ark	Strawberry Hill
C S Berkowitz	East West	J O'Gara	Stroud
Bible Comment	Edenite Soc	Old Bks & Coll	Thelema
Bk Attic	Fields	Old Edtns	Theological
Bk Case-Fres	Folkways	Ollies	Theoria
Bk Nook	Fox & Suther	Our Heritage	Theta
Bk Srvc-San	Franklin	Owl Creek	This Old Hse
Bkfnder-Pen	G J M	Philos Bk Ser	Truth Seeker
Bkpost-Card	Gateway	Philosophical	S Weiser
Bkst-Len	Genessee	Pomander	J Weiss
Bread, Wine	R L George	A & A Prosser	C B Wimsey
G D Brown	Haslam's-St P	Rare Bk Co	Wings Of Eagle
Bunter	Heritage-Son	Ravenstree	Ye Olde Fan
Caravan-Sti	Huntley	Redford	

Remainders

Bk Stacks-Burl	Imagine That	San Jose-San	Strand
Bkends-Napa			

Renaissance

C Ackerman	Albion	P H Bliss	Folger

Krown & S'man   B M Rosenthal   W Salloch   U S Games
J Mancevice   L Rostenberg   E K Schreiber   M D Zambelli
B McKittrick

Reprints

A M S   Edenite Soc   P Lozinski   Strawbridge
P H Bliss   Estes Service   Nationwide   G P Szontagh
M L Cook   Imagine That   A Schnase   Zeitlin Period
Darby   Kregel's

Revolutionary War

R Greenwood   H Nestler   W P Northrop   Northwoods

Rhode Island

Sewards' Folly   Tyson

Kenneth Roberts

J & J Hanrahan   Old Bk Sh-Ken

Rock & Roll

Bk City Coll   Hall's Nostalg

Roycrofters & Elbert Hubbard

N H Brady   D Weber

Russia & Eastern European Region

Bkphil	W S Johnson	P T Mallahan	J P Slattery
A Buschke	W S Johnson	McBlain	Slavic Antiq
Dee Cee	D Ladner	E P Rich	E C Thomas
Dictionary	A Lauberts	Russica	Young Antiquar
Y W Griffin	P Lozinski	Scattergood	J T Zubal
V Janta	M A MacIntosh	S Shmavonian	

Scandinavia

A Christiansen   C Larson

Scholarly Books

W H Allen	Bkery-Ith	El Cascajero	J & J House
Alphabet	Bkie Joint	Elliot's	D Jaffe
Amer Wrlds	T W Burrows	R & D Emerson	Junius
Ancient Cty Pr	J R Butterworth	Grub St	Krown & S'man
Anderson's	Canterbury-Chi	K Grunewald	D Ladner
The Antiquarium	D Carbonneau	Hammer Mtn	Landmark
Ark	Caveat Emptor	B J Hecht	Latin Amer
Attic-Hodg	Christopher's	S Heller	Leekley Srch
Barra	Columbia	Hermitage	J & J Lubrano
Bear	Conversation	Hoffman Resch	R A MacKsey
Ben Franklin	Dolphin-NYC	Hollands'	J W Martin
G A Bernstein	M Du Priest	Holmes-Oak	A E Maxted
Blors	R P Dunaway	Holmes-S F	M McCosh
Bk Stop-Tuc	E K	L Honan	L H McGill
Bk Cellar-Ful	Edenite Soc	J Hood	Memorable
Bk Home	Edgewood	L Hunegs	Metaphysic-Por
Bk Srvc-Ind	Educo	W M Hutter	F Metcalf

Meyer Boswell
Newcomb Hall
North Shore
Old Bk Sh-Morr
Old Oregon
On Paper
Overstock
Pangloss
Princeton Antiq
R & R

Regent St
B M Rosenthal
L J Ryan
A Saifer
Schroeder's
Schuylkill
Science Bkshlf
2nd Fiddle
Secret Sharer

Servant's Knowl
Seville
Significant
Stonehill's
Strand-Rare
P A Stroock
V Tamerlis
Taurus
Theoria

This Old Hse
Tuckers
Twice Sold
Ursus
G Wayner
Wessex
Witherspoon
J Woods-Yak
Ziesing Bros

Science

Acres-Cin
Alpha Omega
Bennett & Marsh
Bk & Tackle
Bkfndrs-Mia

J C Bryan
Buteo
A G Clegg
K Cutler
W & V Dailey

W F Hale
Librarium
Maxwell Sci
Out-Of-Prnt-NYC
A D Santomasso

W H Schab
Scholar's
Shaw-Banfill
L W Smith
Smoky Hill

Science Fiction

Aesir
Allbks
Antiq Bkvestors
Argos
K Armens
As You Like It
AVH Bkshop
Avocet
Bailey Srch
Bakka
Bee Gee's
S C Bernard
Biblioctopus
Bk Baron
Bk Bin-Kin
Bk Sail
Bk Sh-Ket
Bk Case-Pas
Bk Mart
Bk Stop III
Bk Treasury
Bkie
Bkie Joint
Bkshelf-El D
Bk Traders

Bkwrights
C W Brooks
Bunker
J Burger
Cabin In Pines
Canterbury-Geo
Caravan-Sti
Castalia
Caveat Emptor
Change Hobbit
Civic Center
E Clement
Coll's Bkcase
Coll's Ch-Wat
Confederate
Cosmic Aero
Curious-Los G
Curious-East
L W Currey
N Dame
G & H De La Ree
Debra
Diff Drum-Sea
P C Dillon
D Discher

J Distefano
Dragon's Lair
A Egan
Fant Archives
Fantasy
Ferryman Ant
E Fithian
A T Ford
Francis & Yell
Fransen's
G N Gabbard
C Garvin
J T Gatto
R L George
D & P Gilbert
K Glackin
Greenblatt
P Greene
A Gud
F M Halpern
C Held
L Herndon
R Hittel
Hooked On
Horizon

G Houseman
J S Iavarone
Imagine That
J D S
Jack's Used
Janus-Hun
Kay's
J B Keeler
R Kristiansen
La Mesa
J Landau
B R Levin
Little Prof
Little Read
Longhorn
Maverick
McClintock
J McGovern
I Mendoza
Merlin's
Merlin's Closet
Midnight-Mar
Midway
Million Year
G R Minkoff

Mostly-Farm
D R Nelson
N'Woods Funnies
Nostalgia
J & J O'Donoghue
O'Leary's
Odyssey
Old Corner
Old Glory
Old Bk St-Akr
Orpheus
P'back Paradise
Passaic
Paul's

D Peterson
L Pipes
B Plant
Print Dev-Mil
Ralston
Raven
Reedmor
Reston's
A G Robinson, Jr
Rodden's
S & S
H & R Salerno
Sample-Sea
H Satty

Science Fantasy
Sci Fict
A Sherlock
Sidney's
W R Slater
Somerset
R A Squires
Stan's
Theta
R Todd
Valley Bk City
Village-Mass
Wards Corner
Wayside

West L A Center
West's Agency
F J Wilhelm
M C Wilson
J M Winters
Wooden Spoon
J Woods-Yak
Words Worth
H Yellin
Yellowstone
Yesteryear-Nam
S Yudkin
Ziesing Bros

Sculpture

Museum Gall   Olana

Search Service, with Stock

A To Z
Aardvark's-Orl
Abbies
Acorn
Acres-Tre
Action Bks
Adams
J Addams
B Agranoff
Al's
Aldine
All B & P
All Photo
All Pts View
Allbks
Allen
Amer Print
Antiq Sh-Ste
Antiquus
Appalachia
F Armstrong
Astronomy
Atlantic
Attic
J Bailey

S Ballinger
Barjon's
Barrow
Bazaar
Ben Franklin
Bengta Woo
Bibliophile-Pas
Bird's Nest
Blacktail Mtn
P H Bliss
Blitz
Bk Baron
Bk Gall-Whit
Bk Hse-Will
Bk Sh-Boise
Bk Stall-Cin
Bk Case-Pas
Bk Cellar-Tem
Bk Cottage
Bk Exch-Mis
Bk Fndr-Genev
Bk Fndrs-NYC
Bk Gall-Gai
Bk Hse-Pla
Bk Look-War

Bk Place-Col
Bk Ranger
Bk St-West
Bkfndrs-Bol
Bkfndrs Unltd
Bkie Joint
Bkmailer
Bkman Arcady
Bks On File-Uni
Bks Then & Now
Bksh-War
Bksource
Bkstock
Bkstop-Laf
Bkst-Vern
Bk Traders
Bradford
Brainard
Brassers
Brennan
Mrs L M Brew
Buccaneer
Buckabest
Burke's
T W Burrows

Bygone
Cabin In Pines
Cache
Call Me Ishmael
Cameron's
Campbell's
Canterbury-Geo
Caravan-Sti
D Carbonneau
Carmel
Carmichael's
Caveat Emptor
Change Hobbit
Christian-Mil
Cinema-Sea
Colleen's
College Hill
Columbia
Computer Locate
Comstock's
Copper Fox
Crabtree
D J
Davis & Schorr

Day's
H O Dendurent
M H Detweiler
Diamond-Mon
Diff St
Dobbs
Donan
Eight-Cent
Elliot's
L E Evans
Fant Archives
B Farnsworth
Ferryman Ant
S Finer
Fireside
C G Fisher
P T Fisher
Forest Park
Gateway
L Gereghty
Ghent Bkworm
D & M E Gilford
Givens
G F Glaeve
Golden Hill
J R Goodwin
R Greenwood
D Grossblatt
Gundy's
Gutenberg's
T Harper
F Hawkins
S Heller
H C Hensel
Hermit's
Hinds
Hobby Helpers
D Hood
J Hood
Hummingbird
Hunted
A C Hunter
R F Hutson
I Am I
International
A Jacobs
Jay's
Jenny Lind

K N
L S Kaiser
Kestrel
Kneedeep
B Koenig's
Kwasniewski
D Lachance
J Landau
Las Lenguas
R Lasley
Leekley Srch
Lilac Hedge
Lincoln-O P
Literary Seal
P M Lumb
B Lynch
Magazine Center
Magazine
Magic Mtn
Manuscript
Marion Antiq
S Marx
Mason's-Wab
T Mawson
J McGovern
J S McKenna
McLean
J O McMeans
Metaphsic-L A
J Meyerson
J Michaels
F Michelli-Nwk
F Michelli-Ogu
Midvale
E Miller
Mitchell's-San
Monroe
L A Moore, Sr
C Morelle
Murray's
Nautica
'neath The Elms
Needham
W D Nelson
Nemaha
Northern Lights
Novel Exper

Nutmeg
Observatory
Old Delavan
Old Favorites
Ollies
R & M Orner
J Owen
Ozark
Pacificana
Paper Chase Sch
P'back Paradise
Paragon Gall
M R Parks
Parnassus Svce
E Pasoti
Peggatty
Perception Plus
Peterson Bk Co
D V Pfeifer
A J Phiebig
W Pierce
H J Popinski
Prairie Archive
Princeton Antiq
Quill & Brush
I Quitzau
Readmore
Red Bank
Reliable
H B Robinson
Ron-Dot
Royal Oak
B J Rule
C A Rush
Russica
S & S
S-T
Sail Loft-Summ
Sail Loft-Wint
Schneemann
L Schnell
Scribbling
Seabook
2nd Debut
2nd Story
Servant's Knowl
Shamus

T W Shaw
J & V Shelton
Shuey
Silver Door
D Sloan's
Smith's-Brew
Snowbound
South Side
R Speray
P Sperling
Sterling Valley
P Stockman
I Stormgart
Strawbridge
Suncircle
R M Sylvester
Tainters
Talbothay's
Taos
Tappin
B Tauscher
Theatrebooks
Theoria
This Old Hse
Thrifty Reader
T W Tingle
Tower Hse
Tracery
Trackside
Treehorn
H T Trueb
Tuckers
M Twyce
Tyson
Used-Dye
Von Blons
Wayward
L Weidler
Whaling
E C Williams
T Williams
Wolf's Head
C Wright
Yesterday's-Hot
S Yudkin
B Zaremba
Ziesing Bros

Search Service, without Stock

C Ackerman	L E Carpenter	Inn	Regent St
Aide	Centauri	Jokal	C A Rush
Amer Opinion	Chamisa	R T Kennedy	S & S
Argos	Chappaqua	J Kidston	L St Clair
Backpocket	Chicago	T M Knaus	Savran's
Bk Addict-Albu	Coll's Libr	C Larson	Science Bkshlf
Bk Barn-Bea	Dan's	H B Leech	Spencer
Bk Center-Ath	De Ville	Mermaid	R B Taylor
Bk Gall-Whit	D Discher	Metaphysic-Por	10 O'Clock
Bk Peddlers	Donan	Mexbooks	13 Colonies
Bk Nook	E F Dunlap	E Miller	Treasures
Bk Quest	Edgewood	L A Moore, Sr	M L Tyrrell
Bk Srch-Spr	Mrs C Fallert	Old Curiosity	Under Cover-Sha
Bk Sh-Salt	Fordham	Old Harbor	Under Cover-Cle
Bkfnder-Pen	Forest	Oxford	R E Underhill
Bkhunter-NYC	K Glackin	O Patterson	J H Weinberg
Bkpost-Card	Golden Hill	Peninsula Bksch	Whistler's
Bksearch-Fri	Greet & Read	Perryman	Williams
B Boss	Heritage-Son	Pinocchio's	A G Ziagos
J C Buckley	Hobson's Ch	Reedmor	Zollingers
Bunter	Homesteader		

Self Help

Examino	Metaphsic-L A	Sebastopol	R G Wilborn
Landau			

Self-Sufficiency

Examino	Homesteader	Used-Dye

Series Books for Boys & Girls

Adventure	Dr Nostlgia	Red Bridge	Wise Owl
T Catledge	H H Eastman	Temares	Zellner's
Coll's Bkcase	R L George		

Sets

Appelfeld	L S Granby	R E Lewis	Suncircle
J N Bartfield	B J Hecht	Midnight-Mar	Wahrenbrock's
P H Bliss	S Heller	N R S	L & H Weitz
Bkery-Ith	G Houle	Starr-Bost	Thomas J Wise
British Stamp	Hunted	Starr-Camb	Witherspoon
C Farkas			

Sexology

Elysian Fields	C J Sheiner	I Stormgart

Shakers

H Nestler	F P Wood

Shakespeare

As You Like It	H B Diamond	G Hubert	M M E Maxwell
Coll's Crnr	Folger	W Madden	Sons Of Liberty

Sheet Music

Blue Eye	L S Levy	Paper Person	J V Sichel
Dennis	Nickelodeon		

Ships & The Sea

Antheil	B Finch	R Keene	Shorey
Caravan-L A	Howland	E Moran	

Shooting & Firearms

Amer Eagle	Cortese	Global	S Spindel
K Andersen	Mrs K R Dorn	High Ridge	Sporting
Blacktail Mtn	P J Drabeck	Highwood	Sportsman's
Bk Mart Anx-San	A A Dunn	M Marcher	P Sterne
Cabinet Of	T Durflinger	I J Oelgart	G H Suhm
Callahan & Co	Eagle	G Pettinger	L Thompson
Chestnut Ridge	Gall Old West	S R Smith	H Volker
Conrad's	C E Gardiner	Soldier	

Show Business

Cosmopolitan	Meyerbks	Village-Hud

Signed, Limited Editions

A S Fischler	Francis & Yell	Ohio Bkhntr	Signed Limited

604 S. 15th
San Jose Calif.
95112

PO B 2403
Sepulveda
Calif 91.343

564 E. Townview
mansfield ohio
44907

PO B 631
Port Washington
ny
ny 11050

When in California, Visit Santa Barbara's 5 A.B.A.A. Members:

Drew's Book Shop
27 E. Canon Perdido
966-3311
Literature, Americana, Ephemera, Maps, Prints

Daniel E. Guice: Bookseller
1116 N. Milpas Street
965-8888
Early Printing, Science, Medicine,
Continental Scholarship

Milton Hammer — Books
819 Anacapa Street
966-4666
Literature, Americana, Californiana,
Maps, Prints

Joseph the Provider — Books
Suite 201
903 State Street
962-6862
Modern Literature: First Editions,
Manuscripts, Letters

Maurice F. Neville Rare Books
835 Laguna Street
963-1908
19th & 20th C. Literature: First Editions,
Manuscripts, Letters

All centrally located and within walking distance of each other.
Excellent travel access from Los Angeles or San Francisco areas.

Skating

Cabinet Of   With Pipe

Soccer

Bkwood   Soccer World

Social Sciences

All Pts View   College Nook   Hammer Mtn   Pangloss
Atlanta   Cosmopolitan   Int Univ Bkslrs   Philosophical
W Bledsoe   Dee Cee   Lincoln-O P   R H Rubin
Bk Land-Tor   H B Diamond   H J Mason   L J Ryan
Bk Srch-Bro   Elliot's   Maxwell Sci   R L Sadoff
Bkie Joint   Epist Scholar   Memorable   P Smith
Bks For Every   Folkways   S Millman   Sterling Valley
D Carbonneau   Folkways   New Engl-Benn   Theoria
Catawba River

Societies & Associations & Their Publications

Bkmart-Gar   J R Goodwin

The South

H D Adams   Amer Bks   Bk Basement   J P Cather
K Altau   Beckham's   W M Boulton   Choctaw Traders

| Crabtree | Far Corners-Mob | Hound Dog | P R Rieber |
| Dobbs | F M Hill | J O McMeans | |

South America

Amer Bks	B Fein	H Karno	R C Ramer
Bk Home	Harris Srch	McBlain	Ross Valley
C Dvorak			

South Carolina

| Bird & Bk | Bk Disp-Col | Hampton | J S Pipkin |
| Bk Basement | Bk Trader-Fai | Old Mill | |

South Dakota

Bk Keeper-Mit

Southeastern America

Heartwood   Lighthse

Southwestern America

Adobe	Bargain-San	Grt So'West	B E Pingenot
Alcazar	Boysag	S L Heritage	N Potter
Ancient Cty Bk	Chamisa	Los Artesanos	J D Terry
Assoc Bk Svc	5 Quail	M S Lambeth	Wilson

Spain & The Spanish

J B Nomland

R C Ramer

Seville

Specialized Publications

E D Bullian
Fletcher's

R T Kennedy
Magazine Center

K Mitchell

C A Rush

Sporting

K Altau	J Criscione	Lyrical Ballad	Rising Trout
Amer Eagle	J Cummins	Magazine	A G Robinson, Jr
K Andersen	Daly Coll	J McGovern	2nd Fiddle
Angl & Shoot	T Durflinger	Midvale	R W Smith
Baldwin's Barn	Fleuron	E Moran	S Spindel
Baseball	Gall Old West	Old Dragon's	Sporting Biblio
Big John's	A Gutkin	Old Mystic	Sporting
Blacktail Mtn	D Halloran	Pendragon	Sportsman's
J Bowman	Hennesseys	G Pettinger	G Sullivan
Brassers	Highwood	W Pierce	J Sullivan
Bunkhse	Hoffman Resch	Pisces & Cap	Trotting
Calderwoods	D B Howes	K Rais	A Vanasse
Chestnut Ridge	J & C	L L Razek	G Wayner
T Clark	Jenny Lind	Renaissance-Lak	Westfall Spring
Cortese	V Kraft	Rising Trout	Whitlock Farm

Sports

H Abrams-Sta
Bk Addict-Por

Bk Mart
Hall's Nostalg

Rising Trout

A Vanasse

STC & Wing Books

W H Allen	Krown & S'man	Ravenstree	L Schulman
R W Clare	H A Levinson	E P Rich	Trebizond
D E Guice	J Mancevice	J R Sanderson	Ximenes
Hartfield	Meyer Boswell		

Steamships, River Travel, & Steamboats

Autobks E	Inland River	R Keene	H B Leech

John Steinbeck

Danville	S Noto	D Peterson

Stereoviews

A Christiansen	S L Heritage

Stock Market & Wall Street

Abbot	R Bever	H J Mason	M Roenick
G Arndt	Bk Clearing	C E Miller	A Sample
Bargain-San	J L Fraser	S Millman	2nd Debut
M E Battersby	W W Hildreth	K Prag	R M Smythe

Gene Stratton-Porter

Bicentennial	Country Bkshlf	Wake-Brook-Ft L

Jesse Stuart

Coll-Pad	J D S	P & D Kenyon	V Owens

Suffrage

D Miranda	Women's Words

Surveying & Surveys

E E Lindh

Technology

Acres-Cin	Bks Unltd-Nat	S Finer	McDuffies
Antiq Scientist	Bkworm & Silver	Geological	H Nestler
Ark	J C Bryan	G Hall, Jr	E Offenbacher
Astronomy	Chatham	Hawley's Island	N M Pawlett
Auslender	E Clement	Hive	Radiographics
S D Beare	Colleen's	M S Hollander	Riverow
G A Bernstein	College Nook	Indolent Antiq	J Roby
Bk Clearing	Cornhill	Jokal	B & L Root'berg
Bk Stall-Roc	T Durflinger	Kennedy's	Rupprecht's
Bkcell	W H Edgerton	Knight's	A Saifer
Bkpost-Dal	Elgen	Kwasniewski	A D Santomasso
Bks For Every	Farley's	C Magee	Science Bkshlf

Significant   P Smith   Univelt   Zeitlin & Ver B
L W Smith   Stuart's   G Wilson

Television

Crofter's   J T Gatto   Hampton

Tennessee

Crabtree   F M Hill
Enterprise   Mrs Thomason
Fox-Mad   G E Webb, Jr

Nicola Tesla

R J Kalanja   W P Northrop   R G Wilborn

Texas

Alcazar   Bk Cellar-Tem   B E Pingenot   Von Blons
Amer So'West   Bkpost-Dal   Red River   R S Walton
Arjay   Brick Row   Rosengren's   Wilson
R Bandas   M S Lambeth   J D Terry   Ye Olde Fan
Barber's   Old Bkshelf   Trackside

Textiles

Bks Embroid   R Halpern   R L Shep   Swiss Village
M Chapman-Coll   S & H Meller

Theatre

Backstage	Corner-NYC	Y W Griffin	Lennies
Ballet	Dish Hollow	R T Jordan	M M E Maxwell
Coll's List	Genealogists	La Scala	

Theology

Cartesian	Loft	R O Roberts	Theological

Tobacco & Smoking

Abra Cadavar	C E Clift	O Schreyer	G Sullivan
Antiq Tobacco	International	B Shaler	With Pipe
R Bleiweiss	C E Miller		

Trade Cards

J & W Bursten	Fortunate Fnds	W F Mobley	Yesteryear-Nam

Trade Catalogues

Albert	Fortunate Fnds	McDuffies	I M Roth
Bkworm & Silver	A & R Gardiner	H Nestler	A Saifer
J & W Bursten	G L Granger	L L Razek	S Shuart
C Chandler	Jean's	M Roenick	R Verhines
Coll-Pad	J & L Mallis		

Transcendentalism & Transcendentalists

Thoreau Lyceum   H T Trueb

Transgenderism

Elysian Fields   Willmann-Bell

Transportation

Autobks E   Bk Harbor   E Moran

Travel

Big John's   Cole's-La J   W F Hale   Junction
Bkpress   Forsyth Travel   R Halpern   Old Edtns

Travel Guides

Abbot   P R Feltus   W B O'Neill   B M Rieger
H Ebensten   E Musial   J Packard   J P Slattery

Treasure Hunting

Examino   San Fernando

Mark Twain

Corn Mill   A C Fox   R A Lowenstein   B Thatcher

20th Century Literature

Joseph Provider   J B Nomland   Riverrun   Talisman
Limestone Hills   J Petty

Typography & Type Specimens

J W Beattie	W A Graf	D L O'Neal	Stationarius
P C Beyer	G L Granger	Oak Knoll	Taurus
Bks In Trans	R J Hoffman	N & N Pavlov	Under Cover-Sha
Chiswick	G Klemm	Plane Tree	Under Cover-Cle
Colophon	P Krapp	Richardsons	R L Veatch
J E Conner	G Lange	S O Saxe	Wilsey Square
Davison	Midnight-West	S R Shapiro	C B Wimsey
Enterprise	Mt Falcon		

UFOs

Arcturus   D E Whelan

U.S. Government Publications

Bkmart-Gar	Civic Center	W P Northrop	S Ward
Bkmart-Gar	Q M Dabney	E Short	Western Hemi
J S Canner	5 Quail	D Testa	

Useful Publications for Bookdealers

| AB Bookman's | Abpc | Mandeville |

Useful Publications for Book Collectors

| Amer Bk Coll | Bk Mart (Mag) |

Utah

| Bk Sh-Salt | Kats | Ute-Or-Ida |

Vegetarianism

| Red River | Sunny | Vegetarian Soc |

Vermont

Carry Back   M Dunn

Victorian Literature

G Deeds   Log Cabin

Violins

A Christiansen   H Goodkind   Maestro   O Shapiro

Virginia

C Ackerman   Appleland   L Evans   A Lauberts
K Altau   Corner Shelf-Cul   Heartwood

Visual Synthesizers

Argus   E R Bowes

Voyages, Travels, & Exploration

Aah!   Academic   Acres-Cin   Aloha Bk
R E Abel   Acadia   R H Adelson   Arabest

W G Arader III
Arctician
Argonaut
Arkway
Asian-NYC
At The Sign
Autos & Autos
Baird Press
Barnette's
D L Bauman
Bayview
J W Beattie
W E Beaver
J Bekker
Bennett & Marsh
F A Berk
G A Bernstein
Bick & Barc
H Black's
W Blake
Bk Addict-Albu
Bk Bin-Kin
Bk Chest
Bk Den East
Bk Ranger
Bk Srch-Bro
Bk Sh-Salt
Bked Up
Bkleggers
Bkst-Vern
R V Boswell
E R Bowes
Branford
J Burnett
Caravan-Marit
R F Casavant
Cellar
Chamblin
Chestnut Ridge
A H Clark
N Copeland
J Criscione
Cross Hill
J Cummins
Curiosity-Eau
Current
D Davis
E Davis

Davison
Diablo
R Diamond
M C Dooling
P J Drabeck
C Dvorak
I Ehrlich
Elgen
E Enzler
F & I
A Fair
B Finch
R Fitch
Floating Mtn
Forsyth Travel
P D French
Fron Amer
A & R Gardiner
R G Gill
M Ginsberg
Globe-Chic
Gryphon's Lair
A Gutkin
H W K
H Halbach
J H Hale
M Hammer
J Harder
L C Harper
T Harper
Heritage-L A
S L Heritage
J A Hill
C Hinchliffe
Hist Real
N W Hoffman
M S Hollander
Holy Land
D Hood
V Howard
J C Huckans
M Hudson
K Huntress
J & J House
Janus-Hun
R W Jimerson
Johnson & Small

J Johnson
H R Kahn
K Karmiole
J J Keleher
Keramos
J Kidston
D & E Lake
E J Lefkowicz
J G Leishman
Lib Quebecoise
L N Lien
Lowe Antiques
R F Lucas
J Majer
J & L Mallis
Maps & Bks
R W Mattila
F Mavis
J P McGahern
Mermaid
T T Moebs
E Morrill
Mtn Travel
Nautica
K Nebenzahl
W D Nelson
S N Halas
New Steamship
J Norman
W B O'Neill
Observatory
M Ockett
Okanagan
Old Harbor
Old Lou Books
Old Mill
S Orr
Ottenberg Bks
Pacific Writers
Pacificana
A W Paine
G Pettinger
J Pollock
E B Power
R C Ramer
Rancho
Randall Hse

Raven
Wm Reese Co
Rendezvous
W Reuben-NYC
W Reuben-Aus
Richardsons
R H Richshafer
B M Rieger
J D Rittenhouse
R Robertson
C L Robinson-Wi
C L Robinson-Ma
Scharf Art
Scotia
Seabook
Sergio
Seville
S Shmavonian
J M Skutel
R B Stephenson
H L Stern
H Stevens Son
Sun Dance
Sykes & Fla
G P Szontagh
Tattered Cover
Tech Info-Doc
Temple Bar
Terramedia
G Totty
Travellers'
Trebizond
G H Tweney
W Van Devanter
C J Vega
H Volker
Wahrenbrock's
R S Walton
Wantagh
R M Weatherford
West Side
Whaling
T Williams
W P Wolfe
Yesterday's-Wes
M Zervas
I Zucker

War

At The Sign
R Dworcyk

Harold's

Jay's

B E Pingenot

Watchtower Books & Jehovah's Witnesses

M G Alfs

R O Estes, Sr

Jehovah's

Ron-Dot

Waterfowl & Shore Birds

E E Lindh

J E Norris

H. G. Wells

M Tanditash

West Virginia

Bishop Of Bks
Inland River

Major's
J Petty

Trans Allegheny

Wolf's Head

Western Americana

A Pts Northe	Dawson's	Guidon	Ohio Bkhntr
Aardvark-Tuc	De La Pena	D Henson	Old Corner
J P Adzima	H & E Deines	S L Heritage	H N Ottaway
Alpha Omega	J Distefano	Hermitage	W & L Pinkney
K Altau	D R Doerres	R Hittel	Ralston
Amer Bk & Gal	Douglas	Holmes-Oak	Rancho
H R Andrews	Mrs L Douglas	Holmes-S F	J E Reynolds
Authors Of West	J Dowd	V Howard	Ross Valley
B & G	J Dykes	M Hunley	Shorey
Backpocket	Et Cetera	Jack London	Sidney's
Big John's	L Evans	E F Keenan	Summerhouse
Bisbee	Firstborn	Knutson's	Talisman
Bishop Of Bks	A S Fischler	E Lubbe	Taos
Bloch & Co	Gall Old West	T N Luther	Trail To Y'day
Bk Habit	M Ginsberg	McDuffies	G Tramp
Bk Den-San	Glenn	Memory Aisle	Ute-Or-Ida
W J B Burger	Grady's	Michael's	Van Norman
Burkwood	Graedon	Mitchell's-San	R S Walton
Cache	R Greenwood	Northern Lights	O E Warrick
D M Chase	A M Griffiths	W P Northrop	Yesteryear-Nam
Cosmic Aero	D Grossblatt	No'West	B Yolleck

Western Books

A S Fischler	T Minckler	Stan's	Yellowstone
Hobby Hse	W Pierce	D W Starry, Sr	Zellner's

Western New York State

Lift Bridge-Bro	E Musial

Western Pennsylvania

Erie   E E Lindh   Trans Allegheny   Tuckers

Whaling

B & B	Cross Hill	J Johnson	Scotia
Bayview	F & I	R Keene	Seabook
Bk Habit	B Finch	E J Lefkowicz	E Short
Bkfndrs Hawaii	High Ridge	Lowe Antiques	Spector
Bryant's	C Hinchliffe	R F Lucas	Sun Dance
J Burnett	Int'l Hobbies	E Moore	Whaling
J Clinton	D Jaffe	Nautica	

Wierd Fiction

G & H De La Ree   L Diehl

Harold Bell Wight

P & H   J L Wheeler

Wines

Bkwood	Corner-NYC	Hsehold Words	Wine & Food
K Caughren	C F Hamsa		

Wireless Communication History

Biblio's Dream   N Copeland   Radiographics   A D Santomasso

Wisconsin

Bob's-App   Winsted   Wise Owl

Women & Feminism

J Addams	V Burgman	S W Katz	2nd Life
Addison	Carmichael's	Little Read	Sisterhood
Al's	Common Reader	C Lowenberg	I Stormgart
Amer Print	Coventry	Magic Mtn	K W Sutcliffe
Americanist	Daly Coll	Memor Amer	Swiss Village
Austin	Deskins/Greene	F Metcalf	J Taylor
Bigelows' Quill	Diff Drum-Sea	Oblong	10 Pound
A Bloom's	Froghollow	Old Bks-Brun	Twice Sold
Bk Sh-Boise	Goodwin & Zein	J L Polley	Wayward
Bk Cellar-Ful	P Greene	Poor Farm	S Wetstone
Bk Land-Tor	J M Hays	D J Preece	R Wilkerson
Bk Stacks-Burl	Horse In Attic	D F Proctor	Women's Words
Bkshelf-Cla	International	Riverside Mail	Words Worth
Bkst-Len	R T Jordan	2nd Debut	

Woodcut Books

H J Besnia	K Buck	Ravine Cottage	J G Stanoff
Bk Block-Gree	Christiania	W H Schab	Ukiyo-E
Bks In Trans	R W Clare	Signed Limited	

World War II Battlefield Art

Autobks E   R A Lowenstein

World Wars

Antheil   Fuller's   P K Slocum   M C Wilson
Edgewood   P T Mallahan

World's Fairs

Hobby Helpers   L Laws   E Orth

Writing Instruction

Backpocket   Librarius

Wyoming

Backpocket   E F Keenan   Summerhouse

Yachts, Yachting, & Sailing

Caravan-Marit   Cross Hill   D W McLennan   Unicorn-Eas
J Clinton   Howland

Zeppelin & Dirigibles

Crofter's   D R Doerres

Zoology

Buteo	East West	Loft	Sharp's
J J Nadolny	E V Glaser	Mayflower	S Finer
Action Bks	E Klein	Metaphsic-L A	Bkie
Albatross	Fields	Mostly-Farm	Bk Sh-Sou
All B & P	G J M	Oxford	Gateway
Bkpost-Card	G Houseman	Perry's Antiq	Globe-L A
City Bk & Coin	G Sullivan	Philos Bk Ser	Hermeticus
Cosmic Aero	G Hubert	Print Dev-Mil	Thomolsen
Curious-Los G	H T Trueb	S Weiser	U S Games
D E Whelan	J E Conner	San Jose-San	W McDonnell
De Haviland	J Bekker	Sebastopol	Ye Olde Fan
D Spencer	L Sloan		

Anthony Fair

Fine Books

Autograph Letters

Architectural, Literary &
Natural History Drawings

274 Madison Avenue

New York City 10016

Telephone (212) 685 2475

By Appointment Only

Alabama

Birmingham
J P Cather
Fort Payne
G Wayner

Geneva
Allenson-Breck

Huntsville
W M Boulton

Mobile
Far Corners-Mob

Alaska

Anchorage
B Nelson
E Short

Fairbanks
Bkst-Fai

Sitka
Observatory
Old Harbor

Alberta

Calgary
Heritage-Cal

T Williams
R C Scace

Edmonton
Adan

Arizona

Bisbee
Bisbee

Cottonwood
D E Hahn

Douglas
Chiricahua

Flagstaff
L Diehl

Phoenix
B Porter
R Todd
Prescott
J L Parker
Scottsdale
V A Bradley
Guidon
Tempe
Marlil

Tombstone
Rosetree Inn
Tucson
Aardvark-Tuc
Antiquariat
Baseball
Bk Stop-Tuc
D C Dickinson
Hinds
Janus-Tuc

Period Ludw
B Sackheim
Tucson
Wellton
Ravenstree

Arkansas

El Dorado
Bkshelf-El D
Eureka Springs
Kingfisher

Fayetteville
Dickson St
So By S'West

Hot Springs
Yesterday's-Hot

British Columbia

Kelowna
Mosaic
Okanagan
Maple Ridge
Terry's Better
No. Vancouver
Academic
S C Lunsford
Johnson & Small

Qn Charl. City
B Ellis
Richmond
Ainslie
Sidney
Thunderbird
Tofino
Cj Hinke

Vancouver
T Rutherford
S McIntyre
E R Bowes
W Hoffer
Windhover
Ahrens

Victoria
Haunted Bksh
Sager's
Scotia

California

Albany
Mtn Travel
Ross Valley
Sand Dollar
Altadena
Balaclava
Anaheim
Bk Baron
Cypress-Park
Hse Of Bks-Ana
Aptos
H Schickler
J G Stanoff
Strawbridge
Atherton
D Peterson
Auburn
R Hansen

Balboa
Peninsula Antiq
Baldwin Park
C E Miller
J Ray
Bellflower
Ostby's
Berkeley
Albion Graphics
Anacapa
Ark
R Bleiweiss
Cartesian
K Caughren
Creative Arts
C Docheff
J R Goodwin
Hsehold Words
Invisible

I Jackson
Moe's
J B Muns
Regent St
Scattergood
Serendipity
S Shmavonian
Toad Hall
Urban
Whaling
Beverly Hills
H A Levinson
Scriptorium
Buena Park
Singer Comm
Burbank
H B Diamond
Milestone Auto

Burlingame
V Howard
Peninsula Bksch
K Prag
Calexico
R Valdez
Cambria
T Coffman
Campbell
Campbell-Camp
Canoga Park
Clipper Ship
Cardiff
Aide
Bkpost-Card
Carlsbad
J Hansen
Memorabilia

Los Osos
D Lachance
Mariposa
Bk Connect
Country Craft
Martinez
Joyce
Mendocino
Hermeticus
Menlo Park
J G Leishman
Mitch's
Wessex
Mill Valley
Ethnograph Arts
Mission Viejo
G F Kolbe
Moke Hill
R G Wilborn
Montclair
This Old Hse
Monterey
Bk End-Mon
Old Monterey
Moraga
C E Clift
Napa
Bkends-Napa
Vol One Used
National City
Bks Unltd-Nat
South Bay
North Hollywood
N E Lyon
Sharp's
Valley Bk City
Northridge
H Yellin
Norwalk
Mil-Air
Oakhurst
Seashell Treas
Oakland
Aah!
J & J Berger
Bk Stall-Oak
Dance Etc
P R Feltus
P D French
Gull
Holmes-Oak
Marple
A R Milkerit

No'West
R Perata
Western
Ontario
Hunted
Orange
Bk Sail
Indolent Antiq
Oregon House
M Mahoney
Oroville
W Pierce
Pacific Palisades
Fain's First
Pacoima
P Jenkins
Palisades
Int'l Bkfndrs
Palo Alto
Buckabest
J Pollock
J P Slattery
W P Wreden
Paramount
Bargain-Par
Pasadena
Bibliophile-Pas
Bk Case-Pas
Hse Of Fict
Weller Victoria
Pine Grove
W J B Burger
Pleasant Hill
F W Smith
Point Richmond
J Landry
Pomona
Acorn
Quincy
Day's
Ramona
Acoma
Rancho Cordova
J Taylor
Rancho Mirage
Mrs D Cook
Rancho Palos Verdes
L Bowling
Rancho Santa Fe
5 Quail
Redlands
Libros Latinos

Redondo Beach
Bailey Srch
Silver Door
Redway
Floating Mtn
Redwood City
Grady's
Reseda
Bkie Joint
Libra
Personal
Richmond
H R Andrews
Sacramento
Angel's
Argus
At The Sign
B Cassidy
Chloe's
Churchilliana
Delta
R L Press
San Anselmo
M Castelli
Diva
Greame Kelley
San Bernardino
D J
San Carlos
W Bledsoe
Carlos
San Clemente
Dobbs
San Diego
atticus
Bargain-San
Cape Cod-San
Corn Mill
Golden Hill
P Howard
J & J House
L Kohrs
Peri Lithon
J Roby
Truth Seeker
Univelt
Wahrenbrock's
San Dimas
P & D Kenyon
San Fernando
San Fernando
San Francisco
Aardvark-S F
About Music

Albatross
Anglican Bib
Antiquus
Argonaut
Arkadyan
Arts & Lett
W Berner
Bound Pleas
Brick Row
K Buck
CBAG-S F
Civic Center
L Collins
R Dean
Drama
T Durflinger
Bkman-Gran
Fantasy
Fields
A Hills
Holmes-S F
J Howell
F L Kovacs
Lake Law
E Lubbe
Maelstrom
Magazine
Manning's
R W Mayer
Meyer Boswell
Miller-Fruchart
Mother Tongue
J Norman
Old Bk Sh-S F
J Packard
Randall Hse
B M Rosenthal
San Franciscian
S F Mystery
J Scopazzi
Sergio
Spencer
K Starosciak
Strawberry Hill
Transition
Walt Whitman
Yellow Press
San Gabriel
M L Gore
San Jose
A S Fischler
Gilfillan
Perry's Antiq
San Jose-San

San Luis Obispo
Confederate
Novel Exper

San Marino
C P Gould

San Mateo
Bk St-San

San Pedro
Billiard

San Rafael
M S Hollander
R E Lewis
Sandpiper

San Raphael
C Blomgren
R W Jimerson

Santa Ana
Encyclopedias
R Greenwood
D Henson
W Lillywhite
Pacific Law

Santa Barbara
Abraxas
Again
Bk Den-San
Drew's
D E Guice
H Halbach
M Hammer
Joseph Provider
M A MacIntosh
B Morrow
M F Neville
2nd Debut
M A Silver
S Vogel-San
Volkhoff & Von
Westfall Spring

Santa Clara
Mitchell's-San

Santa Cruz
Bk Srvc-San
L S Kaiser

Santa Monica
Arthritis
Euclid
F & I
G J M
Rancho
Sunny
Vegetarian Soc

Santa Rosa
V Burgman
Cipriano's
Papermill
Treehorn

Saratoga
L'estampe

Sausalito
Electric Glory
E V Glaser

Scotts Valley
Chimney Sweep

Sebastopol
D M Chase
Sebastopol

Sepulveda
Francis & Yell
L Gereghty
B Lynch

Sherman Oaks
A C Fox
Fraser's
A Jacobs
Nickelodeon
B & L Root'berg

Simi Valley
W P Shepard
H T Trueb

Solana Beach
Bk Swap

Sonora
Heritage-Son

Soquel
Abreyde
Bay Side

South Pasadena
M Hunley

Spring Valley
Bunker

Stockton
Bkmark-Sto
J Breen
Maxwell's

Studio City
F A Berk
E M Katt
T C Packard

Sunland
G Krueger

Sunnyvale
Cortese
N T Hopper

Thousand Oaks
J Juszyk

Tiburon
Pendleton Publ

Tollhouse
Air Age

Toluca Lake
D Spencer

Topanga
Boulevard

Torrance
B Finch

Torrence
Bk Buddy
Bk Land-Tor

Trinidad
Inprint

Turlock
Bks In Trans
Garciagarst

Universal City
B & G
D M Sanchez

Van Nuys
R J Hoffman
J Makarewich
L St Clair

Venice
Mariner's Unltd

Ventura
Adventure Kids
2nd Time Around

Vista
Bk Habit

Walnut Creek
Diablo
Hooked On
G Hubert

Watsonville
Bks For Every

Weaverville
Blitz

Westlake Village
221

Whittier
Out Of Prnt-Whi

Willits
J E Reynolds

Wilmington
Int'l Hobbies

Woodland Hills
Okman's
R W Sabbot

Colorado

Boulder
Brillig Works
R D Greenlee
Ivycrest
Rue Morgue

Brighton
L Sloan

Colorado Springs
Bk Home

Denver
Amadeus
W J Bkhunter
Colls' Cntr-Den
Court Place

Hermitage
Tattered Cover

Fort Collins
H & E Deines

Old Corner
Suncircle
Grand Junction
Conrad's
Greeley
Mt Falcon

Lakewood
E Fithian

Littleton
Prospector

Loveland
Cache

Norwood
Colo Bkman

Sedalia
A M Griffiths

Wheat Ridge
J Bailey

Connecticut

Bantam
R G Gill
Bethany
The Antiquarium
Whitlock Farm
Bethel
D M Jacobs
A W Paine
Bethlehem
Bethlehem
Branford
Branford
Bridgeport
Chimney Smoke
H V Ryan
Chester
Howe
Colebrook
Colebrook
Rinhart Gall
Collinsville
Country Lane
Cos Cob
Harrington's
Coventry
Printery
J Woods-Cov
Danbury
A G Weindling
Darien
W H Edgerton
East Hampton
M Roenick
East Hartford
Bkie
Fairfield
W Blake
J M Skutel

Falls Village
R & D Emerson
Geological
Farmington
Mostly-Farm
Georgetown
Canterbury-Geo
Glenbrook
Auslender
Goshen
Angl & Shoot
I J Oelgart
Granby
W & L Pinkney
Greenwich
Bk Block-Gree
Tower Hse
Hamden
Amer Wrlds
Bkcell
Hartford
W E Hallberg
B McBride
S Wetstone
Harwinton
W Madden
Kensington
J J Nadolny
D J Preece
Manchester
R MacKendrick
Mansfield Center
S B Amdur
Middletown
P H Bliss
Milldale
Print Dev-Mil
Morris
R Shuhi

Mount Carmel
Antiq Bks
Naugatuck
M C Dooling
New Caanan
J & L Mallis
New Canaan
New Canaan
New Haven
Bryn Mawr-N Hav
Edgewood
S L Heritage
H Miller
R Norton
O'Conn Y'year
Pharos
B A Pinchot
Wm Reese Co
W Schiefer
R W Smith-N Hav
C A Stonehill
Whitlock's
New Milford
Scarlet Letter
Newtown
East & West
Niantic
S N Bean
Norfolk
J Craig
North Haven
19th Cent Photo
North Stonington
Cartographics
Northford
Elliot's
Norwalk
Dan's

H J Mason
F Paws
Old Mystic
Old Mystic
Orange
I Am I
Pawcatuck
Raven
Ridgefield
J Mashman
Salisbury
Boysag
Lion's Head
Sandy Hook
Chiswick
Simsbury
Toxophilite
South Woodstock
C B Wood III
Southport
A Dumler
Museum Gall
L Witten
Stamford
Davison
A & R Gardiner
Stonington
Seaport
Stratford
P C Beyer
R B Sirrine
Torrington
Nutmeg
S Powell
Trumbull
J P Adzima
Washington
Crofter's

Watertown
Cabinet Of

West Cornwall
D Benson
B Farnsworth
Poor Farm

West Granby
Yesterday's-Wes

West Haven
Fuller's

West Redding
P Sterne

Westport
P C Dillon
Guthman
Turkey Hill

Wethersfield
E Tatro

Whitneyville
D Ladner

Willimantic
Ziesing Bros

Wilton
Archives Hist

Windham
E Moody

Windsor
C L Robinson-Wi

Winsted
Attic-Wins

Woodstock
S T Oakley, Jr

Delaware

Greenville
Bks-Gre

New Castle
Oak Knoll

Newark
R M Eisenberg
McMahon

Wilmington
S D Beare
Palma

District of Columbia

Washington
Bick & Barc
Bked Up
Q M Dabney
Earthworks
Estate
Folger

D & M E Gilford
W F Hale
Holy Land
Illustrated Ant
International
Lambda Rising
Latin Amer

S B Lebo
Old Print Gall
Old Prntd Word
L Pipes
Plane Tree
2nd Story

O Shapiro
L Smith
Stuart's
W Van Devanter
Wayward
Yesterday's-Was

Florida

Atlantic Beach
Tappin

Boca Raton
Bks & Thngs-Boc
H Herst, Jr

Chuluota
Mickler's

Clearwater
Theta

Cocoa
O Patterson

Coral Gables
Bk Warehouse

Delray Beach
F Goldman
Pel's

Eustis
Raintree

Fern Park
T Catledge

Fort Lauderdale
R Hittel
Wake-Brook-Ft L

Gainesville
Bk Gall-Gai

Jacksonville
Chamblin
E F Kramer

M N McQuerry
San Jose-Jack
San Marco
Surrencys

Jensen Beach
A D Santomasso

Lake Wales
Bk Mart (Mag)

Lake Worth
A T Ford

Margate
Amer Lib Srvce

Miami
All B & P
Banyan

Miami Beach
Bkfndrs-Mia

Naples
Bk St-Nap

R Demarest
Nugent & Assoc

Newberry
D E Whelan

North Fort Myers
J H Reuther

North Miami
A To Z

Orlando
Aardvark's-Orl

Palm Beach
C Ackerman
J Owen
C M Robinson

Pensacola
Bkfnder-Pen
Farley's
Galvez
Long's-Pen

Pensacula
Seville

Pompano Beach
Happy Source
Lantern

Sarasota
Aceto
Fleuron
J W Harmand
Parker's
Townsends

Seminole
Brassers

St Augustine
A Mueller

St Petersburg
J C Daub
Haslam's-St P
Lighthse

Stuart
Horticultural
Jolie's

Tampa
E K Powell
J & V Shelton

Vero Beach
Eagle's-Vero

Wales
Bk Caravan

West Palm Beach
Bk Fair
Used-West

Winter Haven
Bk Traders
K W Nims

Winter Park
T Phelps

Georgia

Altanta
R Bemis

Athens
Bk Center-Ath

Atlanta
H D Adams
Atlanta
Bk Studio
J Burnett
T L McCook
J O McMeans
Memorable
Miller's

T T Moebs
Old New York
Oxford
Yesteryear-Atl

Augusta
K T Adamson

Avondale Estates
Bk Srch-Avon

Conyers
H C Blackerby

Decatur
Bk Dispensary

Bk Cottage
Hound Dog

Marietta
Midnight-Mar

Rome
Coosa Valley
G S Herron

Savannah
Bk Lady
L E Evans
J Levine

Sharpsburg
H Bridges

Temple
Perryman

Thomasville
P R Rieber

Tybee Island
Bkman Arcady

Warner Robins
Bksh-War

Hawaii

Hilo
Bkfndrs Hawaii

Honolulu
Academy-Hon

Pacific Bk Hse
Pacific Writers

Kailua
tusitala

Kaneohe
Aloha Bk

Wailuku Maui
S N Halas

Idaho

Boise
Bk Sh-Boise

Nampa
Yesteryear-Nam

Illinois

Barrington
Old Dragon's
Renascence

Berkeley
R Lasley

Berwyn
H J Popinski

Bloomingdale
Slavic Antiq

Brookfield
Yellowstone

Champaign
Stonehill's

Chicago
Abraham Lincoln
R Adamiak
R H Adams
J Addams
Articles Of War
M B Beal
Beasley
Bkleggers
Bkseller's Row
J M W Borg
Canterbury-Chi
G J Cielec
Creedmoor
East West
Globe-Chic
Hamill & Barker
Hanzel Gall
E Jaksto
K N
E Krebs
N L Laird
L Laws
London-Chi
Marshall Field

K Nebenzahl
R G Newman
J O'Gara
J E Pearson
E Phalen
C T Powner
A & A Prosser
Rogers Park
J Rybski
Schneemann
H L Stern
J Sullivan
Unicorn-Chi
F J Wilhelm
Zollingers

Chicago Heights
Chicago

Cicero
J M Bruna

Clarendon Hills
No'West Auct

Crystal Lake
Fireside

Decatur
D V Keck

Dekalb
R Verhines

Downers Grove
T W Burrows

Evanston
Athenaeum
Bunter
Kennedy's

Farmersville
E C Thomas

Freeport
Bk End-Free

Galena
Valley-Gal

Galesburg
Van Norman

Geneva
T J Joyce

Glenview
A Maita

Glenwood
Meyerbks

Highland
Swiss Village

Highland Park
Titles

Hillsboro
L Weidler

Hinsdale
Mrs C Fallert
Trotting

Hoffman Estates
Stevensons

La Grange
Brainard
Colophon
J W Martin

Lake Bluff
E F Keenan

Lake Forest
J & C
Renaissance-Lak
O W Tuthill

Lincoln
Yesteryear-Lin

Marshall
M Frazier

Monee
P Krapp

Mount Prospect
Jack's Used

Normal
Kent's Crossing

Northbrook
Leiden
Scribbling

Northfield
M Goldsholl

Oak Park
O Davies
Goodwin & Zein
J Klein
J McGovern
E P Rich
B Wheel

Olympia Fields
Old Verities

Palatine
R H Cady

Paris
T T Foley

Peoria
Junction

Prospect Heights
V Kraft

Quincy
Treetops

Ridgefarm
D & D

Rockford
D Blomberg
Bk Stall-Roc

Rolling Meadows
C Hacker

Skokie
S Alsberg
Historic News

Springfield
Prairie Archive

St Charles
J Dowd
7 Oaks

Tinley Park
C Magee

Urbana
Burkwood

Vernon Hills
Bkst-Vern

Wauconda
Srch Srvce-Wau

Wheaton
First Impress
R O Roberts

Wilmette
Cogitator

Winthrop Harbor
Leekley Srch

Indiana

Bloomington
Caveat Emptor
Christopher's
K Rais
R Speray
G Steigerwald

Carmel
Carmel
J P Leeds

Chesterton
Country Bkshlf
G B Manasek

Clarksville
Bkshelf-Cla

Dyer
Used-Dye

Elberfeld
L Schnell

Elkhart
Bkstack-Elk

Evansville
Bk Broker
M L Cook

Farmland
C E Law

Fort Wayne
Chantiicleer
Forest Park

Indianapolis
Back Tracts
Bk Srvc-Ind
Bks Unltd-Ind
J Finney

Hoosier Bksh
O J Imel
W S Johnson
W S Johnson
Odds & Eads
E Pasoti

La Porte
Hoosier School

Marriston
Blue River

Muncie
R King

New Albany
J R Long

Richmond
R R Rhoads

South Bend
Barnette's
Binders Press
Bk Sh-Sou

Terre Haute
E H Bevington

Wabash
Mason's-Wab

Walkerton
Lion Ent

West Lafayette
Midnight-West

Iowa

Akron
Broken Kettle

Ames
K Huntress
Little Read

Cherokee
Bkseller-Cher

Davenport
Able Beam
Peterson Bk Co
Source

Des Moines
McBlain

Dubuque
Checker
Inn

Iowa City
K Armens
W A Graf

Maquoketa
Andromeda

Russell
G Pettinger

West Des Moines
Diff Drum-Wes

Wilton
D R Doerres

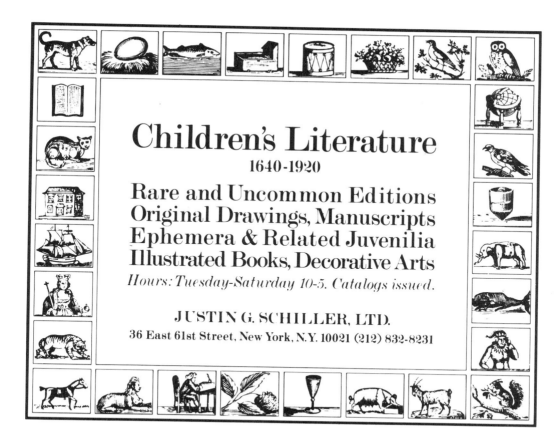
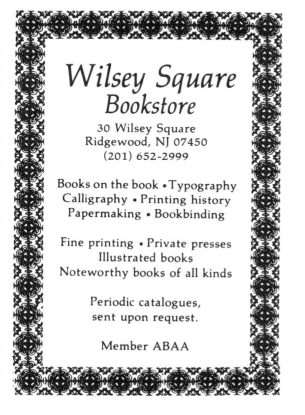

Kansas

Goff
Nemaha

Kansas City
E Llewellyn

Lawrence
J Hood

Manhattan
Univ Bk St-Man

Prairie Village
Whistler's

Shawnee Mission
Forsyth Travel
T N Luther

Wichita
Al's

H N Ottaway
P & H

Kentucky

Covington
Trade & Sell

Harrodsburg
E Davis

Hopkinsville
Pennyroyal

Lexington
Craighse-Mall
Craighse-Pat
Eagle
Sail Loft-Wint

Louisville
Carmichael's

W C Gates
G T McWhorter
D S Mull
Old Lou Books
V Owens
Philatelic
S-T
D Smith

Paducah
Coll-Pad

Louisiana

Baton Rouge
Claitor's
T Clark

Bernice
J & W

Lafayette
C F Hamsa

New Orleans
Amer Opinion
Beckham's

De Ville
R & R

Shreveport
Ark-La-Tex

City Bk & Coin
Red River

Maine

Bangor
H O Dendurent
Ex Libris-Ban

Bath
Cross Hill

Berwick
J Pitchforth

Bingham
N'Woods Funnies

Boothbay
E C Williams

Brewer
Medical

Bridgton
Bridgton

Brunswick
L Cross
Old Bks-Brun

Bryant Pond
M Ockett

Buckfield
P Ledlie

Burnham
J B Reynolds

Camden
L Berliawsky

Deer Isle
Skeans & Cliff

Ellsworth
Bedford's

Eustis
MacDonald's Mil

Farmington Falls
Barn Sale

Freeport
Bk Cellar-Fre

Gardiner
Bunkhse

Hallowell
L Tebbetts

Kennebunk
Old Bk Sh-Ken

Lewiston
Estes Service
Hobby Hse
D Isaacson

Litchfield
M E Owen

Livermore Falls
Tri-Town

Madison
Snowbound

Manchester
C L Robinson-Ma

Newcastle
Sail Loft-Summ

North Monmouth
J B Keeler

Ogunquit
F Michelli-Ogu

Orono
Nimue

Pittsfield
Winter Farm

Portland
Bk Addict-Por
N Copeland
F M O'Brien

Springvale
H H Eastman
F P Wood

Spruce Head
Lobster Lane

Stockton Springs
A B W MacEwen

Stonington
G F Bush

Wells
R MacDougall

Manitoba

Winnipeg
B Lysecki
F A L Mathewson

K Mitchell
J J Keleher

Maryland

Annapolis
Dragoman

Baldwin
Artcraft

Baltimore
Arc Bks
M Braiterman
A Cheslock
Chirorgical
J E Conner
C C Davis
A J Gutman
Harris Auct
E A Lehwald
L S Levy
R A MacKsey

D F Proctor
Remington's
C A Rush
Sherlock

Bethesda
Folkways
Folkways
Quill & Brush
R W Smith

Bowie
B & K Stamps
Heritage-Bow

Brinklow
Old Hickory

College Park
M Chapman-Coll
J Dykes

Columbia
J Gach

Easton
Callahan & Co
Unicorn-Eas

Elkton
C Farkas

Ellicott City
Deeds
G Klemm

Gaithersburg
D Frohnsdorff

Galesville
Firstborn

Glen Echo
Print Portfolio

Greenbelt
E D Bullian
L Seeborg

Kensington
Atherton's
J C Rather

La Plata
S Ward

Laurel
Elm

Lutherville
Drusilla's

Port Tobacco
Old Quenzel
Rockville
S C Bernard
Carrocell
Salisbury
Kardy's

Silver Spring
J A Desch
M T Hall
Silver Springs
Hirschtritt's
Sykesville
J Schochet

Timonium
Little Prof

Towson
Greet & Read

Westminster
Christian

Wheaton
Mooers

Massachusetts

Abington
F G Walett
Acton
Annie's-Act
Acton Centre
J R Becker
Adams
2nd Life
Amesbury
Antiq Scientist
Amherst
Valley-Amh
Andover
J A Hess
Arlington
Hall's Nostalg
Perception Plus
Print Dev-Arl
Worldwide-Arl
Ashfield
Yesterday's-Ash
Ashley Falls
History House
Assonet
O H Brady
Auburn
K Andersen
Beck
Dish Hollow
Bellingham
Cath Bk Coll
Belmont
R McCarthy
Bernardston
Astronomy
Beverly
J S McKenna

Blandford
R F Lucas
Boston
Ars Libri
Artistic End
AVH Bkshop
Bkfndrs Unltd
Boston Annex
Brattle
Bromer
M A Bromsen
J S Canner
Cheng & Tsui
Childs Gall
Choreogr
Curious-Bost
Glad Day-Bos
Goodsp'd's-Beac
Goodsp'd's-Milk
Harcourt Bind
R Kristiansen
Lowe Antiques
G H Mahfuz
C G Martignette
E Morrill
Starr-Bost
I Stormgart
Vintage-Bost
Young Antiquar
Braintree
Organ Lit
Xanadu
Brewster
D B Howes
Smith's-Brew
Brockton
Bk Mart
Stan's
Brookline
T G Boss

B A James
D Miranda
Wait Godot
A Wilder
Brookline Village
Horse In Attic
Byfield
H E Rohr
Cambridge
Asian-Cam
Blue Rider
Daly Coll
N Dame
Grolier
Hofmann & Free
In Our Time
Mandrake
Million Year
Pangloss
Science Fantasy
Starr-Camb
Temple Bar
R Wilkerson
Words Worth
B Zaremba
Canton
Ishtar
Chapel
Savoy
Charlestown
Atlantic
Chestnut Hill
Bk & Tackle
S S Carver
Cohasset
A E Maxted
Concord
Barrow

New Albion
Thoreau Lyceum
Conway
R L Merriam
Danvers
Back Number
Deerfield
M D Sackman
East Longmeadow
W D Hall
East Sandwich
Titcomb's
Easthampton
Taurus
Fairhaven
E J Lefkowicz
Framingham
R B Desmarais
Franklin
J A Smith
Georgetown
K & J Field
Gloucester
10 Pound
Great Barrington
G R Minkoff
Harvard
G Arndt
Harwich Port
Knight's
Haverhill
C Morelle
Hingham
Hingham
Huntington
Cookery Bkery

Hyannis
Wake-Brook-Hyan
Jamaica Plain
Howland
P'back Paradise
Lenox
Bkst-Len
Leominster
W T Gavin
Lexington
Echo
Lowell
J H Weinberg
A G Ziagos
Lunenburg
G Totty
Malden
G R Osgood, Jr
Marblehead
I Galis
Lorenz Books
Mermaid
'Neath The Elms
Melrose
A Sample
Millis
B E Cassie
Nantucket Island
Bkwrights
Natick
Annie's-Nat
New Bedford
D R Nelson
New Salem
Common Reader
Newburyport
B Gould
J F Hendsey
F E Reynolds
S Scharoun

Newton
Bk Coll-Newt
Bks Embroid
Rendells
S Schlossberg
North Abington
K C Owings Jr
North Amherst
Magnalia
North Weymouth
British Stamp
Northampton
Bigelows' Quill
Dwyer's
Omega
Oak Bluffs
Bk Den East
Onset
J A Dermont
Orange
D B Belcher
Palmer
Fox Hill
Open Creel
Pittsfield
Imagine That
D V Pfeifer
2nd Floor
Provincetown
Bryant's
Randolph
B & B
Salem
Saxifrage
Santuit
Liberty Lore
Sharon
M Ginsberg
P L Stern

Sheffield
H S Mott
Somerville
W Dordick
South Dartmouth
K W Sutcliffe
South Gardner
Irene's
South Hamilton
Elmcress
South Lee
J & J Lubrano
South Yarmouth
T Small
Springfield
Murray's
Sterling
Sterling
Sterling Junction
H J Besnia
Stockbridge
J R Sanderson
Stoughton
R H Rubin
H J Vickey
Western Hemi
Stow
Bazemore's
Sturbridge
2nd Fiddle
Sunderland
Oinonen Auct
Templeton
P C Richards
Topsfield
Amer Eagle
Turner's Falls
S Finer

Waltham
H M Burstein
Wayland
R F Casavant
Wellesley
Old Bks & Coll
Terramedia
West Bridgewater
Bk St-West
West Roxbury
L H Finn
West Stockbridge
D Elsberg
Westborough
Annie's-Wes
L Honan
Westfield
G H Suhm
Weston
M & S
Westport
P Lozinski
Whitman
E Panos
Wilbraham
W F Mobley
Murray
D Tessier
Williamstown
M W Dowhan
Williams
Winchendon
Theological
Worcester
Isaiah Thomas
J Mancevice
Yarmouth Port
Parnassus Svce

Michigan

Addison
Diff St

Albion
Pisces & Cap

Allen
Antiq Michiana

Alpena
F Hawkins

Ann Arbor
David's
Hartfield
Keramos
Leaves Of Grass

Old Curiosity
E B Power
Science Bkshlf
West Side

Wine & Food
Wooden Spoon
Auburn Heights
Marion Antiq
Battle Creek
Memory Aisle
Belding
Global
Chelsea
Eagle's-Chel
Dearborn
Alpine
Detroit
Cellar
J K King
Redford
D E Wojack
Dundee
Willmann-Bell
East Lansing
Curious-East
J L Lepczyk

Eaton Rapids
A G Clegg
Ferndale
Mayflower
Flint
D Sloan's
Franklin
W R Harris
Grand Rapids
Argos
Baker
Don's
Kregel's
Philos Bk Ser
Grosse Point Park
Grub St
Hastings
Bks Etc-Hast
Houghton
Grt Lake
Jackson
G Tramp

Kalamazoo
Bicentennial
P J Pirages
Lawton
Bohling
Livonia
C Chandler
Mount Clemens
O Oughtred
Niles
Casperson
Okemos
G L Granger
Oxford
Thrifty Reader
Parchmont
Yesterday's-Par
Petoskey
Bk World
Pontiac
A G Robinson, Jr

Richland
J C Buckley
Rochester
B J Rule
D Weber
Roscommon
R Yorty
Royal Oak
Much Loved
Rupprecht's
Saugatuck
Call Me Ishmael
St Joseph
Curiosity-St J
Suttons Bay
L L Razek
Three Oaks
D C Allen
Traverse City
Arnold's
Highwood

Minnesota

Anoka
J & J O'Donoghue
Duluth
M Kilen
Excelsior
M McCosh
Grand Marais
W Chadde
Mankato
Once Read
Minneapolis
M G Alfs
Allen
Biermaier's

Blue Moon
Bk Dales
Bkmailer
Caissa
Dinkytown
L Hunegs
L N Lien
Loft
E Rovick
Savran's
Scientia

Moorhead
V Koppelman

Rochester
Northern Lights

St Cloud
Amer Bks
Tree Hse

St Paul
E L Anderson
Harold's
G Lange
J & M Laurie
H McKee
Midway

S & S
Vintage-St P

Staples
Christiania
B Parrington

Wayzata
Ross & Haines

Willmar
Borene

Winona
M Twyce

Mississippi

Jackson	**Kiln**	**Ocean Springs**	**Ridgeland**
Nouveau	Mrs L M Brew	W M Hutter	Choctaw Traders

Missouri

Blue Eye
Blue Eye

Clayton
Library Ltd

Columbia
Adams
Columbia
H B Robinson

Crestwood
Readmore

Festus
L Thompson

Hannibal
B Thatcher

Hartville
R O Estes, Sr

Independence
Darian

Ironton
B E McCaslin

Kansas City
W J Cassidy
Glenn
K Grunewald
Red Bridge
Smoky Hill

Lebanon
D & P Gilbert

Moberly
Court's

O'Fallon
W G Bazan

Rolla
L J Bain

Sedalia
Bkman-Sed
C Payton

Seligman
Centauri

Springfield
ABC Theological

St Louis
Adventure
R P Dunaway
E F Dunlap
A Garnett
D Halloran
Marvelous
Sangamon
S Vogel-St L

University City
Paul's

Warsaw
Ozark

Montana

Billings
Barjon's
T Minckler

Bozeman
Sage

Kalispell
Blacktail Mtn

Lakeside
Gall Old West

Missoula
Bird's Nest
Bk Exch-Mis
Sidney's

Plains
D A Lawyer

Nebraska

Fremont
Examino

Grand Island
Bargain-Gran

Lincoln
Long's-Lin
1023

Omaha
D N Dupley

Mostly-Oma
O E Warrick

Sioux City
Bk Barn-Sio

Nevada

Las Vegas
K Appel
Bk Stop III

Gambler's
Gundy's

Reno
Unique Stall

New Brunswick

Fredericton
Arctician
L Hill

St Andrews
Pansy Patch

Sussex
R & A MacKay

New Hampshire

Bradford
Kalonbooks

Contoocook
Women's Words

Derry
B Babcock

Durham
N Houle

Enfield
H Reichner

Exeter
Adams Brown
Landscape

Francestown
Typographeum

Franklin
E Clement

Haverhill
Carry Back

Hillsboro
Shadow

Jaffrey Center
R B Stephenson

Laconia
Barn Loft

Littleton
Village-Lit

Manchester
B Boss
Sons Of Liberty

Marlborough
Homestead

Nashua
D N Harding
P Henderson

North Conway
No Conway

North Weare Village
Sykes & Fla

Peterborough
D L O'Neal

Portsmouth
J & J Hanrahan
C A Noon

Old Bk St-Port
P A Rousssel
Randolph
Ravine Cottage
Rochester
Half Price

Rumney
E Olcott
Rumney Village
Stinson Hse
Salisbury
E C Fales

Temple
Abbies
Tainters

Warner
O'Neills

Westmoreland
Hurley

Windham
Gryphon's Lair

New Jersey

Asbury Park
White's
Atlantic City
D L Bauman
Deskins/Greene
Princeton Antiq
Servant's Knowl
Basking Ridge
A Christiansen
Berkeley Heights
Paper & Ink
Bernardsville
Bkstock
Edtns Ltd
Boonton
Aeroprint
Old Tyme
Brick Town
R W Spellman
Brielle
Escargot
Cedar Grove
L M Gottlieb
Cherry Hill
Evergreen
Clifton
AB Bookman's
Closter
H W Brewer
Cranbury
Cranbury
C L Feick
Cream Ridge
Bread, Wine
Dover
L Loewenthal
Edison
Edison Hall

Englewood
L Balish
Bk St-Engl
K Lopez
R A Paulson
Fairview
Junius
Peacock
Flemington
Bk Roundup
People's
Freehold
Rare Bk Co
Glen Gardner
Windage Farm
Glen Rock
Artifacts
Hackensack
W T Clermont
J M Winters
Haddonfield
Wings Of Eagle
Hazlet
B Dawson
Hopewell
E Woodburn
Imlaystown
Edenite Soc
Kendall Park
De Victor's
Kenilworth
Oz & Ends
Lakewood
M Kronovet
Lincroft
Past History
Livingston
L Stamelman

Long Valley
Calderwoods
Madison
Chatham
Marlboro
Jay's
Metuchen
Bel Canto
Montclair
A Schram
P Smith
Wangner's
Morristown
Old Bk Sh-Morr
Newark
J C Bryan
A Iuspa
F Michelli-Nwk
New Jersey
North Newark
D Testa
Norwood
W J Johnson
Ocean Grove
Morrell's
Park Ridge
Noyes
Passaic
Passaic
Paterson
Reliable
Pennington
Bk Peddlers
Plainfield
Bk Hse-Pla
P M
Plainsboro
Green River

La Scala
Magic Mtn
Pleasantville
J Rubinfine
Princeton
J J Felcone
Scholar's
Witherspoon
Rahway
Apothecary
W H Helfand
Rancocas
Sporting
Red Bank
Red Bank
Ridgewood
Wilsey Square
Rochelle Park
L W Smith
Rutherford
Chestnut Ridge
Saddle River
G & H De La Ree
Sea Girt
Soccer World
Sea Isle City
R B Taylor
South Egg Harbor
Heinoldt
Summit
E S Hickok
Teaneck
J Goldman
M Waldstein
Tenafly
Coll's Crnr
J C O'Connor
R & M Orner

Trenton
Acres-Tre
Cathryn

Union
J V Sichel

Union City
Bks On File-Uni

Verona
S Koschal

Waldwick
H Nestler

Wayne
R F Hutson

West Caldwell
Antic Hay

West Orange
A Saifer

Westfield
Hobbit

Westmont
Richardsons

Westwood
Bkwood

Whippany
M J Yuill

Willingboro
K Cutler

New Mexico

Albuquerque
Adobe
Bk Addict-Albu
Bks By Mail
Chafey's
Chamisa
J Distefano
El Piasano

Hummingbird
J D Rittenhouse

Corrales
P H Samuels

Las Vegas
Los Artesanos

Los Alamos
J Harder

Santa Fe
Ancient Cty Bk
Ancient Cty Pr
De La Pena
R Fitch
Grt So'West
Marg & Moss
N Potter
J B Shaw

Taos
Rendezvous
Taos

New York

Adams Center
E G Blankman

Albany
Albion
Bryn Mawr-Alb
J S Iavarone
London-Alb
Page One
Question Mark
T W Shaw

Albertson
S Apfelbaum

Amenia
Totteridge

Amherst
K T Ransom

Amityville
F R Gardner
K Lang

Amsterdam
Reston's

Ancramdale
J F Schultz

Andes
Treasures

Babylon
Autobks E

Baldwin
Baldwin
J Bambach

Baldwin Place
Thomas J Wise

Bayport
Maestro

Bayside
C E Gardiner
S Stewart
Thomolsen

Bedford
J Bowman
Pages

Bethpage
F Mavis

Binghamton
Biblio's Dream

Brewster
Olana

Brockport
Lift Bridge-Bro

Bronx
Abbot
C Baron
H Clenick
Denbry
P J Drabeck
Jokal
S Lupack
H Satty
C Steir

Bronxville
N T Smith

Brooklyn
G A Bernstein
Bk Srch-Bro
Bklyn Gall
City Wide
Dance Mart
B Fein
Footnote
Fricelli
Grand
Judaica Bk Agy
Main St
Memor Amer
J Meyerson
S Millman
N'tl Libry
Nationwide
Opera Box
Pogonia
Revisionist
C J Sheiner
Towson

Buffalo
C Held
T D Mahoney
Old Edtns

Caledonia
D Fay

Camden
C J Boardman

Canaan
S R Smith

Canton
Jenison's

Catskill
Pan

Cazenovia
Froghollow
J C Huckans
Pan-Amer
S Resnick

Center Moriches
Paper Chase Sch

Chappaqua
Chappaqua

Clarence
Vi & Si's

Clinton Corners
Seabook

Cobleskill
C G Fisher

Cooperstown
Hoffman Lane
W Monie

Corning
Bk Exch-Corn
Bkworm-Cor

Cornwall
T N Haviland

Cornwallville
Hope Farm

Croton-On-Hudson
B Chaney Jr
Croton
Old Bk Rm-Cro

Deansboro
Berry Hill

Delmar
Lincoln Hill

Dobbs Ferry
F Arone
N & N Pavlov

East Aurora
N H Brady

East Chatham
Librarium

East Northport
M & M

Eastchester
B Weiss

Edmeston
I Quitzau

Elizabethtown
L W Currey

Elma
As You Like It

Elmhurst
Elysian Fields
A Gud
V Janta

Elmsford
Maxwell Sci

Endicott
R E Donovan

Fairport
Lift Bridge-Fai

Far Rockaway
Baron

Farmingdale
Overstock

Fleischmanns
Purple Mtn

Flushing
H Feldstein
M Halpern
Spiratione

Fly Creek
Fly Creek

Forest Hills
Biblion
S E Rubenstein
Theoria

Freeport
Wantagh

Fresh Meadows
New Steamship

Gardiner
Bkmart-Gar

Geneseo
H Tanner

Geneva
Adrian's
Bk Fndr-Genev

Getzville
R W Clare

Glen Head
C Dvorak
Plandome

Goldens Bridge
E J Kearin

Gowanda
Old Bk Rm-Gow

Great Neck
Core Coll
M M Kraus
S Penner

Great River
G F S

Greenport
Burton's

Greenwich
Owl Pen

Hamilton
Colgate

Harriman
A C Hunter

Harrison
Barbara's
Harbor Hill

Hartsdale
K Schick

Hartwick
R Butterfield

Hastings-On-Hudson
Riverrun
C K Travis

Hauppauge
H & R Salerno

Hempstead
Womrath's

Hilton
Coll's Libr
Colls Library

Hopewell Junction
D Hirsch

Hudson Falls
Village-Hud

Hunter
Benjamin Autogr

Huntington
L Galinsky
North Shore

Huntington Station
J Cashman
Janus-Hun

Irvington-On-Hudson
E Andrews

Islip
Fortune Finders

Ithaca
Bkery-Ith
C Garvin
Ithaca Hse

Jackson Heights
S E Blumenauer
M A Schaefer
Spector

Jamaica
Caravan-Marit
J E Schober

Jamestown
Twice Sold

Jericho
P A Stroock

Johnstown
Mrs K R Dorn
Tryon Cnty

Kew Gardens
Austin
M E Bennett
E Offenbacher

Kew Gardens Hills
Ukiyo-E

Kings Point
H Minkoff

Lafayette
H J Shoebridge

Lake Grove
B Shaler

Lake Placid
With Pipe

Lansingburgh
W F Broderick

Larchmont
F A Bernett
Bk Clearing
Dog Inc
Ex Libris Mazel
H Goodkind

Liberty
Eight-Cent

Lido Beach
S Spindel

Lima
Hobby Helpers

Lindenhurst
Herp Exch

Liverpool
Johnson & O'D

RARE BOOKS

667 Madison Avenue (at 61st St.) New York, New York 10021

BLACK SUN BOOKS
Suite 305 (212) 688-6622
10:00 A.M.-5:00 P.M.
Monday-Saturday & by appointment
First Editions. Rare Books.
Illustrated Books. Private Press Books.
Fine Old & Modern Master Drawings.

JAMES CUMMINS, BOOKSELLER
Suite 1005 (212) 371-4151
Monday-Saturday 10:00 A.M.-5:00 P.M.
Rare Books. Literature. Press Books.
Exploration. Color Plate. Sporting.
Books of the 1890's.

LEONARD FOX, LTD.
Suite 410 (212) 888-5480
10:00 A.M.-5:00 P.M. Monday-Friday
Illustrated Books. Reference Works.
& Posters relating to Art Nouveau.
Art Deco, & Fashion.

HARMER JOHNSON BOOKS LTD.
Suite 906 (212) 752-1189
10:00 A.M.-5:00 P.M. Monday-Saturday
Art Reference: Greek, Roman, Egyptian,
Western Asiatic, African, South Pacific,
Pre-Columbian, American Indian,
and Eskimo.

HOUSE OF BOOKS, LTD.
Suite 901 (212) 755-5998
20th Century First Editions.
Autograph Material.

JAMES LOWE AUTOGRAPHS, LTD.
Suite 709 (212) 889-8204
11:00 A.M.-6:00 P.M. Monday-Saturday
Signed and Limited Editions. Historic and
Literary Autographs.
Manuscripts and Documents.
Americana. Original Photography.

WALTER REUBEN INC.
Suite 1006 (212) 752-8508
10:00 A.M.-6:00 P.M.
Tuesday-Saturday & By Appointment.
Rare Maps and Atlases. Americana (North
& South).
Literature (First & Foreign Editions).
Voyages. Travels.

TREBIZOND RARE BOOKS
Suite 207 (212) 371-1980
9:30 A.M.-5:30 P.M.
Monday-Friday & by appointment
English, Continental and American Books.
Literature and Travel.

URSUS BOOKS, LTD.
Suite 704 (212) 838-1012
9:00 A.M.-5:00 P.M. Monday-Friday
Saturday 10:00 A.M.-4:00 P.M.
Rare Books, Art Reference, Fine Press Books,
Illustrated Books.
Rare & Decorative Prints.
Books About Books.

Catalogues issued by each dealer.

Livingston
A Frisch

Long Beach
Landau

Mahopac
R A Lowenstein

Malverne
Our Heritage

Mamaroneck
P P Appel
Christoffersen
Littwin & Fel
V Tamerlis

Manhasset
M Zervas

Medina
C Ross

Millbrook
Christian-Mil
A P Collins
Copper Fox

Millerton
Oblong

Mineola
William-Roberts

Minetto
Talbothay's

Monroe
C S Berkowitz

Monsey
W Loewy

Monticello
Lubrecht & Cram

Mount Kisco
Fox & Suther

Neponsit
Hemlock

New City
L H McGill

New Hyde Park
J Criscione

New Rochelle
Cat Center
Fordham

New York
A M S
Academy-NYC
Adler's
J G Amadeo
Abpc
Amer Bk Coll
Ampersand
Antiq Bksllrs

Appelfeld
Argosy
Arkway
J E Arnay
Asian Amer
Asian-NYC
Backworks
Ballet
C V Barnes
Barnstable
Barra
J N Bartfield
Belanske & Lev
P Berry
Bibliophile-NYC
Black Sun
Bk Fndrs-NYC
Bk Ranger
Bk Friends
Bkhunter-NYC
Bks & Thngs-NYC
Brentano's-NYC
M Breslauer
Broude Bros
R K Brown
Brownstone
J Buck
J H Burke
J & W Bursten
A Buschke
D Carbonneau
Carnegie
R Chalfin
Christie's
Cityana Gall
Colls' Edtns
Comic Art
Corner-NYC
Country Connect
J Cummins
M R Cutler
H C Daitz
Dauber & Pine
De Simon
Dolphin-NYC
Donan
M Du Priest
P C Duschnes
E K
H Ebensten
A Egan
El Cascajero
A Elsner
Ex Libris-NYC
Facsimile
A Fair
Fant Archives

P T Fisher
J F Fleming
L Fox
R Gardner
J T Gatto
Gem Antiq
Genealogists
V Germack
S Gilman
L Goldschmidt
A Goodman
E Gordon
M Gordon
Gotham
D Gouey
L S Granby
Greenwich
K Gregory
Y W Griffin
A Gutkin
H W K
Hacker Art
R Halpern
C Hamilton
L C Harper
Harris Srch
W S Heinman
F T Heller
J N Herlin
J A Hill
Horchow
G Horowitz
Hse Of Bks Ltd
El Dieff
E Howe
Int Univ Bkslrs
H Johnson
Jolly Roger
R T Jordan
J Jurist
K Karith
R J Kempe
Keshcarrigan
Y Kishi
E Klein
J & P Klemperer
H P Kraus
La Valois
Landmark
Lee & Lee
J Lehr
B Leibowits
D A Lewis
W B Liebmann
Lion Heart
J Lowe
A Lutz

Magazine Center
Maiden Voy
J Majer
Martin's
Mason's
T Mawson
M M E Maxwell
S & H Meller
I Mendoza
Milestone-NYC
Military
Miller & Miller
A H Minters
J C Morel
Moriah
N R S
Neikrug
New Engl-NYC
N Y Bound
H Noble Jr
Oceanic Primitive
Old Block
Old Glory
Old Print Sh
Out-Of-Prnt-NYC
Pageant
P'back Exch
Paragon Gall
Pendragon
Performing Arts
Phillips
Philosophical
Phoenix
Photog's Place
Pomander
Radio City
R C Ramer
Reference
W Reuben-NYC
R Richards
Rivendell
M S Rosenberg
L Rostenberg
Russica
C F Safir
S O Saxe
W H Schab
J G Schiller
O Schreyer
Sci Fict
B Scott
Secret Sharer
S R Shapiro
Sky Bks Int
R Slifer
R M Smythe
Soldier

A Sosenko
SPB
P Sperling
Sporting Biblio
Steinberg
Strand-Rare
Strand
G Sullivan
Swann
M Tanditash
Theatrebooks
Trebizond
P Tumarkin
D Tunick
U S Games
University Pl
Ursus
C J Vega
Victoria-NYC
S Weiser
L & H Weitz
Weyhe
P Williams
F Wilson
Witkin
Wittenborn
World Wide-NYC
Wurlitzer-Bruck
Ximenes
M N Young
M D Zambelli
Zita
I Zucker

Niagra Falls
D Sauber

North Bellmore
Antheil

Northport
Bayview

Nyack
Dee Cee

Oakland Gardens
H A Luft

Oceanside
Action Bks
Oceanside

Old Forge
Wildwood

Oneonta
Carney
Serpent & Eagle

Ossining
J Lazarus
W Salloch

Owego
Riverow

Oxford
Paper Person

Palmyra
K G Arthurton
P Stockman

Peekskill
T Trace

Penfield
Ayrshire

Penn Yan
D & M Krueger

Piermont
Pier

Pine Island
W McDonnell

Plainview
Bengta Woo
H Galewitz

Plandome
Temares

Plattsburgh
Corner Stone

Pleasantville
Colonial
A Wittenborn

Port Washington
Signed Limited

Potsdam
Cabin In Pines

Poughkeepsie
Dugout & Depot
Griffin
3 Arts
R E Underhill

Pultneyville
Yankee Peddler

Queens
J F F

Rego Park
Orsay

Rhinebeck
Baird Press

Richmond Hill
G Snyder

Riverdale
E K Schreiber

Rochester
Abra Cadavar
R L Collins
R Diamond
Genessee

Rockville Centre
Addison
Bk Chest
Coll's List
H M Darvick
Elgen
P Greene

Rocky Point
E Moran

Roslyn
S Marx

Roslyn Heights
B Resnik

Rye
High Ridge
Super

Sands Points
Cornwall Hse

Saranac Lake
Adirondack

Saratoga
Hennesseys

Saratoga Springs
Lyrical Ballad

Scarsdale
J D Hawkins
A Schnase

Schenectady
Hammer Mtn
N W Hoffman

Scotia
Arcturus
Hawley's Island

Severance
Northwoods

Sloatsburg
Liberty Rock

Smithtown
Cadenza
G B I
R L Veatch

Southampton
R Keene

Staten Island
Bk End-Sta
H McMillen

Stone Ridge
Ridge

Stony Brook
H E Heinrich

Syracuse
E Monarski

Sterling Valley
R M Sylvester

Tonawanda
E Musial

Tuckahoe
Amer Bk & Gal

Uniondale
College Nook

Upper Nyack
Ben Franklin

Utica
R Asaro

Valhalla
Educo

Valley Cottage
Aleph-Bet

Valley Stream
C Appelbaum

Vestal
Indian Head

Wading River
J & R Casten

Warwick
Bk Look-War
Warwick

West Hempstead
Eubiotics

Westbury
J Giller

White Plains
Bk Gall-Whit
A J Phiebig
E B Shields

Williamsville
Tan Bark

Woodmere
J Granat

Woodside
Alron

Woodstock
N Cowen
3 Geese

Wynantskill
aGatherin'

Yonkers
Alicat
All Photo
Green Thought

Newfoundland

St Johns
Maps & Bks

North Carolina

Asheville
Bk Mart-Ash

Charlotte
Carolina
Little Hundred
B L Means

Elizabeth City
Autos & Autos

Fairmont
Bk Trader-Fai

Greensboro
Browsery
Dictionary

Highlands
Cyrano's

Hillsborough
Antiques-Hil
C B Wimsey

Jamestown
Pacificana

Morganton
Catawba River

New Bern
Keith & Martin

Pittsboro
Resurrection

Raleigh
October Farm

Wendell
Broadfoot's

West Durham
Old Galen's

West Troy
Grandpa's Hse

North Dakota

Devils Lake
H O Berg

Nova Scotia

Halifax
Schooner
Nautica

Windsor
L S Loomer

Wolfville
Odd Bk

Ohio

Akron
Bkseller-Akr
Donegan
B P Ferrini
Old Bk St-Akr

Alliance
Odyssey

Athens
Hock-Hocking

Bartlow
L E Carpenter

Beachwood
S Heller

Bluffton
D Gratz

Bolivar
Bkfndrs-Bol

Carey
R G Hayman

Cincinnati
Acres-Cin
B Agranoff
Albert
Bk Stall-Cin
R H Richshafer
Significant
J Wade

Cleveland
Bibliopolis-Cle
Bloch & Co

A L Feldman
Kay's
Radiographics
Under Cover-Cle
J T Zubal

Cleveland Heights
Coventry

Columbus
P H North, Jr
L J Ryan
Shaw-Banfill
Trail To Y'day

Conneaut
F Metcalf

Dayton
Bk Stop-Day
Burt's
Dragon's Lair
J D S
Morningside-Oak
Morningside-Pob

Fairborn
Back Row
Bkery-Fai

Greensburg
Ron-Dot

Hilliard
Bkphil

Hudson
D Davis

Kettering
Bk Sh-Ket

Lima
L A Moore, Sr

Mansfield
Ohio Bkhntr

Massillon
Village-Mass

Miamisburg
G Armitage

Mount Vernon
Owl Creek

North Canton
Literary Seal

North Olmsted
C Larson

Norwalk
E Miller
I M Roth

Parkman
P Ellis

Poland
Alpha Omega

Reynoldsburg
Ambelrs
Conversation

Shaker Heights
Under Cover-Sha

South Euclid
Paper Peddlers

Springfield
Bkhaven-Spr

Sylvania
Borderland

Toledo
G D Brown
K G Gaisser

Vienna
P F Miller

Warren
McClintock

Waterville
Coll's Ch-Wat

Willoughby Hills
B Mraz

Wooster
Hist Real
D Moore

Worthington
Looking Glass

Yellow Springs
G Houseman

Youngstown
C Butcher
A Cohen

Oklahoma

Edmond
R Bever

Inola
J Hall

Lawton
G F Edwards

Oklahoma City
M Marcher A Pts

Northe
Arcane
Michael's

Stillwater
Caravan-Sti

Ontario

Amherstburg
Bullock's

Bewdley
7 Seas

Cobalt
Highway

Combermere
Madonna Hse

Downsview
De Haviland

Grimsby
D W McLennan

Guelph
J Weiss
Nostalgia
Rising Trout

Hamilton
J Rush

Hensall
J W Smith

Kingston
Heinemann's
Bk Bin-Kin

London
Attic

Manotick
Sportsman's

Mississauga
Book-Miss

Ohskweken
Iroqrafts

Ottawa
Mrs A L Ashton
K Benson
Bk Bazaar
J P McGahern
C Hinchliffe
Dyment
H Black's

Owen Sound
Ginger

Rockton
Pomona Exch

St Catharines
Hannelore

Tarzwell
J Kidston

Thorold
J Burtniak

Toronto
Coach Hse
Hyman & Son-Tor
Bk Fiend
G E C Barnes
Glad Day-Tor
D Mason
Grt No'West
St Nicholas
Acadia
Montgomery
S Temple
D & E Lake
Canada Bk Auct
Old Favorites

B Yolleck
Other
Travellers'
Alphabet
Atticus-Tor
H Anson-Cart
D Hood
Hortolus
G Wilson
About
Bakka
L A Wallrich
Abelard
W Nelson
A Sherlock
D W Goudy

Weston
P L Jackson

Wiarton
Readables

Oregon

Albany
B McMaster

Astoria
K Glackin

Beaverton
Bk Barn-Bea
E & M Ediger

Bend
Maverick

Corvallis
Avocet

Dallas
A A Dunn

Dundee
Authors Of West

Eugene
Backstage
Bk Fair-Eug
J Michaels

Gold Hill
B L Bibby

Medford
Applegate

Newberg
Ken-L-Questor

Noti
S Arden

Portland
R E Abel
A Bloom's

Cameron's
Green Dolphin
Hollands'
Midvale
Old Oregon

Salem
D Bearce
Manuscript
C Seluzicki

Pennsylvania

Aliquippa
R A Palket

Allentown
Amer Mail Auct
P G Le Van
M L Tyrrell

Allenwood
Otzinachson

Allison Park
Camden Hse

Altoona
Old Bkshed

Ambler
R Batchelder

Ardmore
M E Battersby

Athens
Franklin

Bethlehem
D Weiss

Blue Bell
J Goffman

Boyertown
D L Larson
White Hse

Bryn Mawr
Epist Scholar

Carversville
A Vanasse

Chalfont
Dana's Doorway

Chambersburg
G Hall, Jr
C Kellinger

Cochranville
J S Helms

Cornwells Heights
Button

Darby
Darby

Doylestown
Petrilla/Kane
Riverside Mail

Easton
College Hill
Debra
Hive

Quadrant
Zellner's

Erie
Erie

Fairview Village
B Godshall

Ferndale
Gateway

Gettysburg
Obsolescence

Gilbert
C Derowitsch

Glen Rock
Family Album

Harrisburg
H B Leech

Hatboro
Legacy

Hatfield
Jean's

Huntingdon Valley
Mystery Manor

Jenkintown
Bkst-Jenk
Hobson's Ch
Medical Manor
R L Sadoff

Kane
S Shuart

Kennett Square
T MacAluso

King Of Prussia
W G Arader III

Lancaster
Bk Haven-Law

Levittown
R Robertson

Lumberville
G Steele

Mars
Gene & Kit's

Mechanicsburg
W Thomas

Meshoppen
Big John's

Mount Penn
J E De Turck

New Hope
Graedon

New Oxford
W L Zeigler

New Wilmington
J Fisher

Newtown Square
S & C Najarian

North East
Cantrells'

North Huntington
E E Lindh

Paoli
A Brutico Jr
J E Norris

Philadelphia
W H Allen
G H Arrow
Bk Mark-Phil
A Carduner
B C Carltiz
Y Goldman
F M Halpern
B J Hecht
B R Kemp
G S MacManus
B McKittrick
Olympia
Palinurus
Reedmor
Riling Arms
Rittenhse
Schuylkill
C Sessler

Phoenixville
Valley Forge

Pittsburgh
P E Baracca
Bk Srch-Pit
H R Emler
P C Hull
Lamp
D Richards
Scharf Art
B Schmid

Schoyer's
Tuckers

Pottstown
Americanist
S F Cullins'

Reading
S F Chapin
Mystery Hse
Rockland

Revere
J H Woolmer

Rillton
Hoffman Resch

Rouseville
T Harper

Sayre
Valley-Say

Selingsgrove
D J Ernst

Sellersville
Jenny Lind

Shippensburg
D W Starry, Sr

Souderton
M H Detweiler

St Peters
Mexbooks

State College
H Abrams-Sta
R F Perotti

Swarthmore
Bksource

Trafford
R J Kalanja

Warren
E C Miller

Washington
T Sullivan

Waverly
Waverly

Wayne
J W Beattie
Bk Shelf-Way

West Chester
Baldwin's Barn

Williamsport
T Hughes

Wynnewood
E Moore

Wyoming
Hermit's

Quebec

Montmorency
L La Berge
Montreal
Stryker's
Westmount
Word
J A Benoit
Guerin Editeur
Lib Quebecoise

Sindell Res
P Dumas
J J Lefebvre
I MacKenzie
Mansfield
G Woolmer
Biblio
G Javitch
Dr L M Lande

J H Hale
H R Kahn
I Ehrlich
Diamond-Mon
W De Freitas
Bibliog Of Dog

Pierrefonds
H Volker

Pointe Claire
Page 2
W P Wolfe

Quebec
J Gagnon

Westmount
Tech Info-Doc

Rhode Island

Bristol
Current
Foster
Lincoln-O P
Hope Valley
J Clinton
Jamestown
E J Craig

Kingston
W T O'Malley
Newport
Anchor & Dol
Armchair Sailor
Corner-Newp
Peacedale
Sign Of Unicorn

Providence
Markey & Asp
Merlin's Closet
Metacomet
Sewards' Folly
Tyson

Warwick
Fortunate Fnds

Longo Auct
J W Morritt

Westerley
Wayside

Saskatchewan

Regina
Blue Jay
R Spafford

South Carolina

Beaufort
Beaufort

Charleston
Bk Basement
Old Mill

Columbia
Bk Disp-Col
Bk Place-Col

Greenwood
Noahs Ark
B M Rieger

Hodges
Attic-Hodg

Myrtle Beach
Bird & Bk

Newberry
Hampton

Rock Hill
J S Pipkin

South Dakota

Mitchell
Bk Keeper-Mit

Vermillion
Buteo
Stationarius

Webster
Dakota

Tennessee

Brentwood
J L Heflin, Jr

Cleveland
Bk Shelf-Cle
R L George

Crossville
Purple Bkcase

Dyersburg
M Hudson

Kingsport
F M Hill

Knoxville
R R Allen
Andover Square
Donaldsons

Madison
Fox-Mad

Memphis
Burke's

Old South
Ollies

Nashville
Battery
Cumberland
C Elder
Methodist

Paris
G E Webb, Jr

Ripley
Enterprise

Signal Mountain
Crabtree

White Creek
Mrs Thomason

Texas

Amarillo
Amer So'West

Arlington
Bk Quest

Austin
Arjay
D Bissett
Jenkins

Longhorn
W Reuben-Aus
W T Taylor

T W Tingle
R S Walton

Bryan
Fron Amer

Conroe
Gierspeck & Rop

Dallas
Aldredge
Bk Bin-Dal
Bkpost-Dal
D Grossblatt
L Herndon
Las Lenguas
Library-Dal
J R Mara
P'backs Plus
Tracery
Wilson

Dickinson
Schroeder's

Eagle Pass
B E Pingenot

El Paso
Alcazar

Fort Worth
Barber's

Friendswood
Bksearch-Fri

Galveston
Old Bkshelf

Glen Rose
Limestone Hills

Houston
Bk Case-Hou
Chickadee
Colleen's
Detering
From Another
W W Hildreth
Montrose
Norumbega
Old Bk & Cur
G P Szontagh
Trackside

Keene
J L Wheeler

Lake Jackson
J Burger

New Boston
G N Gabbard

Plano
M Gibbs

Portland
P Kufus

Salado
Fletcher's

San Angelo
Info
Ye Olde Fan

San Antonio
All Pts View
Bk Mart-San
Bk Mart Anx-San
Gutenberg's
M S Lambeth

On Paper
W R Orbelo
Rosengren's

Stphenville
F Armstrong

Temple
R Bandas
Bk Cellar-Tem

Terrell
Bks & Thngs-Ter

Victoria
J Petty

Waco
Von Blons

Waxahachie
C Wright

Wichita Falls
J D Terry

Utah

Park City
Kats

Salt Lake City
S Ballinger

J Bekker
Bk Sh-Salt

Brennan
Cosmic Aero

West Jordan
Ute-Or-Ida

Vermont

Arlington
Kwasniewski

Bennington
Bradford
J M Hays
New Engl-Benn

Brattleboro
Bk Cellar-Brat
K Leach

Burlington
Bk Stacks-Burl

Bygone
J L Fraser

Castleton
Northeast

Greensboro Bend
Ferryman Ant

Hartford
Stanley

Manchester
J Appleseed

Manchester Center
Kneedeep

Morristown Corners
Brick Hse

Newport
M Dunn

North Bennington
J Johnson

North Pomfret
R H Adelson

Plainfield
B Koenig's

Putney
Lilac Hedge
Unique Antiq

Rutland
Tuttle Antiq

Springfield
Abatis

West Brattleboro
Bear

Windsor
Celtic Cross

Virginia

Alexandria
Associates
Jennies
I Rouse
Seminary
Strictly
S Yudkin
Arlington
Bk Ends-Arl
Bk Hse-Arl
Find A Bk
D Jaffe
Quizzicum
Berryville
Va Bk Co
Bristol
B Tauscher
Charlottesville
Daedalus
Forest
Heartwood
Newcomb Hall
N M Pawlett
Culpeper
Corner Shelf-Cul
Fairfax
Allbks

Antiq Tobacco
P M Lumb
Falls Church
Ajay Ent
A Lauberts
Front Royal
Royal Oak
Harrisonburg
Log Cabin
Ivy
J N Showalter
Lynchburg
Dr Nostlgia
Givens
Manassas
Canine Conn
Mc Dowell
J R Levien
McLean
McLean
Mount Crawford
L Evans
Store
New Castle
J Landau

Newport News
C W Brooks
Norfolk
Ghent Bkworm
H C Hensel
Wards Corner
Oakton
Bkfinders-Fair
Petersburg
L Ginsberg
Portsmouth
Metaphysic-Por
Reston
W B O'Neill
13 Colonies
Richmond
Coll's Old
Shamus
Waves
Roanoke
N Bond
Springfield
T Alford
Bk Srch-Spr
Camelot

Staunton
Woodspurge
Vienna
Audubon
J A Reisler
Virginia Beach
W S Hay
Waynesboro
K Altau
Williamsburg
Bk Hse-Will
Bkpress
Eu Be Co
H Stevens Son
Winchester
Appleland
Woodbridge
Rockaway
Woodstock
O O Evans
Wytheviile
Bkworm & Silver

Virgin Islands

Christiansted, St Croix
Jeltrups'

Washington

Anderson Island
Fransen's

Bellevue
P T Mallahan

Bellingham
Amer Print
R A Mezoff

Clarkston
Peggatty

Friday Harbor
Boardwalk

Kenmore
Mandeville

Kent
R T Kennedy

Lopez
R L Shep

Monroe
R M Weatherford

Morton
Koths

Olympia
Bk St-Oly
Browser's

Opportunity
McDuffies

Prosser
Bkmark-Pro

Redmond
D M H Lowe

Renton
M R Parks

Seattle
Cinema-Sea
Comstock's

Dennis
Diff Drum-Sea
Golden Age
Holistic Health
Horizon
D Ishii
Knutson's
R W Mattila
P Miller
Ottenberg Bks
S Ottenberg
J L Polley
Raymer's
Sample-Sea
Shorey
G H Tweney

Sequim
R H Redding

Spokane
Clark's

Tacoma
Bk Gall-Tac
Bks Black Bass
O'Leary's
South Side

Vancouver
G L Estabrook
D Perier

Wentachee
Homesteader

Yakima
Bk Nook
J Woods-Yak

West Virginia

Bluefield
Appalachia

Charlestown
Major's

Morgantown
Pinocchio's

R E Robinson
Wolf's Head

Shepherdstown
E Driscoll

Walker
Trans Allegheny

Washington
Inland River

Wheeling
Bishop Of Bks

Williamsburg
Stroud

Wisconsin

Appleton
Bob's-App

Big Bend
Arabest

Brown Deer
Bee Gee's

Delavan
Old Delavan

Eau Claire
Curiosity-Eau

Elm Grove
West's Agency

Lake Delton
Wise Owl

Madison
Blors
Bks Then & Now
P G Waite
D Ward

Marshfield
W B Fye

Mazomanie
G J Rausch

Merrimac
D Chapman

Milwaukee	Renaissance-Mil	**Phillips**	**Stevens Point**
Aesir	W E Schroeder	Spectrum	Antiq Sh-Ste
Bkst-Mil		**Racine**	
Castalia	**Mount Horeb**	D Doonan	
Constant Reader	G F Glaeve	**Sparta**	
R Dworcyk	Lust Auct	W E Beaver	
Fir Tree			
	New Holstein	**Spring Green**	**Watertown**
	C J Bedore	Winsted	Baptist Bourse

Wyoming

Casper	**Dayton**	**Sheridan**	**Sundance**
Corner-Cas	Summerhouse	Mrs L Douglas	Backpocket
Lange's			

American Book Collector has computerized all the names, addresses, and book specialties for the 3,000 dealers found in this directory and for a growing list of dealers who will appear in subsequent editions. We can provide mailing labels for these dealers, selected by specialty if you wish, at reasonable cost. Write for our price schedule. *ABC,* 274 Madison Avenue, New York, N.Y. 10016.

American Book Collector is North America's most readable and interesting magazine for book collectors. Write today for our free subscription brochure. *ABC,* 274 Madison Avenue, New York, N.Y. 10016.